الجواهر اللماعة

The Radiant Jewels

For Summoning the Kings of Jinn at the Right Time and Hour

Attributed to

ʿAlī Abū Ḥayy Allāh al-Marzūqī

Translated from Arabic by

John Friend

JOHN FRIEND
PUBLISHING

John Friend Publishing

THE RADIANT JEWELS

الجواهر اللماعة

◊

Second edition, revised and corrected, 2026.

A complete translation of *al-Jawāhir al-Lammāʿa* (The Radiant Jewels).

◊

TRANSLATOR John Friend

PUBLISHER John Friend Publishing

SERIES Arabic Islamicate Occult Manuscripts in Translation, Volume 5

Contents

Translator's Note

This edition presents *The Radiant Jewels* (*al-Jawāhir al-Lammāʿa*), attributed to ʿAlī Abū Ḥayy Allāh al-Marzūqī (c. 15th century). Arabic terms follow IJMES romanization with full diacritical marks.

Barbarous names (*ʿajamī*) — sequences of letters meant to be pronounced as written — are transliterated exactly and presented alongside the original Arabic script, never translated.

Talismanic seals and magic squares are reproduced as images from the source manuscript. Where the source is illegible, the translator has noted the lacuna rather than invent content.

—*John Friend*

John Friend is a nom de plume. Behind it is an esotericist, occultist, scholar, and translator who has spent years immersed in the Arabic manuscript tradition — reading what most academics catalog but never open, and translating what has never before appeared in any Western language. His work sits at the crossroads of Islamic esotericism, Solomonic magic, and the living tradition of *ʿilm al-ḥurūf* (the science of letters). He translates not as an outsider looking in, but as a student of the tradition itself.

This book is translated from a printed Arabic text. This edition handles its material according to fixed rules, so that the reader always knows what is original and what is editorial judgment.

Prayers, adjurations, and inscribed formulae are presented in three layers: the English meaning, an exact romanized transliteration, and the original Arabic script. The transliteration and Arabic lines are the scholarly record: what stands in them is precisely what the source yields, and nothing more.

Where the scribe left a deliberate blank for the practitioner to insert a name, the English renders the slot as "so-and-so" or "the named person," following the text's own idiom. A small numeral such as ٢ (2) or ٣ (3) after a word is the scribe's repetition mark, indicating the word is to be spoken that many times; the English renders it "(twice)" or "(three times)."

Barbarous names — the untranslatable names of power — are transliterated exactly and never interpreted. Talismanic figures, number squares, and seals are reproduced photographically from the source printing.

Where the source cannot be read — ink lost to damage, a stain, or a binding edge — the transliteration and Arabic layers carry *(...)*. No name, number, or sacred formula in this book is a guess.

The printed copy from which this edition was made lacks two pages near the end of the Conclusion. The text ends where the copy ends; nothing has been supplied in their place.

The Author's Preface

In the Name of God, the Most Gracious, the Most Merciful.

Bismi Allāh al-Raḥmān al-Raḥīm

بسم الله الرحمن الرحيم

Praise be to God, the Lord of all creation, with abundant praise that meets His blessings and matches His increase. I bear witness that there is no god but God alone, having no partner — a testimony by which the one who speaks it attains great honour and mighty glory on the Day of Resurrection and Rising. And I bear witness that our master and our prophet Muḥammad is His servant and His messenger, the treasury of the sciences and the secrets, and the master of the godfearing and the righteous. May God bless him and grant him peace, and his family and his companions, possessors of lofty glories and noble secrets.

Al-ḥamdu li-llāhi rabbi al-ʿālamīn, ḥamdan kathīran yuwāfī niʿamahu wa-yukāfiʾu mazīdahu. Wa-ashhadu an lā ilāha illā Allāhu waḥdahu lā sharīka lahu, shahādatan yanālu qāʾiluhā al-sharafa al-ʿaẓīma wa-l-ʿizza al-jasīma yawma al-baʿthi wa-l-nushūr. Wa-ashhadu anna sayyidanā wa-nabiyyanā Muḥammadan ʿabduhu wa-rasūluhu, kanzu al-ʿulūmi wa-l-asrār, wa-sayyidu al-atqiyāʾi al-abrār. Ṣallā Allāhu ʿalayhi wa-

sallama wa-ʿalā ālihi wa-aṣḥābihi dhawī al-mafākhiri al-ʿaliyyati wa-l-asrāri al-jalīla.

الحمد لله رب العالمين حمدا كثيرا يوافي نعمه ويكافئ مزيده. وأشهد أن لا إله إلا الله وحده لا شريك له شهادة ينال قائلها الشرف العظيم والعز الجسيم يوم البعث والنشور. وأشهد أن سيدنا ونبينا محمدا عبده ورسوله كنز العلوم والأسرار. وسيد الأتقياء الأبرار. صلى الله عليه وسلم وعلى آله وأصحابه ذوي المفاخر العلية والأسرار الجليلة.

As for what follows: the most exalted of the sciences and the most refined of them, the noblest of aims and the most sublime of them, is the science of the secrets of the names and the letters; for it is the science that acquaints the one who practises it with the secrets of the higher and the lower worlds and with the beholding of the spiritual spirits, and that gives him power to obtain whatever matters he desires — such as the treatment of illnesses hard to cure, which the physicians are helpless to remedy, like palsy, leprosy, lovesickness and madness; the rescue of the wronged from the hands of tyrants; the seeing of things far apart; the drawing near of what is distant and the driving away of what is near; the joining together of those who are estranged; the disclosure of hidden things; the drawing of delights and the repelling of harms; and other purposes beyond all counting, which come to no limit.

Many eminent imams have written upon this art, such as the Imam Abū Ḥāmid al-Ghazālī, the Imam Abū al-ʿAbbās al-Būnī, Thābit ibn Qurra al-Ḥarrānī, Abū Maʿshar al-Balkhī, Abū Bakr al-Khwārizmī, Khalaf ibn Yūsuf al-Dasmāsānī, Salīm ibn Thābit al-Baghdādī, and others. When I had examined many of their books and had seen of their secrets what cannot be numbered, God, glorified and exalted, inspired me to lay down something of these secrets and blessings in a concise book, in the hope that I might earn a righteous prayer from a brother in God Most High which would profit me before the Creator of all creatures.

So I gathered this abridgement, small in bulk and great in benefit, and arranged it upon an introduction, three purposes and a conclusion. The Introduction sets out the merit of this science and the conditions for practising it. The First Purpose gives a brief selection from the secrets of the letters. The Second Purpose gives a number of the secrets of the magic squares, and above all the threefold square of the Imam al-Ghazālī. The Third Purpose sets out a goodly number of the secrets of the divine names and the Qur'anic verses. The Conclusion gives scattered benefits from spiritual medicine, the rules of reckoning, and the precious properties. And I have named it:

The Radiant Jewels for Summoning the Kings of the Jinn at the Time and the Hour (al-Jawāhir al-Lammāʿa fī Istiḥḍār Mulūk al-Jinn fī al-Waqt wa-l-Sāʿa)

May God bring benefit to His servants through it, and make it a cause of triumph on the Day of the Promise. Amen.

Nafaʿa Allāhu bihi al-ʿibāda wa-jaʿalahu sababan li-l-fawzi yawma al-mīʿādi, āmīn.

نفع الله به العباد وجعله سببا للفوز يوم الميعاد آمين

The time has now come to begin upon what is intended; so I say, and with God lies gracious acceptance.

Introduction: The Merit of This Science and the Conditions for Practising It (al-Muqaddima fī Bayān Faḍl Hādhā al-ʿIlm wa-Shurūṭ Mumārasatih)

Know that the science of wisdom washes souls clean of the filth of the darkened nature, just as soap washes clothes. When the soul comes to know wisdom it yearns and longs for the world of spirits, turns away from the bodily appetites that deal death to the living soul, and is delivered from the secrets of the appetites and from their snares, in which the people of knowledge have been caught. Buqrāṭ said: He is no sage who knows the path and then swerved away from it. Refuting ignorance is not itself knowledge, and no one is truly alive who does not strive for the deliverance of his own soul. Socrates said: The living man is not the one who eats and drinks, who prefers his appetites and kills the living soul by plunging into the desires of the lower self. The living man is rather he who knows that the pleasures which have passed are gone, and who is certain that what is yet to come is like what has passed in having no settledness and no permanence.

Then know that the masters of this science have combined the most delightful of the sciences with the noblest of rank, because it acquaints its practitioner, through practice, with the secrets of the higher and the lower worlds. By it he is enabled to behold the spiritual beings, to address them, to mingle with them, to become as one of them, and to act in all matters according to what lies within his power. He treats the diseases whose cure is difficult, before which the most eminent physicians are helpless, such as palsy, leprosy, lovesickness, madness, and brain fever. He brings together those who are estranged and set far apart, and he separates those who have joined together upon that with which the Lord of the worlds is not pleased.

He conveys from the spirits the tidings of events that are to happen before they occur, so that their harm may be guarded against. He uncovers hidden things whose marks have grown faint and whose traces have been effaced, so that they may be put to use instead of being lost. He rescues the oppressed from the hands of tyrannical oppressors. All of that belongs to the secrets and the blessings that God, glorified and exalted, deposited in the Names, the verses, and the letters, which He inspired in His righteous servants and made manifest at their hands in fulfilment of His noble promise in His generous saying:

Call upon Me; I will answer you.

Udʿūnī astajib lakum

ادعوني أستجب لكم

In reality it is supplication, and it is an act of worship that is required, as is evident.

The Twenty-Seven Conditions of the Work

For working with this science there are conditions without which none of its operations is sound. They are many, and some have brought them up to twenty-seven conditions:

1. Certainty: This is settled conviction that the operation will bear its result, for whoever performs one of these operations and then doubts it will not be benefited by that operation. The Prophet, may God bless him and grant him peace, said:

Call upon God while you are certain of being answered.

Udʿū Allāha wa-antum mūqinūna bi-l-ijāba

ادعوا الله وأنتم موقنون بالإجابة

2. Perseverance in the service, without boredom or weariness: If the seeker serves a name, or a magic square, or something else, and finds no fruit of it, he must not break off from his work, nor leave off returning to it; for whoever strives finds, and every diligent man has his share. The way of the seeker of this science is the way of the lover: if he sits back from seeking it he will never attain it at all, but if he persists in his pursuit he will attain it, even after a time.

3. Concealment: This is that you do it in an empty place where no one sees you, and that you say to no one, “I have done such-and-such,” or “I am doing such-and-such.” It has come in the report:

Seek help in the fulfilling of your needs through concealment.

Ista'īnū 'alā qaḍā'i ḥawā'ijikum bi-l-kitmān

استعينوا على قضاء حوائجكم بالكتمان

4. Godfearing piety: Included in it are abandoning the eating of what is unlawful, refraining from harming created beings, bearing injury, doing no injury, leaving off lying and backbiting and tale-bearing, keeping to truthfulness and to sincere counsel toward created beings, the common people and the elect alike, and looking upon them with the eye of tenderness and mercy and compassion. The scholars and the sages have agreed that the more the possessor of this science turns toward the doing of good, the more successful his operations are, because whoever fears God Most High, God makes everything subject to him and obedient to him.

5. That he not dispute with the spiritual beings over a matter they desire of him, or to which they direct him for some purpose, because they fulfil no purpose unless it accords with the noble Law and is free of every doubtful thing.

6. That he not employ them in mean matters that can be obtained without them, because that is an insult to them and a diminishing of their due, in that he employs them in contemptible things.

7. That the soul of the one who practises this science be a living soul, one that does not turn toward base matters nor toward perishing pleasures; rather its concern must be to acquire exalted ranks and noble stations.

8. Specifying the two persons between whom you wish to bring about love or enmity, or the one from whom you wish to remove harm, or to bring some injury upon him, by his build, his colour, his likeness, and his condition, whether he is tall or short, a boy, a youth, or a man of middle age. The mention of his name and his mother's name, if she is known, stands in place of this identification; and if she is not known, Ḥawwāʾ stands in place of his mother's name. Identification is stronger than naming, and stronger than either is to join the two together.

9. The Ninth Condition: That he secure the time of the operation against inattention and error, and that he not busy himself with the work while his mind is occupied with family, or wealth, or joy, or grief, or fear; rather, his mind must be empty of all of that.

10. The Tenth Condition: That he commit to memory the oath by which he adjures the spiritual beings, memorizing it soundly so that he does not stumble in it, and that he not be content to read it by looking at a tablet or a book, for that occupies the heart, takes away the humility that is required, and cuts the soul off from the complete orientation that is the greatest of the pillars.

11. The Eleventh Condition: The general authorization, which is known and obtained by taking it and receiving it from

the shaykhs. Whoever has not obtained it, though he has obtained the knowledge, his work is like a child with no father to whom he may be attributed.

On the Operations Proper to Each Planet

12. The Twelfth Condition: Observance of the astrological correspondences and the celestial observations, so that every operation is performed at the time that suits it.

Thus, everything that involves winning the affection of a king or a minister, or extracting a treasure from the hoards of kings, or setting right a craft or a farm, or binding a tongue, or undoing a talisman, is attributed to the Moon. Everything that involves bringing out what lies buried, or turning the heart of a learned man toward you, or bringing on a sickness of the soul, or binding a tongue, is attributed to Mercury. Everything that involves affection, arousal, diversion, joy, and chastisement, and whatever resembles these, is attributed to Venus. Everything that involves coercion, mastery, awe, sovereignty, and ostentation, and the gaining of honour, high station, and abundant gold, and whatever resembles these, is attributed to the Sun. Everything that involves setting one man over another, or parting those who love one another, or casting enmity and hatred between them, or laying waste to lands, or causing sickness, or stirring up strife, or bringing ruin, and whatever resembles these, is attributed to Mars. Everything bound up with setting a livelihood in order and keeping it so, or with adornment and looking well in the eyes of people, or with undoing a talisman, or with binding the tongue of a wicked man, and whatever resembles these, is attributed to Jupiter. Everything belonging to the doors of separation, destruction, and hatred, and to the binding of desire and the binding of sleep, and whatever resembles these, is attributed to Saturn.

Whatever operation is attributed to two planets leaves you free to choose: you may seek your need under whichever of the two you wish, or you may watch for their conjunction in a single sign, which is more complete and better, if you wish to observe the celestial aspects.

The Table of the Planetary Hours

The learned have distributed the hours of the days and the nights among the seven planets, assigning every hour to a planet. They began with the first hour of the day of Saturday, which they assigned to Saturn, and the hour after it to Jupiter, and so on to the twelfth hour of the night of Saturday, which they assigned to the Moon; and for this they set out the table that you see here:

Hour	Saturday Day / Wednesday Night	Sunday Day / Thursday Night	Monday Day / Friday Night	Tuesday Day / Saturday Night	Wednesday Day / Sunday Night	Thursday Day / Monday Night	Friday Day / Tuesday Night
1	Saturn	Sun	Moon	Mars	Mercury	Jupiter	Venus
2	Jupiter	Venus	Saturn	Sun	Moon	Mars	Mercury
3	Mars	Mercury	Jupiter	Venus	Saturn	Sun	Moon
4	Sun	Moon	Mars	Mercury	Jupiter	Venus	Saturn
5	Venus	Saturn	Sun	Moon	Mars	Mercury	Jupiter
6	Mercury	Jupiter	Venus	Saturn	Sun	Moon	Mars
7	Moon	Mars	Mercury	Jupiter	Venus	Saturn	Sun

Hour	Saturday Day / Wednesday Night	Sunday Day / Thursday Night	Monday Day / Friday Night	Tuesday Day / Saturday Night	Wednesday Day / Sunday Night	Thursday Day / Monday Night	Friday Day / Tuesday Night
8	Saturn	Sun	Moon	Mars	Mercury	Jupiter	Venus
9	Jupiter	Venus	Saturn	Sun	Moon	Mars	Mercury
10	Mars	Mercury	Jupiter	Venus	Saturn	Sun	Moon
11	Sun	Moon	Mars	Mercury	Jupiter	Venus	Saturn
12	Venus	Saturn	Sun	Moon	Mars	Mercury	Jupiter

The method of working with it is that you enter with the hour sought under the day sought, or under the night sought, and you will find the planet to which that hour is attributed. Know that the measure of the hour here is not equal to the measure of the clock hour; rather it increases or decreases according to the length or the shortness of the day or of the night, because the day and the night here are reckoned by the rising of the sun and its setting. What lies between sunrise and sunset, and the reverse of it, is the measure of the day or of the night. This measure is then divided into twelve parts, and each part is attributed to a planet, as you have seen.

Conditions of Diet, Election, and Incense

(13) That the practitioner keep the stomach free of excess food, except for what cannot be done without.

(14) That the practitioner avoid eating animals and whatever comes out of them.

(15) That he avoid eating everything that has a foul odour, such as garlic and onion.

(16) Astrological election. This is a condition particular to whatever is written or engraved upon metal or stone.

(17) That every operation be fumigated with the incense proper to it, according to what the learned have set out in detail for each request among the requests, for they assigned them only by correspondence. One group has said that it is enough to fumigate it with the incense of the planet to which it is attributed; and they assigned to every planet an incense for attraction and an incense for repelling, and they laid down a table for that, of which here is the explanation:

Planet	Incense of Attraction	Incense of Repelling
Saturn	Liquid storax and male frankincense	Asafoetida, sulfur, and the hair of a black cat
Jupiter	Yellow sandalwood, Qimārī aloeswood, and ambergris	Yellow sandalwood
Mars	Yellow sandalwood and male frankincense	The blood of a goat slaughtered on a Tuesday, and opium
Sun	Nadd, camphor, musk, and ambergris	Camphor
Venus	Male frankincense, benzoin, aloeswood, and mastic	Male frankincense
Mercury	Blue bdellium and male frankincense	Male frankincense and liquid storax
Moon	Onycha, ladanum, and male frankincense	Male frankincense

Some of them confined themselves to fumigating with male frankincense and coriander in every operation, whether of good or of ill, and it was stipulated that the coriander be whole grains, sound, and free of breakage and of weevils.

(18) That the practitioner maintain his garments and his body in a state of cleanliness, and that his place be likewise clean; and there enters into this the writing instrument, the ink, the parchment and whatever stands in its stead, whether of metal or of something else.

(19) That he face the noble qibla.

(20) That what is written be arranged according to its original form and its position. If it is a verse or a Name, then no later word is to be set before the one that precedes it, nor a later letter before one that comes before it; and if it is a magic square, the movement within it is to follow the succession of the numbers in their natural order. Even so, for every word, Name, or number that he writes, he should accompany the writing of it with the utterance that denotes it.

(21) That the oath appropriate to each operation be recited over it, according to the detail recorded under each of the purposes, as will come in its explanation, God Most High willing.

(22) That the digits in the magic squares be written in the Indian script, for in it lies the secret.

(23) That the writing of the letters and the digits be made beautiful, so that it is in a fine hand; and that the dimensions of the magic squares be fixed, their divisions made, and their sides made equal, so that there is no disparity in them at all, neither in length, nor in breadth, nor in the diagonal. That is the likelier to win their acceptance from the spirits appointed to their service, for their tastes are refined; and the more beautiful the hand, and

the more exact and even the magic square, the more its possessor is loved by them, beauty being met with its like.

(24) That blessings be sent upon the Prophet, God bless him and grant him peace, before the work and after it, because of the hadith:

Supplication between two blessings upon me is not turned back.

al-Du'ā' bayna al-ṣalātayni 'alayya lā yuraddu

الدعاء بين الصلاتين علي لا يرد

And the form of blessing upon him, God bless him and grant him peace, is:

O God, bless our master and our patron Muḥammad the Prophet, and his family and his Companions, and grant them peace, to the number of Your creatures, the contentment of Your own self, the weight of Your Throne, and the ink of Your words.

Allāhumma ṣalli 'alā sayyidinā wa-mawlānā Muḥammadin al-nabiyyi wa-'alā ālihi wa-ṣaḥbihi wa-sallim 'adada khalqika wa-riḍā'a nafsika wa-zinata 'arshika wa-midāda kalimātika

اللهم صل على سيدنا ومولانا محمد النبي وعلى آله وصحبه وسلم عدد خلقك ورضاء نفسك وزنة عرشك ومداد كلماتك

On Seeking Guidance and the Choice of Days

(25) That the practitioner seek guidance before every operation, so that he may proceed with clear insight regarding his affair. Its manner is that the practitioner pray two rak'as, reciting in the first of them, after al-Fātiḥa, Sūrat al-Kāfirūn, and in the second

Sūrat al-Ikhlāṣ. When he has given the closing salutation, he recites this supplication:

O God, I seek Your guidance through Your knowledge, I seek Your power through Your power, and I ask You of Your immense bounty to make plain to me the outcome of my affair in such-and-such a matter (and here he mentions his need); for if it be good, expand my breast for it and grant me success in doing it, and if it be evil, turn it away from me and turn me away from it. Truly You have power over everything.

Allāhumma innī astakhīruka bi-ʿilmika wa-astaqdiruka bi-qudratika wa-asʾaluka min faḍlika al-ʿaẓīm an tubayyina lī ʿāqibata amrī fī al-shayʾ al-fulānī (wa-yadhkuru ḥājatahu), fa-in kāna khayran fa-ishraḥ lahu ṣadrī wa-waffiqnī li-ʿamalihi, wa-in kāna sharran fa-iṣrifhu ʿannī wa-iṣrifnī ʿanhu innaka ʿalā kulli shayʾin qadīr.

اللهم إني أستخيرك بعلمك وأستقدرك بقدرتك وأسألك من فضلك العظيم أن تبين لي عاقبة أمري في الشيء الفلاني ويذكر حاجته، فإن كان خيرا فاشرح له صدري ووفقني لعمله، وإن كان شرا فاصرفه عني واصرفني عنه إنك على كل شيء قدير

He says it three times, or seven. Then, if after that he finds in his heart an expansion and an inclination toward the operation, let him perform it assured of success and of obtaining what he intends; and if he finds constriction, let him leave it and not do it, for it may well be a cause of harm to him. Let the seeking of guidance be with presence of heart and full wakefulness toward the power of God Most High, for He it is who encompasses affairs in their realities and their outcomes.

(26) That the day of the operation be undotted when the operation is for good. The dotted days in every Arabic lunar month are seven: the third, the fifth, the thirteenth, the sixteenth, the twenty-first, the twenty-fourth, and the twenty-fifth. Some of them have set down a fine rule for this, saying:

Your lover tends your passion; will nights return with the rebuff of hope? Whatever is dotted, its ill fortune has shown itself; and whatever is undotted, good fortune has come to pass.

Muḥibbuka yarʿā hawāka fa-hal taʿūdu layālī bi-ṣaddi al-amal
Fa-mā kāna manqūṭan badā naḥsuhu wa-mā kāna muhmalan fa-saʿdun ḥaṣal

محبك يرعى هواك فهل تعود ليالي بصد الأمل فما كان منقوطا بدا
نحسه وما كان مهملا فسعد حصل

(27) That the works of good be performed while the moon is increasing, and the works of harm in the days when it is dark. These are twenty-seven conditions; should the seeker of this science observe them, his operations shall succeed. God is the granter of success to what is right, and to Him are the return and the final home.

The First Purpose: A Brief Account of the Secrets of the Letters (al-Maqṣad al-Awwal fī Dhikr Nubdha min Asrār al-Ḥurūf)

Know that the letters have many secrets, which none perceives save those of His servants whom God Most High has chosen. Operating with the letters has many methods, of which we here confine ourselves to three: the first is the method of elicitation, the second the method of blending, and the third the method of the spirit.

The Method of Elicitation

As for the method of elicitation, it is a mighty elixir for drawing in delights and a noble antidote for repelling harms. By it the practitioner operates in all that he seeks among the works, and it is a treasure among the hidden treasures which many people have not reached.

It has three modes: graphic, alphabetic, and numerical.

The graphic mode is that you set down each letter according to its nature. Its example in the name Zayd is: ز ي د.

The alphabetic mode is that you set down each letter according to its pronunciation, by uttering the name of that letter. Its example in the name Zayd is: زاي . ياء . دال.

The numerical mode is of two kinds. The expanded is that you set down the name, each letter according to the pronunciation of the name of its number. Its example in the name Zayd is: س ب ع ا ر ب ع ة — ع ش ر ة — ة. The abbreviated is that you set down the name by the letters of the sum of its number. Its example in the name Zayd is: ا ك, because the zāy is seven, the yā' is ten, and the dāl is four; their sum is twenty-one, and its utterance is ا ك.

The benefit of them all is one, for the pivot rests only upon the result and the division, and both are obtained from each of them. So when you desire any operation among the works, whether for good or for harm, set out the name of the seeker, the one sought, and the need in a single line, then break it down until the zimām comes out. Its example, in the joining of Zayd and 'Amr in love, is in the following manner:

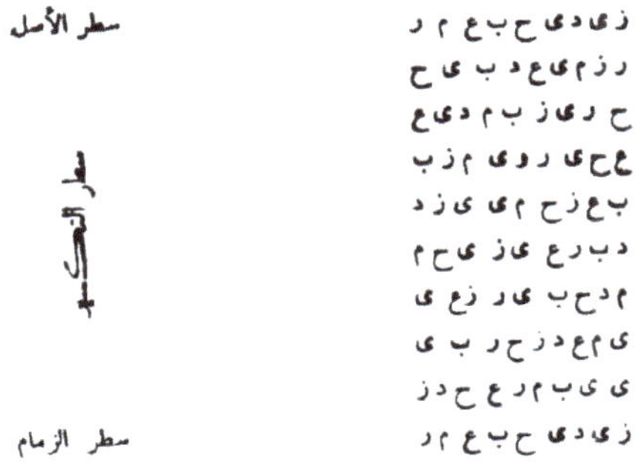

The letter-breaking arrangement: the line of origin, the line of breaking, and the line of the zimām

You then write these extracted lines, apart from the line of the zimām, upon a sheet of paper, and you write the oath upon its back. The way of extracting them is that you take the first three letters and the other three letters from the first line, which is the line of origin, and the first three letters and the last three from the line that comes before the line of the zimām, and to each set of three by itself you add Īl. In the example given, they come out as:

Barbarous names: Zayd Īl, ʿAmr Īl, Yaybāʾīl, Ḥadazāyīl

زيد إيل عمر إيل يبائيل حدزاييل

Then you take the whole numerical value of the line of origin — and it has also been said that you take the whole value of the lines of breaking apart from the line of the zimām, though the first is the better known — and you make that total speak in letters, and you add Īl to them, and from it you draw out the name of the spirit that governs the four named above, which stand in the service of the letters of the operation you have stated. So the name of the governor in this operation is Zamshāyīl (زمشاييل), because its total is 347, and its letters spell out ز م ش.

The manner of writing it is that, for each letter of the letters that voice the said total, you take one of the names of God, exalted is He, which has that letter at its beginning; and here they are: Zakī, Muʾmin, Shakūr. You write these names at the head of the reverse of the paper, and after them:

Answer, O Zayd Īl; and you, O ʿAmr Īl, Yaybāʾīl; and you, O Ḥadazāyīl: by the right of the mighty names of God, exalted is He — Zakī, Muʾmin, Shakūr — answer, O noble spirits, and take charge of inclining the heart of Zayd toward ʿAmr, until he loves him with a surpassing love, so that he cannot bear to be parted from him for the blink of an eye, nor for less than that. Answer, and do what I have commanded you, by the right of the king whose command prevails over you, Zamshā'īl.

Ajib yā Zayd Īl wa-anta yā 'Amr Īl Yaybā'īl wa-anta yā Ḥadazāyīl bi-ḥaqq asmā' Allāh ta'ālā al-'iẓām Zakī Mu'min Shakūr, ajībū ayyuhā al-arwāḥ al-kirām wa-tawakkalū bi-ta'ṭīf qalb Zayd 'alā 'Amr ḥattā yuḥibbahu ḥubban zā'idan bi-ḥaythu lā yastaṭī' yufāriqahu ṭarfata 'ayn wa-lā aqall min dhālika, ajībū wa-if'alū mā amartukum bihi bi-ḥaqq al-malik al-ghālib amruhu 'alaykum Zamshā'īl

أجب يا زيد إيل وأنت يا عمر إيل ييبائيل وأنت يا حدزاييل بحق أسماء الله تعالى العظام زكى مؤمن شكور أجيبوا أيها الأرواح الكرام وتوكلوا بتعطيف قلب زيد على عمرو حتى يحبه حبا زائدا بحيث لا يستطيع يفارقه طرفة عين ولا أقل من ذلك أجيبوا وافعلوا ما أمرتكم به بحق الملك الغالب أمره عليكم زمشائيل

Then, when the writing is complete, you hang the paper in a small frame of pomegranate wands above its censer, as was set out before, and you recite the oath over it. The way of that is that you mention the three names of God seven times and then mention the oath once; then you mention the names forty times and the oath once; then you mention the names three hundred times and the oath once.

After that you dispose of this paper according to the nature that prevails in it. If it is fiery, you place it near fire; if it is earthy, you bury it in clean ground, far from the places where feet tread;

if it is airy, you hang it where the wind blows; and if it is watery, you place it near water, in a sea or a well.

The Table of the Balances

The way to know the prevailing nature is that you enter with the letters drawn out from the total of the line of origin into the table that follows, and look for the strongest among them, and act according to its nature. Strength is reckoned here only by weight, so that whatever is heavier in weight is the stronger. Thus the strongest of the letters in each of the four natures is the one holding rank; next to it in strength is the one holding degree, then the one holding the minute, then the second, then the third, then the fourth; and the weakest of them is the one holding the fifth. This is the form of the table, as you see:

الرتبة	الوزن	الحروف المائية	الحروف الهوائية	الحروف الترابية	الحروف النارية
مرتبة	٧	د	ج	ب	ا
درجة	٦	ح	ز	و	ه
دقيقة	٥	ل	ك	ى	ط
ثانية	٤	ع	س	ن	م
ثالثة	٣	ر	ق	ص	ف
رابعة	٢	خ	ث	ت	ش
خامسة	١	غ	ظ	ض	ذ

The table of the elemental letters by rank and weight

Rank	Weight	Fiery letters	Earthy letters	Airy letters	Watery letters
Rank	7	ا	ب	ج	د
Degree	6	ه	و	ز	ح
Minute	5	ط	ي	ك	ل
Second	4	م	ن	س	ع
Third	3	ف	ص	ق	ر
Fourth	2	ش	ت	ث	خ
Fifth	1	ذ	ض	ظ	غ

Some have confined the operation, in works of good, to the seeker's carrying the parchment upon himself, and in works of harm to burying it in the path of the adversary; and the first is the better and the finer. If the letters of the sum of the line of origin are equal in weight, then you are free to direct your operation according to whichever nature you wish. One group held that the first course is to place what is written in the element of air, because it is the strongest of the four elements, then fire, then earth, then water.

Know that if the manner of the work is one of the works of harm, as when you wish to separate Zayd and ʿAmr, for example, then it proceeds upon the pattern already mentioned, exactly as it stands, except that in place of the word "incline" (أميل), which is appended to the letters of the oath, you mention the word "scatter" (طيش). That is because acting in works of good is bound to upper spirits, and the word "incline" belongs to the upper spirits, while in works of harm it is by lower spirits, and the word "scatter" belongs to the lower spirits.

The Manner of Removing Illness and Distress

And if the work is for the removal of an illness, or a distress, or the like, its manner is that you take the name of the illness, if the illness is general and embraces all the limbs, or the name of the diseased limb if the illness is particular to a limb itself. Then you spread that name out into letters by any of the modes set out before, and blend these letters with the letters of the nature opposed to the nature from which that illness arose. It is well known that the nature of the fiery letters is heat and dryness, which is the yellow-bilious nature; the nature of the earthy letters is coldness and dryness, which is the black-bilious nature; the nature of the airy letters is heat and moisture, which is the sanguine nature; and the nature of the watery letters is coldness and moisture, which is the watery nature.

When the blending of the letters of the patient's name, or of his limb, with the letters of the nature has been completed, you make them a single line and break it until the zimām comes out; then you write down everything except the line of the zimām upon paper. Then you take the sum of the letters of the line of origin, and its total is made to speak in letters, and you take for every letter of this utterance one of the Names of God that has that letter at its beginning. You mention these Names over the parchment the number of their sum, while you fumigate with the suitable incense in the manner set out before. When this is complete you give the parchment to the patient, that he may place it upon himself or upon the diseased limb, or you wash it off with water and give it to him to drink; then he is healed by the blessing of the noble Names, and what afflicts him of sickness passes away, by the permission of God Most High.

The Method of Blending

As for the method of blending, it is that you take the two names of the seeker and the one sought and blend them in direct order in works of good and in reverse in works of harm, and make them a single line. If the letters of one of the two names exceed the letters of the other, you join to the deficient one the noblest letters of its spirit. This is done by taking the sum of the number of its letters by the greater reckoning, making them speak in letters, entering with them into the table set out before, and taking from them whichever is of the higher rank, completing the deficiency with it.

An example of that is in Muḥammad and Sharaf: م ش ح ر م ف د. Since the name Sharaf falls short of the name Muḥammad by one letter, we took the sum of the letters of Sharaf, which is 580, because the shīn is three hundred, the rāʾ two hundred, and the fāʾ eighty, and their total is what we have mentioned, and its utterance is ف ث. So we took the letter fāʾ and joined it to its letters, and the line of blending was thus: م ش ح ر م ف د. The fāʾ rather than the thāʾ was taken only because the fāʾ is of the third rank and the thāʾ of the fourth rank, and every sixty of the fourth rank equals one of the third; understand this.

Then, after the blending of the two names, you take the name of the need whose accomplishment is intended, whether it be good, such as love, affection, tenderness, acceptance, gladness and joy, or harm, such as separation, turning away, enmity, expulsion, banishment and the like. You spread it out into letters and blend them with the letters of the two names in the manner already set out. Then you make this line the origin for your work, and break it beginning from the right in works of good and from the left in works of harm, because the right is good fortune and blessing, while the left is evil and ill fortune.

May God grant us and you success in doing good, and may He spare us the evil of every harm. Amen.

Waffaqanā Allāhu wa-iyyāka li-fiʿl al-khayr wa-kafānā sharra kull ḍayr, āmīn.

وفقنا الله وإياك لفعل الخير وكفانا شر كل ضير آمين

When the line of the zimām appears, you take the letters of the breaking.

Then write them on the face of a sheet of parchment. Then take the sum of the name of the seeker, the sum of the name of the one sought, and the sum of the need, and make each sum speak in letters on its own, adding to each of them the suffix, which is Īl in works of good and Ṭaysh in works of harm. Three spirits will then come out for you, and they are the ones who stand in the service of your operation. Then take the total of the three sums, make it speak in letters, add the suffix to it, and from it extract the king who rules over the three spirits mentioned. Then take the letters of the elicitation of the total and enter with them into the table of the balances, and whichever of them you find strongest in rank, take it and write it in the middle of the back of the parchment. Around it write a circle made of as many of the names of God Most High as come easily to you in which that letter stands first, and around this circle write the oath in the manner already described. Then recite the names over it after the total of the three sums, and recite the oath once after the cycle of the units, then once after every ten of the cycle of the tens, then once after every hundred, until the number is completed. Then, when the recitation is finished, dispose of the operation according to what the nature of the secret letter you wrote in the middle of the back of the parchment requires. Fear God Most High in your workings, and do nothing until you have weighed it in the balance of justice and set it against the rules of the purified Law.

May God grant me and you success in what He loves and is pleased with. Amen.

Waffaqanī Allāhu wa-iyyāka li-mā yuḥibbuhu wa-yarḍāhu. Āmīn.

وفقني الله وإياك لما يحبه ويرضاه آمين

The Method of the Spirit

As for the method of the spirit, it is the greatest elixir and the most noble antidote for the fulfilment of needs, the carrying out of desires, and the obtaining of what is sought. The sages and the learned were sparing of it, and they would not grant it except to one in whose trustworthiness and justice their confidence had grown strong, and then only after severe toil and strenuous effort. It is that you take the name of the seeker and the name of the one sought, reckon the letters of each of them on its own by the abjad reckoning, make what results from each of them speak in letters, and blend them into a single line. Then draw a wafq to the number of the resulting letters and fill it in so that its sides and its positions are equal. Then write opposite each cell one of the names of God Most High that begins with the letters of that cell, and opposite each diagonal write the name of the spirit that stands in the service of the letter in that cell. Then write on the back of it:

Answer, O so-and-so, so-and-so.
Ajib yā kadhā kadhā
أجب يا كذا كذا

Then mention the names of the angels charged with the letters of the elicitation, and say:

By the right of Him who said to the heavens and the earth, "Come, willingly or unwillingly," and they said, "We come willingly": answer, and do such-and-such.
Bi-ḥaqqi man qāla li-l-samāwāti wa-l-arḍi i'tiyā ṭawʿan aw karhan qālatā ataynā ṭā'iʿīn ajībū wa-ifʿalū kadhā wa-kadhā
بحق من قال للسموات والأرض ائتيا طوعا أو كرها قالتا أتينا طائعين
أجيبوا وافعلوا كذا وكذا

Then mention your need, and say:

May God bless you and send blessing upon you.

Bāraka Allāhu fīkum wa-ʿalaykum

بارك الله فيكم وعليكم

Then recite the names of God Most High that you wrote in the wafq to the number of the letters of the two names, and recite the oath after each cycle of the cycles of the number. Let all of this be done while you fumigate with male frankincense and coriander, with aloeswood added to them in works of good and sulphur in works of harm. Then dispose of the parchment according to what the prevailing nature requires, in the manner already described.

An example of joining two persons in love, the second of them ʿAmr: the number of the first is 21, and its utterance is ا ك; the number of ʿAmr is 310, and its utterance is ي ش. The wafq therefore comes out fourfold, thus:

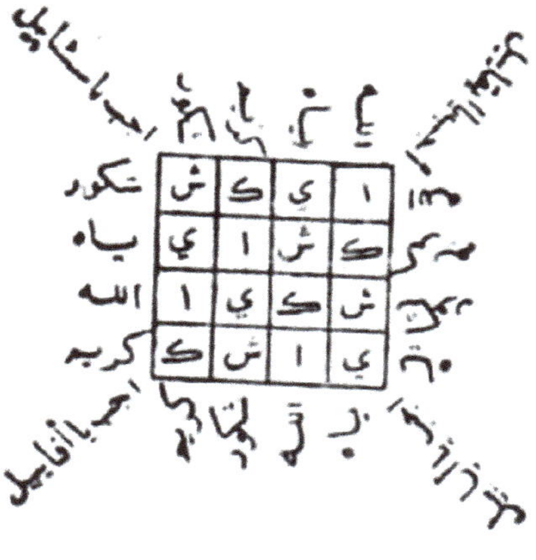

The fourfold wafq

The Table of Letters, Spirits and Names of God

Here is a table setting out for you what belongs to each letter among the upper spirits, the lower spirits, and the names of God Most High, so that you may seek help by it in reaching what is sought. Opposite each letter I have placed its number by the abjad reckoning and by the greater reckoning, to complete the benefit, as you see:

الحروف	عددها بجمل أبجدي	عددها بالجمل الكبير	الأرواح العلوية	الأرواح السفلية	أسماء الله تعالى
ا	١٠	١١١	إبقايل	قباطيش	الله أول آخر تعالى
ب	٢	٣	جايل	حطيش	بر بديع باقي باري، باسط باعث باطن
ج	٣	٥٣	جنايل	جحطيش	جليل جامع جبار
د	٤	٣٥	هلاييل	بهطيش	دائم ديان دافع
ه	٥	٦	وايل	وطيش	هادي
و	٦	١٣	حيايل	بحيطش	ودود واسع وهاب وكيل ولي واحد
ز	٧	١٨	حيايل	بحطيش	زكي واحد والي وارث
ح	٨	٩	طايل	ططيش	حي حسيب حنان حكيم حليم حميد حق حفيظ
ط	٩	١٠	يايل	يطيش	طيب طاهر
ي	١٠	١١	آيايل	باطيش	ياه يوه
ك	٢٠	١٠١	أقاييل	قاطيش	كريم كبير
ل	٣٠	٧١	أعايل	عاطيش	لطيف
م	٤٠	٩٠	صايل	صطيش	مغني معطي مانع مقيت منتقم مجيب مجيد متعال مؤمن مهيمن مالك متين متكبر مصور محصي مبدي معيد محيي مميت ماجد مقتدر
	٥٠	١٠٦	وقاييل	قوطيش	نور نافع
س	٦٠	١٢٠	كقاييل	فكطيش	سلام سريع سميع
ع	٧٠	١٣٠	لبايل	قلطيش	عزيز عليم علي عدل عظيم عفو
ف	٨٠	٨١	أقايل	قاطيش	فرد فاطر فتاح
ص	٩٠	٩٥	صايل	صهطيش	صمد صادق صبور
ق	١٠٠	١٨١	أقتايل	ققاطيش	قادر قدير قوي قهار قابض قيوم قدوس
ر	٢٠٠	٢٠١	أرايل	راطيش	رب رحمن رحيم رءوف رزاق رقيب رشيد
ش	٣٠٠	٣٦٠	ستايل	شسطيش	شهيد شكور
ت	٤٠٠	٤٠١	أمايل	تاطيش	تواب
ث	٥٠٠	٥٠١	أثاييل	ثاطيش	ثابت
خ	٦٠٠	٦٠١	أخايل	خاطيش	خالق خافض
ذ	٧٠٠	٧٢١	القايل	ذلاطيش	ذو الجلال والإكرام
ض	٨٠٠	٨٠١	هضايل	ضهطيش	ضار
ظ	٩٠٠	٩٠١	أظايل	ظاطاش	ظاهر
غ	١٠٠٠	١٠٦٠	سفايل	غسطيش	غفار غني غفور

The table of the letters, their numbers, their upper and lower spirits, and the names of God

Letter	Number by Abjad Reckoning	Number by the Greater Reckoning	Upper Spirits	Lower Spirits	Names of God Most High
ا	10	111	Ibqāyīl (إبقايل)	Qabāṭīsh (قباطيش)	Allāh, Awwal, Ākhir, Taʿālā
ب	2	3	Jāyīl (جايل)	Ḥaṭīsh (حطيش)	Barr, Badīʿ, Bāqī, Bāriʾ, Bāsiṭ, Bāʿith, Bāṭin

Letter	Number by Abjad Reckoning	Number by the Greater Reckoning	Upper Spirits	Lower Spirits	Names of God Most High
ج	3	53	Janāyīl (جنايل)	ʿAjṭīsh (عجطيش)	Jalīl, Jāmiʿ, Jabbār
د	4	35	Halāyīl (هلايل)	Bahṭīsh (بهطيش)	Dāʾim, Dayyān, Dāfiʿ
ه	5	6	Wāyīl (وايل)	Waṭīsh (وطيش)	Hādī
و	6	13	Ḥaybāyīl (حيبايل)	ʿAjṭash (عجطش)	Wadūd, Wāsiʿ, Wahhāb, Wakīl, Walī, Wāḥid
ز	7	18	Ḥaybāyīl (حيبايل)	ʿAṭīsh (عطيش)	Zakī, Wāḥid, Wālī, Wārith
ح	8	9	Ṭāyīl (طايل)	Ṭaṭīsh (ططيش)	Ḥayy, Ḥasīb, Ḥannān, Ḥakīm, Ḥalīm, Ḥamīd, Ḥaqq, Ḥafīẓ
ط	9	10	Yāyīl (يايل)	Yaṭīsh (يطيش)	Ṭayyib, Ṭāhir
ى	10	11	Abāyīl (أبايل)	Yāṭīsh (ياطيش)	Yāh, Yūh
ك	20	101	Aqāyīl (أقايل)	Qāṭīsh (قاطيش)	Karīm, Kabīr
ل	30	71	Aʿāyīl (أعايل)	ʿĀṭīsh (عاطيش)	Laṭīf
م	40	90	Ṣāyīl (صايل)	Ṣaṭīsh (صطيش)	Mughnī, Muʿṭī, Māniʿ, Muqīt, Muntaqim, Mujīb, Majīd, Mutaʿāl, Muʾmin, Muhaymin, Malik, Matīn, Mutakabbir, Muṣawwir, Muḥṣī, Mubdiʾ, Muʿīd, Muḥyī, Mumīt, Mājid, Muqtadir

Letter	Number by Abjad Reckoning	Number by the Greater Reckoning	Upper Spirits	Lower Spirits	Names of God Most High
ن	50	106	Waqāyīl (وقايل)	Qawṭīsh (قوطيش)	Nūr, Nāfiʿ
س	60	120	Kafāyīl (كفايل)	Fakṭīsh (فكطيش)	Salām, Sarīʿ, Samīʿ
ع	70	130	Labāyīl (لبايل)	Qalṭīsh (قلطيش)	ʿAzīz, ʿAlīm, ʿAlī, ʿAdl, ʿAẓīm, ʿAfuww
ف	80	81	Afāyīl (أفايل)	Fāṭīsh (فاطيش)	Fard, Fāṭir, Fattāḥ
ص	90	95	Ṣāyīl (صايل)	Ṣahṭīsh (صهطيش)	Ṣamad, Ṣādiq, Ṣabūr
ق	100	181	Afqāyīl (أفقايل)	Qaqāṭīsh (ققاطيش)	Qādir, Qadīr, Qawī, Qahhār, Qābiḍ, Qayyūm, Quddūs
ر	200	201	Arāyīl (أرايل)	Rāṭīsh (راطيش)	Rabb, Raḥmān, Raḥīm, Raʾūf, Razzāq, Raqīb, Rashīd
ش	300	360	Sashāyīl (سشايل)	Shasṭīsh (شسطيش)	Shahīd, Shakūr
ت	400	401	Atāyīl (أتايل)	Tāṭīsh (تاطيش)	Tawwāb
ث	500	501	Athāyīl (أثايل)	Thāṭīsh (ثاطيش)	Thābit
خ	600	601	Akhāyīl (أخايل)	Khāṭīsh (خاطيش)	Khāliq, Khāfiḍ
ذ	700	731	al-Dhāyīl (الذايل)	Dhalāṭīsh (ذلاطيش)	Dhū al-Jalāl wa-l-Ikrām

Letter	Number by Abjad Reckoning	Number by the Greater Reckoning	Upper Spirits	Lower Spirits	Names of God Most High
ض	800	801	Haḍāyīl (هضايل)	Ḍahṭīsh (ضهطيش)	Ḍārr
ظ	900	901	Aẓāyīl (أظايل)	Ẓāṭanish (ظاطنش)	Ẓāhir
غ	1000	1060	Saghāyīl (سغايل)	Ghasṭīsh (غسطيش)	Ghaffār, Ghanī, Ghafūr

You have now learned that every upper spirit is concerned with the works of good, and every lower spirit is concerned with the works of evil. May God grant me and you success in what pleases Him. Amen.

The Second Purpose: A Mention of Some of the Secrets of the Magic Squares (al-Maqṣūd al-Thānī fī Dhikr Nubdha min Asrār al-Awfāq)

Know that the science of the magic squares is a science by which one arrives at the harmonizing of numbers and their equalization across the diagonals and the sides, without repetition.

The magic square is a right-angled surface bounded by four equal sides, divided into equal parts. Straight lines join the divisions of each side to those of the side opposite it, and by them the surface is divided into small squares whose number is the number obtained by squaring the number of the divisions of one of its sides

Then numbers are entered into it, if it is a numerical wafq, the greatest of them according to the number of its cells and set down in graduated order, so that the resulting sums of the rows, columns, and diagonals of its small squares are all equal, without any number occurring twice among them. Or letters are entered into it, if it is a lettered wafq; or words, if it is a worded one; or names, if it is a named one — so that what stands in the uppermost of its crosswise rows is found in every one of its lengthwise rows.

Then know that every wafq has a key (miftāḥ), a lock (mighlāq), a balance (ʿadl), a wafq, an area (misāḥa), a regulator (ḍābiṭ), a limit (ghāya), and a root (aṣl). Knowledge of these eight principles is incumbent upon the seeker, because from each one of these names he extracts an upper angel and a lower helper, and the helper is the servant of the upper angel.

The key is the first number placed in the wafq, and the lock is the last number placed in it. The balance is the sum of the key together with the lock. The wafq is the number of one side among its sides. The area is the sum of the number of the sides of the wafq. The regulator is the sum of the wafq together with the area. The limit is the sum of the number of its sides lengthwise and crosswise; and if you wish, you may say that it is twice the area. The root is the product of its lock by its limit.

On the Planets and Properties of the Squares

Then every wafq from the threefold to the ninefold is attributed to one of the seven planets. The threefold is attributed to Saturn, the fourfold to Jupiter, the fivefold to Mars, the sixfold to the Sun, the sevenfold to Venus, the eightfold to Mercury, and the ninefold to the Moon. As for the tenfold, it is attributed to the sphere of the zodiac; and whatever lies beyond these eight is attributed to no planet in particular.

Each one of these eight wafqs has many properties; most have taken them from the natures of the planets to which the wafqs are attributed, while some have gone to taking them from the letters of the sides of their natural roots. And they said: among the properties of the threefold are attraction, union, endurance, and restoration, and every purpose the name of which begins with the letter jīm (ج). Among the properties of the fourfold are the continuance of righteousness and good, the indication of unseen tidings, and the warding off of harms, and every purpose the name of which begins with the letter dāl (د). Among the properties of the fivefold are awe, passionate longing, excitement, love, and the like of these. Among the properties of the sixfold are governance, allegiance, protection, and safeguarding, and whatever resembles these. Among the properties of the sevenfold are abstinence, the increase of blessing and of wealth, marriages, and the purifying of hearts through love and affection, and whatever is akin to that. Among the properties of the eightfold are preservation, judgement, sweetness of soul, purity of hearts, and their guidance to the straight path. Among the properties of the tenfold are ease, certainty in the oath, and strength in body, in deed, and in speech. The first of the two statements is the better known and the more fitting.

The Method of Filling a Numerical Square

The method of filling every wafq among the numerical wafqs is that you take the number which is required to be entered into the wafq, subtract from it the base (uss) of that wafq, divide the remainder by the number of its side, and enter the quotient in the cell of the key. Then you proceed by an increase of one according to its natural order until it is complete. And if there is a fraction, make it the first of the final cycle and join it to what is due to it; then proceed by an increase of one, as has already been said, until completion.

The method of knowing the base of every wafq is that you add its natural key, which is one, to its lock, which is the end of its cells, and multiply the result by half its side. What comes out is the least number that may be entered into it; then subtract from it the number of its side, and what remains is the base. And if you wish, you may say that it is the product of its lock, after one has been subtracted from it, by half its side.

And every wafq, in its natural arrangement, has many methods. I shall mention of them, if God Most High wills, the nearest and the best known of them, appending to each wafq some mention of its properties and of the benefits of some of it, and seeking blessing through what has been handed down from the righteous servants of God, whom God Most High acquainted with His secrets, so that through them they brought benefit to His servants. So I say, and with God rests the goodness of acceptance:

The Threefold Square and the Seal of al-Ghazālī

As for the threefold square, the form of its natural composition is as follows, and it may also be set out in letters, thus:

د	ط	ب
ج	ه	ز
ح	ا	و

٤	٩	٢
٣	٥	٧
٨	١	٦

The threefold square in numbers and in letters

Its attribution to the Imam Abū Ḥāmid al-Ghazālī became famous, although he was not the one who devised it. It has been said that it belonged to Āṣaf ibn Barkhiyā; it has been said that it was upon the seal of Solomon, and that by it his dominion was completed; and it has been said that it was upon the seal of Adam, since it is his number, and that it was pyramidal, thus:

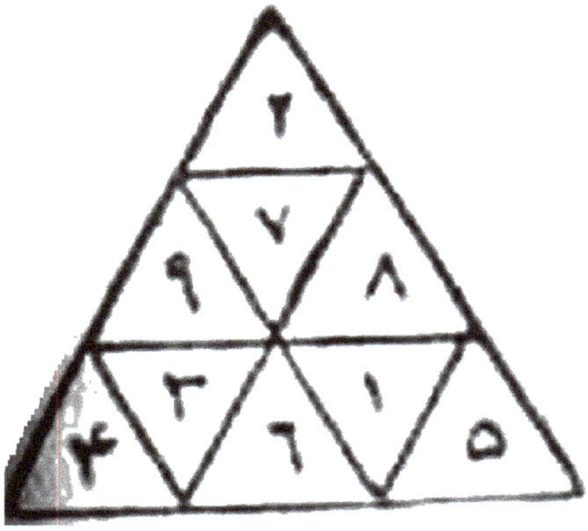

The seal in pyramidal form

When it reached the Imam al-Ghazālī, may God have mercy on him, he applied it to the numbers of كهيعص and حم عسق and extracted for it the five famous verses, and so it was attributed to him.

The Imam al-Ghazālī, may God Most High have mercy on him, said: For a span of time I went about travelling through the lands in search of this blessed seal, until I reached Balkh. When I reached it I was directed to one of the shaykhs, and I asked him about it, and he answered me and said: I have this noble seal with me. So I remained in his service as long as God willed; then he gave it to me and charged me to keep it hidden from the ignorant, because the greatest name of God is in it, so that whoever attains it must not be one who makes a plaything of his religion.

On the Nine Letters of the Seal

The author of *Mustawjibat al-Maḥāmid fī Sharḥ Khātam Abī Ḥāmid* said: Al-Ghazālī attained what he attained only through this blessed seal, and whoever knows it has known the greatest name. Then he said: Its letters were gathered from His saying, may He be exalted, كهيعص, and His saying, حم عسق. It is no objection that these are ten letters while the letters of the square are nine, because the repetition of the letter ʿayn (ع) makes the two of them equal to a single one, so that the letters are nine.

Then, of these letters, some remain in their own state without alteration, and some are altered by subtraction according to what the houses of the square require. Thus the alif (ا) was drawn out from the yāʾ (ي) after the number of the houses of the square had been subtracted from it; the bāʾ (ب) from the kāf (ك) after subtracting eighteen; the jīm (ج) from the qāf (ق), because in the abjad order it is the first of the hundreds, which are the third of the numerical ranks, and for that reason they established the jīm from it; the dāl (د) from the mīm (م) after subtracting nine four times, and then the hā' (ه) is the nearest to it, in its own state; the wāw (و) from the sīn (س) after subtracting nine six times; the zāy (ز) from the 'ayn (ع) after subtracting nine seven times, and the ḥā' (ح) is the nearest to it, in its own state; and the ṭā' (ط) from the ṣād (ص) after subtracting nine nine times.

The Five Verses of the Seal

Then he said: It has five verses which are its secret, and upon them turns the course of its workings and its operations. The first letter of each of these verses is one of the letters of كهيعص, and the last letter of each of them is one of the letters of حم عسق. They are in this order:

Like water which We sent down from the sky, so that it becomes dry stubble which the winds scatter.

Ka-mā'in anzalnāhu mina al-samā'i fa-aṣbaḥa hashīman tadhrūhu al-riyāḥ

(ك) كماء أنزلناه من السماء فأصبح هشيما تذروه الرياح (ح)

He is God, other than whom there is no god, the Knower of the unseen and the witnessed; He is the Most Gracious, the Most Merciful.

Huwa Allāhu alladhī lā ilāha illā huwa ʿālimu al-ghaybi wa-l-shahādati huwa al-Raḥmānu al-Raḥīm

(ه) هو الله الذي لا إله إلا هو عالم الغيب والشهادة هو الرحمن الرحيم (م)

The Day of the Approaching Event, when hearts are at the throats, choking with grief; the wrongdoers will have no devoted friend and no intercessor who is obeyed.

Yawma al-āzifati idhi al-qulūbu ladā al-ḥanājiri kāẓimīna mā lil-ẓālimīna min ḥamīmin wa-lā shafīʿin yuṭāʿ

(ي) يوم الآزفة إذ القلوب لدى الحناجر كاظمين ما للظالمين من حميم ولا شفيع يطاع (ع)

A soul will know what it has brought forward. So I swear by the receding stars, running and setting, and by the night as it draws on, and by the dawn as it breathes.

ʿAlimat nafsun mā aḥḍarat fa-lā uqsimu bi-l-khunnasi al-jawāri al-kunnasi wa-l-layli idhā ʿasʿasa wa-l-ṣubḥi idhā tanaffasa

(ع) علمت نفس ما أحضرت فلا أقسم بالخنس الجوار الكنس والليل إذا عسعس والصبح إذا تنفس (س)

Ṣād. By the Qur'ān full of remembrance. Nay, those who disbelieve are in arrogance and dissension.

Ṣād wa-l-Qur'āni dhī al-dhikri bali alladhīna kafarū fī 'izzatin wa-shiqāq

(ص) ص والقرآن ذي الذكر بل الذين كفروا في عزة وشقاق (ق)

The Manner of Reciting the Five Verses

These verses are its secret and the pivot of its workings only because all of its properties that are to be mentioned hereafter, and the others that we have not mentioned — whether they are properties belonging to it as a whole, or to its single letters, or to its paired letters — are not completed except by reciting these five verses over it forty-five times if the property belongs to the square as a whole, twenty-five times if it belongs to its single letters, and twenty times if it belongs to its paired letters. The single letters are the letters of the two middle sides, the lengthwise one and the crosswise one, namely ا ج ه ز ط; and the paired letters are those that lie in its four corners, namely ب د و ح. The paired letters, taken on their own, are of benefit in all works of good and of felicity, while the single letters, taken on their own, belong properly to works of evil and of harm; and the square in its entirety operates in good and in evil alike.

On the Properties of the Complete Square

Among the properties of the square in its completeness: if a man has been imprisoned and no release is hoped for him, this square is written out for him on Monday after the afternoon prayer upon a sheet of paper, and the prisoner looks into it; his release will be made easy, if God Most High wills.

Among them, for safeguarding goods: this square is written upon whatever holds the goods, whether a chest, a cupboard, or the like. They will not be stolen; and if they are stolen, the thief will appear at once, his affair will be made public, and he will become known.

Among them, for easing the delivery of a woman whose childbirth is hard: this square is written upon three pieces of unfired pottery. Two of them are laid upon her thighs and the third is hung between her eyes, on condition that the writing be done in the first hour of Saturday. The ascendant should be the sign of Sagittarius and the moon in Cancer; but this is seldom accomplished except by one who has obtained it before the need arose.

Its Uses for Love, Intimacy and Stirring Desire

Among them, for love and affection: write the square in its completeness upon nine dates with a fine pen, then recite over it once:

So We returned him to his mother, that her eye might be comforted and that she might not grieve. Come forward, O so-and-so son of so-and-so, to so-and-so daughter of so-and-so, by Him who said: There is no god but I, so worship Me; and I cast upon you love from Me, that you might be formed under My eye; had you spent all that is in the earth you could not have joined their hearts, but God joined them, for He is Mighty, Wise; come forward and do not fear, you are among the secure; and We gathered them all together; has there come upon man a span of time in which he was not a thing remembered? We created man from a mingled drop, to try him. Thus does God incline so-and-so son of so-and-so with love for so-and-so daughter of so-and-so.

Fa-radadnāhu ilā ummihi kay taqarra ʿaynuhā wa-lā taḥzana. Aqbil yā fulān ibn fulāna ilā fulāna bint fulāna bi-lladhī qāla lā ilāha illā anā fa-ʿbudnī, wa-alqaytu ʿalayka maḥabbatan minnī wa-li-tuṣnaʿa ʿalā ʿaynī, law anfaqta mā fī al-arḍi jamīʿan mā allafta bayna qulūbihim wa-lākinna Allāha allafa baynahum innahu ʿazīzun ḥakīm, aqbil wa-lā takhaf innaka mina al-āminīn fa-jamaʿnāhum jamʿan, hal atā ʿalā al-insāni ḥīnun mina al-dahri lam yakun shayʾan madhkūran, innā khalaqnā al-insāna min nuṭfatin amshājin nabtalīh. Kadhālika yumīlu Allāhu fulān ibn fulāna bi-maḥabbati fulāna bint fulāna.

فرددناه إلى أمه كي تقر عينها ولا تحزن، أقبل يا فلان ابن فلانة إلى فلانة بنت فلانة بالذي قال لا إله إلا أنا فاعبدني، وألقيت عليك محبة مني ولتصنع على عيني، لو أنفقت ما في الأرض جميعا ما ألفت بين قلوبهم ولكن الله ألف بينهم إنه عزيز حكيم، أقبل ولا تخف إنك من الآمنين فجمعناهم جمعا، هل أتى على الإنسان حين من الدهر لم يكن شيئا مذكورا، إنا خلقنا الإنسان من نطفة أمشاج نبتليه، كذلك يميل الله فلان ابن فلانة بمحبة فلانة بنت فلانة

Then fumigate them with male frankincense and liquid storax and feed them to the desired one, for he will love the one who seeks him with an exceeding love. Some of the scholars have allowed a man to restrict himself to writing the letters of the square, each letter upon one date, and that too is good.

Among them, for intimacy: the square is written together with the name of the seeker and the name of his mother in a bowl or the like; it is then washed off and given to the desired one to drink, and it works a mighty thing in the producing of intimacy.

Among them, for stirring desire: write the square with dragon's blood upon your right palm, then strike with it the breast of whomever you wish, and he will follow you.

Its Uses for Asking a Favour and Drawing Hearts

It is set out as two contiguous triangles, one above the other. The single letters are written in their houses in the upper triangle, and the paired letters, reversed, in their houses in the lower triangle, in this manner:

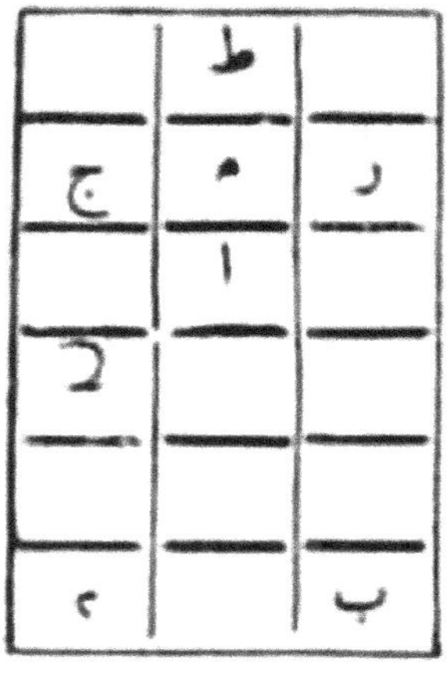

The two contiguous triangles

Then write the name of the desired one and the name of his mother upon another sheet, slip it in between the two squares, carry it with you, go to the desired one and ask of him your need; he will grant it without fail.

Among them, for love and the joining of hearts: make a tablet of silver weighing three dirhams. Gild one of its two faces with gold, and engrave upon the gilded face the single letters in their places, and upon the other face the paired letters in their places. Carry it with you, for it is the utmost in drawing hearts to you, and no one will see you but will love you.

The Frankincense Rite for the Joining of Hearts

Among them, for love, affection, and the joining of hearts: take a large piece of frankincense and write upon it the square in its completeness; then take forty-eight small pieces of frankincense and write upon twelve of them the letter bāʾ (ب), on twelve the letter dāl (د), on twelve the letter wāw (و), and on twelve the letter ḥāʾ (ح); and each group of twelve is set apart by itself. Then take a censer in which there is kindled charcoal, and cast upon it four pebbles of frankincense, so that each pebble stands for one of the paired letters, and recite His saying, exalted is He:

And I have chosen you, so listen to what is revealed.

Wa-anā ikhtartuka fa-stamiʿ li-mā yūḥā

وأنا اخترتك فاستمع لما يوحى

Recite it twenty times, the number of the sum of the paired letters; then recite the adjuration once. Then take four more pebbles, a second group, in the manner described, and cast them into the fire, and recite His saying, exalted is He:

And I cast upon you love from Me.

Wa-alqaytu ʿalayka maḥabbatan minnī

وألقيت عليك محبة مني

Recite it twenty times, and the adjuration once. Then take four pebbles, a third group, in the same way, and cast them into the fire, and recite His saying, exalted is He:

And I fashioned you for Myself.

Wa-ṣṭanaʿtuka li-nafsī

واصطنعتك لنفسي

Recite it twenty times, and the adjuration once. Then do the same with the remaining pebbles, four by four. Over the fourth group of four, recite:

And We brought him near in secret communion. And We raised him to a lofty station.

Wa-qarrabnāhu najiyyā. Wa-rafaʿnāhu makānan ʿaliyyā

وقربناه نجيا ، ورفعناه مكانا عليا

And over the fifth:

When they saw him they held him in awe and cut their hands, and said: God forbid! This is no mortal; this is none but a noble angel.

Fa-lammā ra'aynahu akbarnahu wa-qaṭṭaʿna aydiyahunna wa-qulna ḥāsha li-llāhi mā hādhā basharan in hādhā illā malakun karīm

فلما رأينه أكبرنه وقطعن أيديهن وقلن حاش لله ما هذا بشرا إن هذا إلا ملك كريم

And over the sixth:

And the king said: Bring him to me. When the messenger came to him, he said: Return to your lord and ask him what was the case of the women who cut their hands; surely my Lord is aware of their guile. He said: What was your affair when you sought to seduce Joseph from himself? They said: God forbid! We know no evil of him. The wife of the ʿAzīz said: Now the truth has come to light; it was I who sought to seduce him from himself, and he is indeed of the truthful. That was so he might know that I did not betray him in secret, and that God does not guide the guile of the treacherous. And the king said: Bring him to me, that I may reserve him for myself. And when he had spoken with him he said: Today you are established and trusted with us.

Wa-qāla al-maliku i'tūnī bihi fa-lammā jā'ahu al-rasūlu qāla irjiʿ ilā rabbika fa-s'alhu mā bālu al-niswati allātī qaṭṭaʿna aydiyahunna inna rabbī bi-kaydihinna ʿalīm. Qāla mā

khaṭbukunna idh rāwadtunna Yūsufa ʿan nafsihi qulna ḥāsha li-llāhi mā ʿalimnā ʿalayhi min sūʾ. Qālat imraʾatu al-ʿazīzi al-āna ḥaṣḥaṣa al-ḥaqqu anā rāwadtuhu ʿan nafsihi wa-innahu la-mina al-ṣādiqīn. Dhālika li-yaʿlama annī lam akhunhu bi-l-ghaybi wa-anna Allāha lā yahdī kayda al-khāʾinīn. Wa-qāla al-maliku iʾtūnī bihi astakhliṣhu li-nafsī fa-lammā kallamahu qāla innaka al-yawma ladaynā makīnun amīn

وقال الملك ائتوني به فلما جاءه الرسول قال ارجع إلى ربك فاسأله ما بال النسوة اللاتي قطعن أيديهن إن ربي بكيدهن عليم . قال ما خطبكن إذ راودتن يوسف عن نفسه قلن حاش لله ما علمنا عليه من سوء ، قالت امرأة العزيز الآن حصحص الحق أنا راودته عن نفسه وإنه لمن الصادقين . ذلك ليعلم أني لم أخنه بالغيب وأن الله لا يهدي كيد الخائنين . وقال الملك ائتوني به أستخلصه لنفسي فلما كلمه قال إنك اليوم لدينا مكين أمين

And over the seventh:

And We removed whatever rancour was in their breasts, so that they became brothers.

Wa-nazaʿnā mā fī ṣudūrihim min ghillin ikhwānā

ونزعنا ما في صدورهم من غل إخوانا

And over the eighth:

They love them as they should love God; but those who believe are stronger in love for God.

Yuḥibbūnahum ka-ḥubbi Allāhi wa-lladhīna āmanū ashaddu ḥubban li-llāh

يحبونهم كحب الله والذين آمنوا أشد حبا لله

And over the ninth:

And among His signs is that He created for you, from yourselves, mates, that you might find rest in them, and He set between you affection and mercy.

Wa-min āyātihi an khalaqa lakum min anfusikum azwājan li-taskunū ilayhā wa-ja'ala baynakum mawaddatan wa-raḥma

ومن آياته أن خلق لكم من أنفسكم أزواجا لتسكنوا إليها وجعل بينكم مودة ورحمة

And over the tenth:

It may be that God will set affection between you and those of them with whom you have been at enmity.

'Asā Allāhu an yaj'ala baynakum wa-bayna alladhīna 'ādaytum minhum mawadda

عسى الله أن يجعل بينكم وبين الذين عاديتم منهم مودة

And over the eleventh:

The Most Merciful will appoint love for them.

Sa-yajʿalu lahumu al-Raḥmānu wuddā

سيجعل لهم الرحمن ودا

And over the twelfth:

And He joined your hearts together, so that by His favour you became brothers.

Fa-allafa bayna qulūbikum fa-aṣbaḥtum bi-niʿmatihi ikhwānā

فألف بين قلوبكم فأصبحتم بنعمته إخوانا

Then cast down the large pebble and recite His saying, exalted is He:

And He joined their hearts together. Had you spent all that is in the earth, you could not have joined their hearts, but God joined them together; surely He is Mighty, Wise.

Wa-allafa bayna qulūbihim law anfaqta mā fī al-arḍi jamīʿan mā allafta bayna qulūbihim wa-lākinna Allāha allafa baynahum innahu ʿazīzun ḥakīm

وألف بين قلوبهم لو أنفقت ما في الأرض جميعا ما ألفت بين قلوبهم ولكن الله ألف بينهم إنه عزيز حكيم

Recite it twenty times, and the adjuration once. After all of that, say:

O God, I ask You by every name that is Yours, by which You have named Yourself, or which You have sent down in Your Book, or taught to any one of Your creation, or kept to Yourself in Your knowledge of the unseen, that You bless and grant peace to our master Muḥammad and to his family and his companions. O God, the hearts of the servants are in Your hand; You turn them however You will. O God, place in the heart of so-and-so son of so-and-so kindness, tenderness, love, affection, delight, joy, fondness, devoted attachment, gentleness, success, accord, reconciliation, amendment, tender care, and compassion toward so-and-so daughter of so-and-so, until he loves her with an immense love and cannot bear to part from her for the blink of an eye, nor for less than that, by the Joiner of hearts and of eyes. O Gatherer of mankind for a day in which there is no doubt, O Beloved, O Loving One, O Lord of the Glorious Throne, O Doer of whatever He wills, surely You have power over all things and are worthy to answer. And may God bless and grant peace to our master Muḥammad, the unlettered Prophet, and his family and his companions.

Allāhumma innī as'aluka bi-kulli ismin huwa laka sammayta bihi nafsaka aw anzaltahu fī kitābika aw ʿallamtahu aḥadan min khalqika aw ista'tharta bihi fī ʿilmi al-ghaybi ʿindaka an tuṣalliya wa-tusallima ʿalā sayyidinā Muḥammadin wa-ʿalā ālihi wa-ṣaḥbihi. Allāhumma inna qulūba al-ʿibādi bi-yadika tuqallibuhā kayfa tashā'. Allāhumma ijʿal fī qalbi fulān ibn fulāna al-luṭfa wa-l-ʿaṭfa wa-l-maḥabbata wa-l-mawaddata wa-l-surūra wa-l-faraḥa wa-l-wudda wa-l-tawadduda wa-l-rifqa wa-l-tawfīqa wa-l-ittifāqa wa-l-ṣulḥa wa-l-iṣlāḥa wa-l-ḥunuwwa wa-l-shafaqata ʿalā fulāna bint fulāna ḥattā yuḥibbahā ḥubban jamman wa-lā yastaṭīʿa an yufāriqahā ṭarfata ʿaynin wa-lā aqalla min dhālika bi-muʾallifi al-qulūbi wa-l-abṣāri yā jāmiʿa al-nāsi li-yawmin lā rayba fīhi yā Ḥabību yā Wadūdu yā Dhā al-ʿArshi al-Majīdi yā Faʿʿālan li-mā yurīdu innaka ʿalā kulli shayʾin qadīrun wa-bi-l-ijābati jadīrun wa-ṣallā Allāhu ʿalā sayyidinā Muḥammadin al-nabiyyi al-ummiyyi wa-ʿalā ālihi wa-ṣaḥbihi wa-sallam

اللهم إني أسألك بكل اسم هو لك سميت به نفسك أو أنزلته في كتابك أو علمته أحدا من خلقك أو استأثرت به في علم الغيب عندك أن تصلي وتسلم على سيدنا محمد وعلى آله وصحبه . اللهم إن قلوب العباد بيدك تقلبها كيف تشاء . اللهم اجعل في قلب فلان ابن فلانة اللطف والعطف والمحبة والمودة والسرور والفرح والود والتودد والرفق والتوفيق والاتفاق والصلح والإصلاح والحنو والشفقة على فلانة بنت فلانة حتى يحبها حبا جما ولا يستطيع أن يفارقها طرفة عين ولا أقل من ذلك بمؤلف القلوب والأبصار يا جامع الناس ليوم لا ريب فيه يا حبيب يا ودود يا ذا العرش المجيد يا فعالا لما يريد إنك على كل شيء قدير وبالإجابة جدير وصلى الله على سيدنا محمد النبي الأمي وعلى آله وصحبه وسلم

Your work will not be finished but that your call has already been answered. Know, then, the worth of what has come to you; and success is from God.

Its Use for the Fulfilment of Needs

Among them, for the fulfilment of needs: take a tablet of silver and engrave the magic square upon it in the first hour of the first

Saturday of the Arabic month; fumigate it with frankincense and coriander, and recite over it His saying, exalted is He:

God will appoint ease after hardship.

Sa-yaj'alu Allāhu ba'da 'usrin yusrā

سيجعل الله بعد عسر يسرا

Recite it forty-five times. Whoever carries it and turns with it toward a need will have that need fulfilled, by the permission of God Most High.

The Rite for Scattering a Sinful Gathering

Among them, for breaking up a gathering assembled upon what does not please God Most High: take a rotten egg and write the magic square upon it in the hour of Saturn, with Mercury in its exaltation, and recite over it His saying, exalted is He:

And We cast among them enmity and hatred until the Day of Resurrection.

Wa-alqaynā baynahumu al-'adāwata wa-l-baghḍā'a ilā yawmi al-qiyāma

وألقينا بينهم العداوة والبغضاء إلى يوم القيامة

Recite it the prescribed number of times. Then break it in the place where they gather, and they will scatter and will not gather again until the Day of Resurrection.

Its Use for Ruining a Tyrant's House

Among its properties is the ruining of the house of a tyrant who has strayed from the religion. Draw a complete magic square and write its letters doubled, every letter three times, in the hour of Saturn on a Saturday, while the Moon is in its fall or joined to a malefic. Then recite over it His saying, exalted is He:

He cast terror into their hearts; they destroyed their houses with their own hands.

Wa-qadhafa fī qulūbihimu al-ruʿba yukhribūna buyūtahum bi-aydīhim

وقذف في قلوبهم الرعب يخربون بيوتهم بأيديهم

Recite this over it one hundred and thirty-five times, then bury it in the house of the tyrant; the house will be ruined and will never be inhabited again.

Its Uses for Colic and for Catching Fish

Among its properties is the healing of colic. Engrave the seal upon a piece of lead, recite the noble Fātiḥa over it forty-five times, and hang it upon the sick man opposite his right side; he will be cured, by permission of God Most High.

Among its properties is the easing of the catching of fish. Engrave the magic square upon a piece of tin weighing three dirhams, and write upon its back:

Perhaps God will bring them all to me. Wherever you may be,
God will bring you all together. When their fish came to them,
breaking the surface on the day of their Sabbath.

ʿAsā Allāhu an yaʾtiyanī bihim jamīʿan. Ayna mā takūnū yaʾti bikumu Allāhu jamīʿan. Idh taʾtīhim ḥītānuhum yawma sabtihim shurraʿan

عسى الله أن يأتيني بهم جميعا أين ما تكونوا يأت بكم الله جميعا إذ تأتيهم حيتانهم يوم سبتهم شرعا

Then recite these three verses over it, each verse forty-five times, and hang the magic square upon the fishing net; the fish will come to it from every side.

Its Use for Strength upon a Journey

Among its properties is the strengthening of the traveller upon his journey and the warding off of exhaustion from him, so that he walks and does not tire. Write the magic square upon gazelle hide, or upon paper made from silk, while the Moon is free of the malefics and joined to a benefic, and write around it these verses:

And We created the heavens and the earth and what is between
them in six days, and no weariness touched Us. Glory be to Him
who carried His servant by night from the Sacred Mosque to the
Farthest Mosque, whose surroundings We have blessed, that We
might show him of Our signs. And you see the mountains,
supposing them fixed, while they pass by as the clouds pass — the
handiwork of God, who has perfected all things. And We
inspired the mother of Moses: Suckle him; then, when you fear

for him, cast him into the river, and do not fear and do not grieve. Indeed, We shall return him to you and make him one of the messengers.

Wa-laqad khalaqnā al-samāwāti wa-l-arḍa wa-mā baynahumā fī sittati ayyāmin wa-mā massanā min lughūb. Subḥāna alladhī asrā bi-ʿabdihi laylan mina al-Masjidi al-Ḥarāmi ilā al-Masjidi al-Aqṣā alladhī bāraknā ḥawlahu li-nuriyahu min āyātinā. Wa-tarā al-jibāla taḥsabuhā jāmidatan wa-hiya tamurru marra al-saḥāb. Ṣunʿa Allāhi alladhī atqana kulla shayʾ. Wa-awḥaynā ilā ummi Mūsā an arḍiʿīhi fa-idhā khifti ʿalayhi fa-alqīhi fī al-yammi wa-lā takhāfī wa-lā taḥzanī innā rāddūhu ilayki wa-jāʿilūhu mina al-mursalīn

ولقد خلقنا السماوات والأرض وما بينهما في ستة أيام وما مسنا من لغوب
سبحان الذي أسرى بعبده ليلا من المسجد الحرام إلى المسجد
الأقصى الذي باركنا حوله لنريه من آياتنا وترى الجبال تحسبها جامدة
وهي تمر مر السحاب صنع الله الذي أتقن كل شيء وأوحينا إلى أم
موسى أن أرضعيه فإذا خفت عليه فألقيه في اليم ولا تخافي ولا تحزني
إنا رادوه إليك وجاعلوه من المرسلين

Then let the traveller hang it upon his thigh or upon his leg. He will walk and never tire, nor grow weary at all, and no thief or highwayman will come near him, by permission of God Most High.

Its Use for Binding Evil Tongues

Among its properties is the binding of tongues, so that no one speaks of you except with good. Write the magic square, and write opposite every cell:

Today We seal their mouths.

Al-yawma nakhtimu ʿalā afwāhihim

اليوم نختم على أفواههم

And around that write:

I have bound the tongues of the creation and of humankind, of every female and male, concerning the bearer of this writing of mine, so that not one of them speaks of him except with good.

ʿAqadtu alsinata al-khalqi wa-l-bashari min kulli unthā wa-dhakarin ʿan ḥāmili kitābī hādhā fa-lā yanṭiqu aḥadun minhum fī ḥaqqihi illā bi-khayr

عقدت ألسنة الخلق والبشر من كل أنثى وذكر عن حامل كتابي هذا فلا ينطق أحد منهم في حقه إلا بخير

The writing is to be made circular with the compasses. Whoever carries it will be guarded from evil tongues, and no one will harm him, by permission of God Most High.

Its Use for Safety from Drowning

Among its properties is the preservation of the traveller, or of the vessel, from drowning. Write the magic square in the first hour of Monday, while the Moon is in its felicity, and write around it these verses:

In the name of God is its course and its mooring. Indeed, my Lord is Forgiving, Merciful. They did not appraise God with the appraisal due to Him, while the whole earth is His handful on the Day of Resurrection and the heavens are folded in His right hand. Glory be to Him, and exalted is He above what they associate with Him.

Bismi Allāhi majrāhā wa-mursāhā inna rabbī la-ghafūrun raḥīm. Wa-mā qadarū Allāha ḥaqqa qadrihi wa-l-arḍu jamīʿan qabḍatuhu yawma al-qiyāmati wa-l-samāwātu maṭwiyyātun bi-yamīnihi subḥānahu wa-taʿālā ʿammā yushrikūn

بسم الله مجراها ومرساها إن ربي لغفور رحيم وما قدروا الله حق قدره والأرض جميعا قبضته يوم القيامة والسماوات مطويات بيمينه سبحانه وتعالى عما يشركون

Then hang it upon the traveller, or at the prow of the ship, and it will be safe from drowning.

Its Use for Loosing One Who Is Bound

Among its properties is the loosing of one who has been bound. Write the magic square in its entirety and encircle it with the verse:

And His word is the truth, and His is the dominion.

Wa-qawluhu al-ḥaqqu wa-lahu al-mulk

وقوله الحق وله الملك

This is to be done in the well-known manner. Upon its four corners write the names of the four angels: Jibrīl, Mīkāʾīl, Isrāfīl and ʿAzrāʾīl (جبريل وميكائيل وإسرافيل وعزرائيل). And write around that:

He released the two seas, meeting one another. It issues from between the backbone and the ribs. When the promise of my Lord comes, He will make it level ground, and the promise of my Lord is true. And We shall turn to whatever deeds they have done and make them scattered dust. So the truth came to pass, and what they were doing was made void.

Maraja al-baḥrayni yaltaqiyān. Yakhruju min bayni al-ṣulbi wa-l-tarā'ib. Fa-idhā jā'a wa'du rabbī ja'alahu dakkā'a wa-kāna wa'du rabbī ḥaqqan. Wa-qadimnā ilā mā 'amilū min 'amalin fa-ja'alnāhu habā'an manthūran. Fa-waqa'a al-ḥaqqu wa-baṭala mā kānū ya'malūn

مرج البحرين يلتقيان يخرج من بين الصلب والترائب فإذا جاء وعد ربي جعله دكاء وكان وعد ربي حقا وقدمنا إلى ما عملوا من عمل فجعلناه هباء منثورا فوقع الحق وبطل ما كانوا يعملون

The writing is to be with musk, saffron and rose water in a glazed vessel. Then it is washed off and given to the bound man to drink, and the knot will be loosed from him and the harm that is in him will depart, by permission of God Most High.

Its Use for Stilling a Child's Weeping

Among its properties is the stopping of the weeping of children. Write the magic square in the manner mentioned above, and write around it:

Then do you marvel at this discourse, and laugh and do not weep? And the voices are hushed before the All-Merciful, so that you hear nothing but a whisper. And they remained in their cave three hundred years, and they added nine.

A-fa-min hādhā al-ḥadīthi ta'jabūna wa-taḍḥakūna wa-lā tabkūn. Wa-khasha'ati al-aṣwātu li-l-Raḥmāni fa-lā tasma'u illā hamsā. Wa-labithū fī kahfihim thalātha mi'atin sinīna wa-izdādū tis'ā

أفمن هذا الحديث تعجبون وتضحكون ولا تبكون وخشعت الأصوات للرحمن فلا تسمع إلا همسا ولبثوا في كهفهم ثلاث مائة سنين وازدادوا تسعا

Then hang it upon the child, and he will be quieted from weeping and will increase in joy and gladness.

Its Use for Undoing Sorcery and Knots

Among its properties is the undoing of magic from one who is bewitched and the loosing of the knot from one who is bound. Write the magic square in the form just described upon a clean piece of cloth or in a basin, and write around it the Verse of the Throne in separated letters, and after it:

As for the sorcery, God will bring it to nothing; indeed, God does not set right the work of the corrupters.

Al-siḥru inna Allāha sayubṭiluhu inna Allāha lā yuṣliḥu 'amala al-mufsidīn

السحر إن الله سيبطله إن الله لا يصلح عمل المفسدين

Then, in the same manner, these words:

I have annulled from such-and-such all the works, the sorceries, the adjurations and the knots. If they were in a leaf, or in roots, or in threads, or in birds, or in fire, or in dust, or in water, or in air, or in stone, or in tree, then void, void, void is what they did and what they used to do.

Abṭaltu ʿan kadhā wa-kadhā jamīʿa al-aʿmāli wa-l-asḥāri wa-l-ʿazāʾimi wa-l-ʿuqadi in kānat fī waraqatin aw ʿurūqin aw khuyūṭin aw ṭuyūrin aw nārin aw turābin aw māʾin aw hawāʾin aw ḥajarin aw shajarin bāṭilun bāṭilun bāṭilun mā ʿamilū wa-mā kānū yaʿmalūn

أبطلت عن كذا وكذا جميع الأعمال والأسحار والعزائم والعقد إن كانت في ورقة أو عروق أو خيوط أو طيور أو نار أو تراب أو ماء أو هواء أو حجر أو شجر باطل باطل باطل ما عملوا وما كانوا يعملون

Then erase that with pure water, and with it let the bewitched or the bound man wash his whole body and drink a draught of it. It will depart from him, by permission of God Most High.

The Method of the Nail for Toothache

Among its properties is the quieting of toothache. Take a piece of walnut wood and make of it a small tablet, and write the magic square upon it in letters. Then take an iron nail and set its point upon the letter alif, and command the sick man to place the forefinger of his right hand upon the place of the pain, and recite His saying, exalted is He, once:

Glorify the name of your Lord, the Most High, who created and proportioned, and who determined and guided.

Sabbiḥi isma rabbika al-aʿlā alladhī khalaqa fa-sawwā wa-lladhī qaddara fa-hadā

سبح اسم ربك الأعلى الذي خلق فسوى والذي قدر فهدى

If his pain is quieted, fix the nail in that letter. If it is not quieted, move it to the letter bāʾ and recite the verses twice; and if it is quieted, fix it there, and if not, move it to the letter jīm and recite the verses three times. In this way the verses are recited at every letter according to its number, until the pain is quieted; and whenever the pain is quieted at a letter, the nail is made fast in that letter. Then give the tablet to the sick man, and let him put it away in a guarded place, for so long as the nail remains fixed in the letter at which the pain departed, the pain will not return to him.

Its Use for Quieting Pain in the Head

Among its properties is the quieting of pain in the head. Write the magic square, and write around it:

Be still, O pain, O pain, by Him for whom is stilled whatever is in the night and the day, and He is the Hearing, the Knowing.

Uskun yā alam yā alam bi-lladhī sakana lahu mā fī al-layli wa-l-nahāri wa-huwa al-samīʿu al-ʿalīm

اسكن يا ألم يا ألم بالذي سكن له ما في الليل والنهار وهو السميع العليم

Then hang it upon the head of the sick man, and he will be healed.

Its Use for Disclosing a Hidden Matter

Among its properties is the disclosing of a hidden matter. Write the magic square upon a sheet, and write around it these verses:

And thus did We show Abraham the kingdom of the heavens and the earth, that he might be among those who are certain. And when Moses came to Our appointed time and his Lord spoke to him, he said, "My Lord, show me, that I may look upon You." Indeed, We have given you al-Kawthar, so pray to your Lord and sacrifice. Indeed, it is the one who hates you who is cut off.

Wa-kadhālika nurī Ibrāhīma malakūta al-samāwāti wa-l-arḍi wa-li-yakūna mina al-mūqinīn. Wa-lammā jā'a Mūsā li-mīqātinā wa-kallamahu rabbuhu qāla rabbi arinī anẓur ilayka. Innā a'ṭaynāka al-kawthara fa-ṣalli li-rabbika wa-nḥar. Inna shāni'aka huwa al-abtar

وكذلك نري إبراهيم ملكوت السماوات والأرض وليكون من الموقنين ولما جاء موسى لميقاتنا وكلمه ربه قال رب أرني أنظر إليك إنا أعطيناك الكوثر فصل لربك وانحر إن شانئك هو الأبتر

Then recite these verses over it forty-five times, and fold the sheet and place it beneath your head, and hold in your mind the matter you wish to have made plain, and speak to no one until you sleep. You will see the matter with your own eyes, and its outcome will be made clear to you, by permission of God Most High.

Its Uses for Summoning the Absent and the Runaway

Among its properties is the summoning of one who is absent. Write the magic square upon a sheet, and write around it nine times:

And I cast upon you love from Me.
Wa-alqaytu ʿalayka maḥabbatan minnī
وألقيت عليك محبة مني

And after it write:

I have set ablaze and inclined and made fly and snatched away the heart of so-and-so, son of so-and-so, with love for so-and-so, daughter of so-and-so, by the right of these noble verses and of this blessed magic square.
Alhabtu wa-ʿaṭaftu wa-ṭayyartu wa-khaṭaftu qalba fulān ibn fulāna bi-maḥabbati fulāna bint fulāna bi-ḥaqqi hādhihi al-āyāti al-sharīfa wa-l-wifqi al-mubārak
ألهبت وعطفت وطيرت وخطفت قلب فلان ابن فلانة بمحبة فلانة بنت فلانة بحق هذه الآيات الشريفة والوفق المبارك

Then put into the sheet a large piece of male frankincense, and with it a portion of sulphur, and cast it into the fire, and recite the verse three hundred and thirteen times. At the head of the three, and at every ten thereafter, mention the charge already stated. The one who is sought will come to the one who seeks him, submissive, his reason bewildered with love of her.

Among its properties is the bringing back of a runaway. Write the magic square upon a sheet, and write upon its back the name of the runaway, on condition that it be set directly facing water. Then recite over it four hundred and five times:

Indeed, He is able to bring him back.

Innahu ʿalā rajʿihi la-qādir

إنه على رجعه لقادر

Then take a heavy stone and set the sheet in the place from which that runaway went out, with the stone above it. He will come back, by permission of God Most High, and he will be absent no longer than the distance of the road.

Its Use for Repelling Snake and Scorpion Venom

Among its properties is the repelling of the venom of snakes and scorpions and the warding of their harm from one who has been stung. Write the magic square in its entirety in a vessel of silver, and set it beneath the stars for seven nights, and every night sit beside it and recite Sūrat Yā Sīn over it forty-five times. When that is complete, keep this vessel by you; and when one who has been stung comes to you, put into this vessel some good oil, or pure water if oil is lacking, and anoint the place of the sting with it. The poison will go and the pain will subside, by the permission of God Most High.

Its Uses for Safety and Awe Before the Powerful

Among them, for safety from every oppressive tyrant and from everyone whose evil is feared: take a piece of purified lead and make from it a tablet weighing nine dirhams, and engrave the square upon it in the hour of Saturn, while it is in its strength or its exaltation. Then recite over it the saying of God Most High:

God will suffice you against them, and He is the Hearing, the Knowing.

Fa-sa-yakfīkahumu Allāhu wa-huwa al-samīʿu al-ʿalīm

فسيكفيكهم الله وهو السميع العليم

Do this 135 times, and fumigate it with liquid storax. Whoever carries this tablet and enters upon a tyrant is safe from his evil, and no harm or injury from him reaches him, by the permission of God Most High.

Among them, for awe in the presence of nobles and judges: the square is written on gazelle parchment with saffron, in the hour of Saturn, or of the Moon and Jupiter while it is in its exaltation, and His name, Most High, ʿAzīz is invoked over it a thousand times. Whoever then carries it upon his head attains his aim.

Its Uses for Sciatica and for Drawing Customers

Among them, for making sciatica depart: take a sheet of silver and write the square upon it in full with a pen of gold, then hang it upon the sciatica, and it will pass away.

Among them, for drawing customers to places of trade: the square is written on a paper, and around it is written His saying, Most High:

And proclaim the pilgrimage among the people; they will come to you on foot and upon every lean mount, coming from every distant mountain pass, that they may witness benefits for themselves.

Wa-adhdhin fī al-nāsi bi-l-ḥajji ya'tūka rijālan wa-'alā kulli ḍāmirin ya'tīna min kulli fajjin 'amīqin li-yashhadū manāfi'a lahum

وأذن في الناس بالحج يأتوك رجالا وعلى كل ضامر يأتين من كل فج عميق ليشهدوا منافع لهم

The verse is recited over it forty-five times, and it is hung up in the place; then customers will come to it from every direction.

Its Use for Removing Worry and Distress

Among them, for the removal of worries and the relief of distress: the square is written on a paper, and around it is written:

And He will heal the breasts of a believing people, and remove the rage of their hearts.

Wa-yashfi ṣudūra qawmin mu'minīna wa-yudhhib ghayẓa qulūbihim

ويشف صدور قوم مؤمنين ويذهب غيظ قلوبهم

This is written three times, in the first hour of Monday. Fumigate it with aloeswood and mastic, and recite Sūrat al-Inshirāḥ over it forty-five times. After that, no worried man carries it without his worry departing, no distressed man without God relieving his distress, no prisoner without being delivered from his prison, no captive without being saved, and no man whose breast is straitened without God expanding his breast. So know the worth of what has reached you.

On the Properties of the Single Letters

As for the single letters: among their properties, for overcoming an opponent, is that you write them upon the nail of the thumb of your left hand, then sit facing the opponent; and whenever he speaks, close your hand upon your thumb. His spirit will shrink, and he will not be able to utter what was in his mind.

Among them, for setting a headache upon the head of a tyrant: the single letters are written on a paper, or engraved upon a tablet of copper weighing five dirhams. Then you recite the saying of God Most High:

In their hearts is a disease, so God increased them in disease, and for them is a painful punishment. Then he cast a look at the stars and said, "Indeed, I am sick."

Fī qulūbihim maraḍun fa-zādahumu Allāhu maraḍan wa-lahum ʿadhābun alīm. Fa-naẓara naẓratan fī al-nujūmi fa-qāla innī saqīm

في قلوبهم مرض فزادهم الله مرضا ولهم عذاب أليم فنظر نظرة في النجوم فقال إني سقيم

Do this 25 times, and fumigate it with sulphur. Then bury it beneath a pillow, or beneath a millstone; the headache will seize that tyrant, and it will not leave him so long as it remains buried.

Among them, for driving away a bad neighbour: the single letters are written on the day of Saturn, in its hour, at the end of an Arabic month, upon an unbaked potsherd with garlic water and black ink. Set the incense of harm going, and recite this adjuration, which is that you say:

Barbarous names: Aṭrash Jaṭūsh Haṭūsh Zaṭūsh Ṭaṭūsh

أطرش جطوش هطوش زطوش ططوش

Take charge, O servants of these names, with the removal of so-and-so son of so-and-so, or so-and-so daughter of so-and-so, and drive him out from this place, before We efface faces and turn them back upon their backs, or curse them as We cursed the companions of the Sabbath; and the command of God is accomplished.

Tawakkalū yā khuddāma hādhihi al-asmā' bi-tarḥīl fulān ibn fulāna aw fulāna bint fulāna, wa-akhrijūhu min hādhā al-makān, min qabli an naṭmisa wujūhan fa-naruddahā 'alā adbārihā aw nal'anahum kamā la'annā aṣḥāba al-sabt, wa-kāna amru Allāhi maf'ūlā

توكلوا يا خدام هذه الأسماء بترحيل فلان ابن فلانة أو فلانة بنت فلانة وأخرجوه من هذا المكان من قبل أن نطمس وجوها فنردها على أدبارها أو نلعنهم كما لعنا أصحاب السبت وكان أمر الله مفعولا

Then bury it in the adversary's path, or beneath the threshold of his house, and he will depart.

And this is the form of the placing of the single letters, as you see:

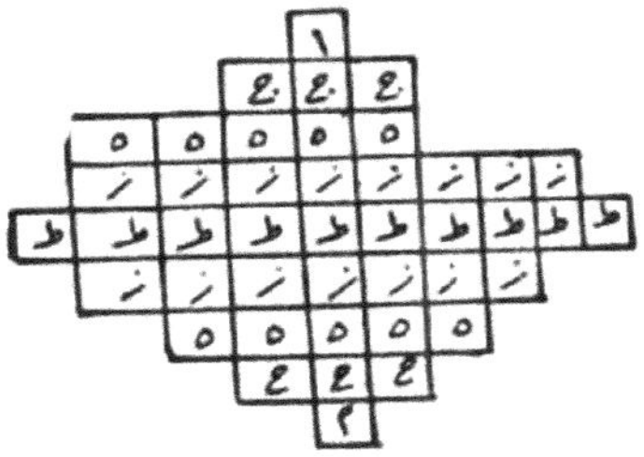

The arrangement of the single letters

Its Use for Sickening a Tyrannical Enemy

Among its uses for sickening the tyrannical enemy: write the single letters in the form already described upon a red strip of cloth, in the first hour of the day of Tuesday or in the eighth, in the name of the one whom you wish to sicken. Recite Sūrat al-Muzzammil over it a thousand times, fumigate it with colocynth and sulphur, then bury it in a dark place. A severe illness will befall the one named, and it will not leave him unless the strip of cloth is taken out and effaced with water.

Its Use for Testing a Woman's Blood

Among its uses for testing the blood of a licentious woman: take a piece of lead and engrave upon it the single letters as set out above, together with the name of the licentious woman and the name of her mother, and around it write:

> And We caused the earth to burst forth with springs, so the waters met for a matter already decreed. And We carried him upon a vessel of planks and nails, running before Our eyes, a

reward for him who had been rejected. In the name of God be its course and its mooring. When the sky is split open, and hearkens to its Lord as in truth it must, and when the earth is stretched out and so-and-so daughter of so-and-so casts forth her blood. Respond, O Aḥmar, and take charge of the flowing of the blood of so-and-so daughter of so-and-so.

Wa-fajjarnā al-arḍa ʿuyūnan fa-iltaqā al-māʾu ʿalā amrin qad qudir, wa-ḥamalnāhu ʿalā dhāti alwāḥin wa-dusur, tajrī bi-aʿyuninā jazāʾan li-man kāna kufir. Bi-smi Allāhi majrāhā wa-mursāhā. Idhā al-samāʾu inshaqqat wa-adhinat li-rabbihā wa-ḥuqqat, wa-idhā al-arḍu muddat wa-alqat fulāna bint fulāna damahā. Ajib yā Aḥmar, wa-tawakkal bi-jarayāni dami fulāna bint fulāna.

وفجرنا الأرض عيونا فالتقى الماء على أمر قد قدر وحملناه على ذات ألواح ودسر تجري بأعيننا جزاء لمن كان كفر بسم الله مجراها ومرساها إذا السماء انشقت وأذنت لربها وحقت و إذا الأرض مدت وألقت فلانة بنت فلانة دمها أجب يا أحمر وتوكل بجريان دم فلانة بنت فلانة

Then pierce the edge of the lead and pass through it a twist of red silk, recite Sūrat al-Zalzala over it forty-five times, fumigate it with red sandalwood and sulphur, then bury it in a running water channel, and the thing desired will come about.

Its Uses for Ruining and Deposing an Oppressor

Among its uses for the ruin of the house of an oppressor: write it in the manner already described upon a clean strip of cloth on the night of the last Saturday of the Arab month, and recite over it the saying of God Most High:

He it is who expelled those who disbelieved among the People of the Book from their homes at the first gathering. You did not think that they would go out, and they thought that their fortresses would protect them from God. But God came upon them from where they had not reckoned, and He cast terror into their hearts, so that they ruined their houses with their own hands.

Huwa alladhī akhraja alladhīna kafarū min ahli al-kitābi min diyārihim li-awwali al-ḥashr. Mā ẓanantum an yakhrujū wa-ẓannū annahum māniʿatuhum ḥuṣūnuhum mina Allāhi fa-atāhumu Allāhu min ḥaythu lam yaḥtasibū wa-qadhafa fī qulūbihimu al-ruʿba yukhribūna buyūtahum bi-aydīhim.

هو الذي أخرج الذين كفروا من أهل الكتاب من ديارهم لأول الحشر ما ظننتم أن يخرجوا وظنوا أنهم مانعتهم حصونهم من الله فأتاهم الله من حيث لم يحتسبوا وقذف في قلوبهم الرعب يخربون بيوتهم بأيديهم

Then take bath-house water and sprinkle it in the house of the adversary after you have dissolved the strip of cloth in it, and the house will be ruined and will never be inhabited again.

Among its uses for the deposing of a tyrannical oppressor: write the single letters as set out above upon a poor white sheet of paper, recite Sūrat al-Raʿd over it forty-five times, and bury it in his house, and he will be deposed.

Its Use for Testing a Sick Person

Among its uses for testing a sick person: write the five letters in the hollow of his palm, or upon his five fingers, and recite over them the saying of God Most High:

And the trumpet will be blown, and whoever is in the heavens and whoever is on the earth will be struck down, save whom God wills. Then it will be blown again, and at once they will be standing, looking on. And when Mūsā came to Our appointed time and his Lord spoke to him, he said: My Lord, show Yourself to me, that I may look upon You. He said: You will not see Me; but look at the mountain, and if it remains firm in its place, then you will see Me. And when his Lord manifested Himself to the mountain, He made it crumble to dust, and Mūsā fell down thunderstruck. When he came to himself he said: Glory be to You, I turn to You in repentance, and I am the first of the believers.

Wa-nufikha fī al-ṣūri fa-ṣaʿiqa man fī al-samāwāti wa-man fī al-arḍi illā man shāʾa Allāh, thumma nufikha fīhi ukhrā fa-idhā hum qiyāmun yanẓurūn. Wa-lammā jāʾa Mūsā li-mīqātinā wa-kallamahu rabbuhu qāla rabbi arinī anẓur ilayk, qāla lan tarānī wa-lākini unẓur ilā al-jabali fa-in istaqarra makānahu fa-sawfa tarānī, fa-lammā tajallā rabbuhu li-l-jabali jaʿalahu dakkan wa-kharra Mūsā ṣaʿiqan, fa-lammā afāqa qāla subḥānaka tubtu ilayka wa-anā awwalu al-muʾminīn.

ونفخ في الصور فصعق من في السماوات ومن في الأرض إلا من شاء الله ثم نفخ فيه أخرى فإذا هم قيام ينظرون ولما جاء موسى لميقاتنا وكلمه ربه

قال رب أرني أنظر إليك قال لن تراني ولكن انظر إلى الجبل فإن استقر مكانه فسوف تراني فلما تجلى ربه للجبل جعله دكا وخر موسى صعقا فلما أفاق قال سبحانك تبت إليك وأنا أول المؤمنين

Recite this twenty-five times. Then look at his state: if he falls into a fit, he is stricken; if he weeps, it is from his nature; and if he laughs, he is envied.

The Egg Rite for Love and Stirring

Among its uses for love and stirring: take an egg on the day of Thursday and write the single letters upon it, together with the name of the one desired and the name of his mother, and write around it:

And the jinn certainly know that they will be brought forth.

Wa-la-qad ʿalimati al-jinnatu innahum la-muḥḍarūn.

ولقد علمت الجنة إنهم لمحضرون

Then bury it beneath a gentle fire, fumigate it with frankincense, benzoin and coriander, and recite over it these names twenty-five times:

Barbarous names: Aykamūlash Haykarūsh Ṭaykarūsh

أيكمولش (...) هيكروش طيكروش

Take charge, O servants of these names, with the stirring and the burning of the heart of so-and-so with love for so-and-so. Quickly, in haste, this very hour.

Tawakkalū yā khuddāma hādhihi al-asmā' bi-tahyīj wa-iḥrāq qalb kadhā wa-kadhā bi-maḥabbat kadhā wa-kadhā, al-waḥā al-'ajal al-sā'a.

توكلوا يا خدام هذه الأسماء بتهييج وإحراق قلب كذا وكذا بمحبة كذا وكذا الوحا العجل الساعة

The Rite for Preventing a Person from Travelling

Among its uses for preventing a person from travelling: you write the single letters reversed, thus: ط ز ه ج ا, upon a rag belonging to the one you wish to prevent from travelling. Then you write his name together with them, hang it upon the tether-peg of a black donkey, and recite these verses as you hang it:

Had they wished to go forth, they would surely have made ready for it some equipment; but God was averse to their being sent forth, so He held them back, and it was said: Sit with those who sit. So We returned him to his mother, that her eye might be comforted, and that she might not grieve, and that she might know that the promise of God is true; but most of them do not know. Then a wall will be set up between them, having a gate; within it is mercy, and outside it, before it, is punishment.

Wa-law arādū al-khurūja la-a'addū lahu 'uddatan wa-lākin kariha Allāhu inbi'āthahum fa-thabbaṭahum wa-qīla uq'udū ma'a al-qā'idīn. Fa-radadnāhu ilā ummihi kay taqarra 'aynuhā

wa-lā taḥzana wa-li-taʿlama anna waʿda Allāhi ḥaqqun wa-lākinna aktharahum lā yaʿlamūn. Fa-ḍuriba baynahum bi-sūrin lahu bābun bāṭinuhu fīhi al-raḥmatu wa-ẓāhiruhu min qibalihi al-ʿadhāb.

ولو أرادوا الخروج لأعدوا له عدة ولكن كره الله انبعاثهم فثبطهم وقيل اقعدوا مع القاعدين فرددناه إلى أمه كي تقر عينها ولا تحزن ولتعلم أن وعد الله حق ولكن أكثرهم لا يعلمون فضرب بينهم بسور له باب باطنه فيه الرحمة وظاهره من قبله العذاب

Recite this twenty-five times. Then sink it into the peg, return the peg to its place, and drive it in while you say:

O peg, I have taken you, and from this place I have pulled you out, and for so-and-so I have set you: he shall not turn aside nor depart save around you.

Ayyuhā al-watad, innī akhadhtuka wa-min hāhunā qalaʿtuka, wa-li-fulānin ṣayyartuka: lā yaḥūlu wa-lā yazūlu illā ḥawlaka.

أيها الوتد إني أخذتك ومن هاهنا قلعتك ولفلان صيرتك لا يحول ولا يزول إلا حولك

He will sit and turn about seven times, and your striking of the peg is to be in the very place from which you pulled it out.

The Rite for Consoling the Lover

Among its uses for consolation: you write the single letters reversed, as before, upon a taro leaf, and you recite over it from the beginning of Sūrat al-Kahf up to His saying, exalted is He:

And none made me forget it but Satan.

Wa-mā ansānīhu illā al-shayṭān.

وما أنسانيه إلا الشيطان

Recite this once. Then recite His saying, exalted is He:

And We had made a covenant with Adam before, but he forgot, and We found in him no resolve.

Wa-la-qad ʿahidnā ilā Ādama min qablu fa-nasiya wa-lam najid lahu ʿazmā.

ولقد عهدنا إلى آدم من قبل فنسي ولم نجد له عزما

Recite this twenty-five times. Then command the lover to lick the single letters with his saliva, for he will be consoled of his beloved and will not return to her.

The Rite for Binding the Tongue of a Ruler

Among its uses for binding the tongue of the ruler, or of whomever you wish among a sultan, a vizier, a judge or another: you write the single letters in their places in the triangle, and beneath them you write the earthy letters, and beneath that:

I have bound the tongue of so-and-so.

ʿAqadtu lisāna kadhā wa-kadhā.

عقدت لسان كذا وكذا

Name whomever you wish, whether an individual or a company, so that he becomes like dust until the Day of Reckoning. Then meet with it whomever you wish, and you will obtain safety from him, and he will speak nothing concerning you but good.

The Rite for Separating Two Unlawfully Joined

Among its uses for separation between two who are joined in a matter that God, exalted is He, does not approve: you draw the single letters twice upon a paper, once at its top and once at its bottom, and between them you write the names of the two persons whose separation is intended. To their right, between the two alifs of the single letters, place the earthy letters; and to their left, between its two ṭā's, the airy letters. Then fumigate it with litharge, recite Sūrat al-Mā'ida over it once, and bury it in a grave that is not visited; they will part and will not come together after that. This is the manner of the writing, as you see:

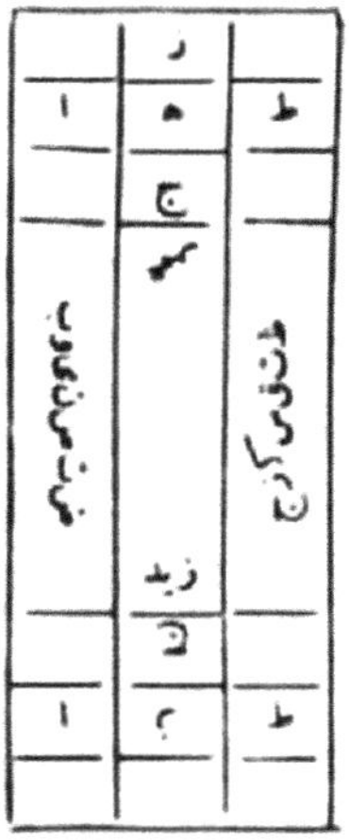

The manner of the writing for separation

The Rite for Drawing a Person from Afar

Among its uses for drawing a person from afar: you write the single letters in the middle of a paper, and around them, on the four sides, the airy letters, thus:

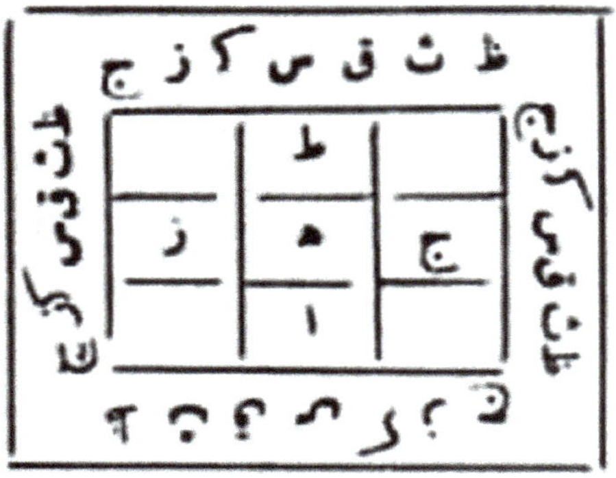

The single letters with the airy letters upon the four sides

And you recite over it His saying, exalted is He:

Has there come upon man a period of time in which he was not a thing mentioned? Indeed, We created man from a mingled drop, that We might try him.

Hal atā ʿalā al-insāni ḥīnun mina al-dahri lam yakun shay'an madhkūrā. Innā khalaqnā al-insāna min nuṭfatin amshājin nabtalīhi.

هل أتى على الإنسان حين من الدهر لم يكن شيئا مذكورا إنا خلقنا الإنسان من نطفة أمشاج نبتليه

Recite this twenty-five times, and each time you say:

Thus does God try so-and-so with love for so-and-so.

Kadhālika yabtalī Allāhu kadhā bi-maḥabbati kadhā.

كذلك يبتلي الله كذا بمحبة كذا

Then hang it in the air, and the one desired will come swiftly and will be delayed only by the distance of the road.

The Rite for Reconciliation and Affection

Among its uses for reconciliation, affection, love and tenderness: you write the single letters in the manner mentioned above, and recite over them:

The Most Merciful will appoint for them affection.

Sa-yajʿalu lahumu al-Raḥmānu wuddā.

سيجعل لهم الرحمن ودا

Recite this one hundred and fifty-nine times. Then let the seeker carry it upon his palm, for the one desired will love him with a surpassing love and will not be heedless of him.

The Rite for Casting Evil and Strife

Among its uses for casting evil and strife among those joined together in what God, exalted is He, does not approve: you write the fiery and the airy letters together with the single letters, and you set the names of the people between them, thus:

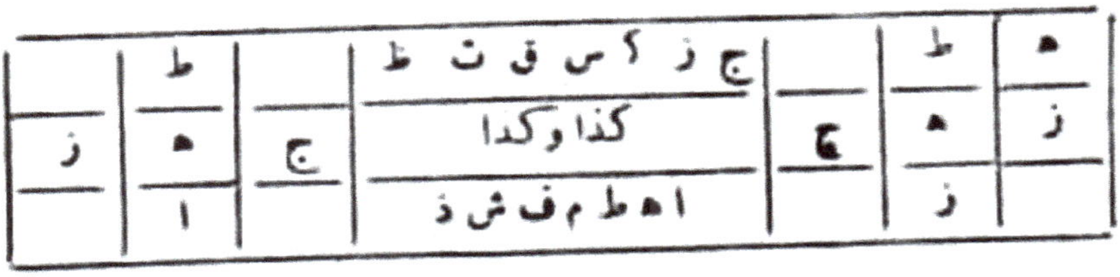

The arrangement for stirring up dispute and separation

And you write around it:

I have cast subjugation and quarrelling between such a one and such a one, like that which is between the cat and the mouse, and between the air and the fire.

Alqaytu al-qahra wa-l-khiṣāma bayna kadhā wa-kadhā kamā allatī bayna al-qiṭṭi wa-l-fāri wa-l-hawā'i wa-l-nār.

ألقيت القهر والخصام بين كذا وكذا كما التي بين القط والفار والهواء والنار

Then fumigate it with litharge, onion, and asafoetida, and bury it in the place where they gather, and they will fall to quarrelling and be parted.

The Rite for the Release of a Prisoner

Among its uses for the release of a prisoner: take a loaf of bread and write upon it the single letters before sunrise on Saturday, and write along with it:

As though, on the day they see what they are promised, they had tarried but an hour. O God, deliver such a one and such a one as You delivered Joseph from the prison and Job from affliction, for You are the most gracious of the gracious and the most merciful of the merciful.

Ka-annahum yawma yarawna mā yū'adūna lam yalbathū illā sā'a. Allāhumma khalliṣ kadhā wa-kadhā kamā khallaṣta Yūsufa mina al-sijni wa-Ayyūba mina al-balā'i, innaka alṭafu al-luṭafā'i wa-arḥamu al-ruḥamā'.

كأنهم يوم يرون ما يوعدون لم يلبثوا إلا ساعة اللهم خلص كذا وكذا كما
خلصت يوسف من السجن وأيوب من البلاء إنك ألطف اللطفاء وأرحم
الرحماء

Then give it to the first beggar who meets you, and the prisoner will come out of his prison.

The Rite for Driving Away Fever

Among its uses for driving away fever: if the fever is a cold one, write for it the single letters together with the fiery letters upon three papers, and fumigate the sick man with one of the papers whenever the fit comes round upon him, and he will be healed. And if the fever is a hot one, write the single letters together with the watery letters in the same way and do likewise, and it will pass away.

On the Paired Letters for Love and Acceptance

As for the paired letters, among their properties for love and acceptance is this: let a man keep up the writing of them upon his forehead with rosewater every morning, saying:

O you who believe, be not like those who vexed Moses; then God cleared him of what they said, and he was honoured in the sight of God.

Yā ayyuhā alladhīna āmanū lā takūnū ka-lladhīna ādhaw Mūsā fa-barra'ahu Allāhu mimmā qālū wa-kāna 'inda Allāhi wajīhā.

يا أيها الذين آمنوا لا تكونوا كالذين آذوا موسى فبرأه الله مما قالوا وكان عند الله وجيها

Then he will meet no one without that person loving him and holding him dear.

And among them: whoever writes them upon gazelle parchment and invokes over it His name, exalted be He, Wadūd (ودود), four hundred times, then Budūḥ (بدوح) four hundred times, and carries it with him, everyone who sees him will love him, and he will be held in awe and his word will be heeded.

And among them: whoever takes an apple with two cheeks, one of them red and the other yellow, and writes upon it with his saliva the paired letters in the first hour or the second hour of the day of Friday or the day of Sunday, and fumigates it with costus and sandalwood, then wraps it in a yellow cloth and gives it as a present to whomever he wishes, whoever smells it will love him with a mighty love and become obedient to his hand.

And among them: whoever recites them twenty times over a knife and cuts with it something of meat or of fruit, everyone who eats of that will love him and will not be able to part from him.

And among them: whoever writes them in a vessel twenty times, then recites them over it four hundred times, then washes the writing off and sprinkles it upon the food of the one desired, or carries something to him by means of it, that person will love him with a love that cuts deep.

And among them: whoever recites them twenty times over the mouth of a water jar that has water in it, everyone who drinks from that jar will love him.

And among them: whoever sets his mouth upon the mouth of his wife and recites them twenty times, then puts his tongue into her mouth, she will love him with an abundant love and will have no power to endure his being apart from her.

And among them: whoever writes them with rosewater in his right palm seven times and recites them over it four hundred times, then turns towards whomever he wishes and touches him with his palm, that person will follow him and love him.

And among them: whoever writes them upon a paper twice and recites over it twenty times, then dries the paper and grinds it up and puts it into the food of whomever he wishes, that person will love him with a vehement love.

The Rite for Love Between Husband and Wife

Among its uses for love between husband and wife: take a hazelnut or an almond that has two kernels and write the paired letters upon each of them; and take a small thin paper and write upon it the name of the seeker and the name of the one sought, interlaced one with the other, thus:

The two names interlaced, as the scribe draws them

Then place it between the two kernels, then wind about them a thread of white silk, and recite the paired letters over them four hundred times, and Hādī (هادي) four hundred times, and Wadūd (ودود) likewise. Then place it in an amulet and let the seeker carry it, and the one he desires will never part from him and will love him with an abundant love.

The Rite for Preventing Miscarriage

Among its uses for preventing the miscarriage of a pregnant human being, animal, or tree: write the paired letters in their four houses on gazelle parchment and recite Sūrat Yā-Sīn over it twenty times, then hang the parchment upon the pregnant one, and she will not miscarry until the term of the pregnancy is complete, by the permission of God Most High.

The Rite for Safety from Thieves and Highwaymen

Among its uses for safety from thieves and highwaymen: if you are in open country or on a frightening road, trace two circles on the ground, one inside the other, and draw the paired letters in the smaller one at its four directions, each letter in its own direction, and in its centre likewise. As you write each letter, say:

His word is the truth, and His is the dominion.

Qawluhu al-ḥaqqu wa-lahu al-mulk

قوله الحق وله الملك

Then sit in the middle of the circle, and the thieves will pass you by and not see you, nor harm you in anything, and they will be kept away from your quarter.

The Rite for the Marriage of an Unwed Girl

Among its uses for the marriage of a girl left unwed: draw the paired letters in a square wafq, letter by letter, and write around it twenty times:

And of everything We created two mates.

Wa-min kulli shay'in khalaqnā zawjayn

ومن كل شيء خلقنا زوجين

Then recite the verse over it one hundred times, and fumigate it with aloeswood, male frankincense, and sandalwood, and at the end of each hundred say:

O God, send to so-and-so a righteous husband, out of Your favour, Your bounty, and Your generosity, O most merciful of the merciful.

Allāhumma ib'ath li-fulāna ba'lan ṣāliḥan min faḍlika wa-jūdika wa-karamika yā arḥama al-rāḥimīn

اللهم ابعث لفلانة بعلا صالحا من فضلك وجودك وكرمك يا أرحم الراحمين

Then hang it upon her, and she will marry swiftly, by the permission of God Most High.

On the Fourfold Square and Its Properties

As for the fourfold square, its form and composition is as follows:

٨	١١	١٤	١
١٣	٢	٧	١٢
٣	١٦	٩	٦
١٠	٥	٤	١٥

The fourfold square

Its base (uss) is thirty, and it has many properties: preservation from calamities, the repelling of harm and injury, the reconciling of estranged hearts, the easing of the breast, the relief of the distressed, might, acceptance, standing, the carrying out of one's word before princes and rulers, and more besides. The time for writing it is the first or the eighth hour of Thursday, and it is well that the Moon should then be in its exaltation.

Whoever writes it on a tin tablet weighing four dirhams, and recites over it the five Qul-suras (al-Qalāqil) — namely Sūrat al-Jinn, Sūrat al-Kāfirūn, Sūrat al-Ikhlāṣ, and the two suras of refuge (al-Muʿawwidhatān) — thirty-four times, and then hangs it upon one struck down, he will come to himself. If he hangs it upon a boy, the boy will be rightly guided and harm and injury will leave him. If he hangs it upon a madman, he will be cured. It has besides this benefits beyond counting, so hold fast to it, for in it is a great secret.

Whoever engraves it on a copper tablet while the Moon is in Sagittarius, fumigates it with sandalwood, and recites Sūrat Yā-Sīn over it in full once, and then carries it with him, people will not be able to bear an hour away from him, so intense is the love. If he puts it in his pocket, his provision will increase, his standing will be great, and he will be safe from the evil of people. If he places it in wealth, it will grow; or in trade, it will profit; or in the middle of a farm, its fruit will thrive; or in a house, its good will increase.

On the Fivefold Square and Its Properties

As for the fivefold square, its form and composition is as follows:

٩	٢١	١٣	٥	١٧
٣	٢٠	٧	٢٤	١١
٢٣	١٤	١	١٨	١٠
١٦	٨	٢٥	١٢	٤
١٥	٢	١٩	٦	٢٢

The fivefold square

Its base is sixty, and it has many properties: the increase of understanding and of intelligence, the repelling of calamity, the bettering of the character of children and the keeping of harm away from them, the attaining of aims, the obtaining of desires, the fulfilling of needs, love, acceptance, tenderness, reconciliation, the drawing of customers, the binding of the tongues of rulers and of others, the subduing of enemies and adversaries and victory over them. It is written with musk and saffron upon gazelle parchment or upon a clean red piece of silk, it is fumigated with mastic, aloeswood and liquid storax, and the noble Fātiḥa is recited over it five times, together with His name, exalted be He, Dayyān (ديان), sixty-five times. Whoever carries it will attain all that I have mentioned, and many times as much again of good things and blessings.

And whoever writes it while the Sun is in the sign of Aries, or the Moon in the sign of Cancer, in a glazed vessel, and recites over it the name aforementioned sixty-five times, and gives it to drink to whomever he wishes, that person will not endure being parted from his love for a single hour.

And whoever writes it in the hour of Mars upon its own day, upon a red strip of cloth, and fumigates it with frankincense and blue bdellium, and recites over it Sūrat al-Mā'ida once, then buries it in the place where they gather for what is unlawful, they will come to hate one another and be parted.

And whoever writes it likewise upon the hoof of a mule and sets it in the house of an oppressor, that house will be laid waste; and if he sets it upon his trade, that trade will stagnate; and if he places it among a company, they will fall to quarrelling and grow blind to one another.

And whoever engraves it upon a tablet of iron in the hour of Mars on the day of Tuesday, and fumigates it with male frankincense and blue pepper, and binds it up in a red strip of cloth and ties it upon his upper arm, then enters in upon a tyrannical king, an unjust ruler, or a stubborn enemy, that man will submit and yield to him, and he will be safe from his evil and his cunning.

On the Sixfold Square and Its Properties

As for the sixfold square, the form of its arrangement is thus:

٣٦	٣٠	٢٤	١٠	٧	١
٢٥	١٩	٣	٣٥	١٧	١٢
٦	١٠	١٤	٢١	٢٨	٢٢
٢٠	٢	٢٩	١١	٣١	١٨
١٥	٢٤	٨	١٧	٥	٢٢
٩	١٦	٣٣	٤	٢٣	٢٦

The sixfold square

Its base is one hundred and five, and its properties are very many and its benefits beyond counting: the fulfilling of needs, the increase of blessing, strength, wealth, prestige, might, eloquence, love and acceptance.

And whoever takes half a mithqāl of gold and makes of it a tablet and engraves this square upon it while the Sun is in its exaltation, and fumigates it with saffron, musk and camphor, and mentions over it His name, exalted be He, Kāfī (كافي), six hundred and sixty-six times, and carries it with him, will attain what we have mentioned and more.

And whoever writes it in the first hour of the day of Sunday upon gazelle parchment or upon yellow paper, with musk, saffron and rosewater, and mentions the noble Name over it a thousand times and carries it with him, will attain strength and authority, and people will take him for their example and follow him in his words and in his deeds.

On the Sevenfold Square and Its Properties

As for the sevenfold square, the form of its arrangement is thus:

٢٣	٤٢	٥	١٧	٢٩	٤٨	١٠
٦	١٨	٣٠	٤٩	١٢	٢٤	٣١
٣١	٤٣	١٣	٢٥	٢٧	٧	١٩
١٤	٢٦	٣٨	١	٣٠	٣٢	٤٤
٣٩	٢	٢١	٣٣	٤٥	٨	٢٧
١٥	٣٤	٤٦	٩	٢٨	٤٠	٣
٤٧	١٠	٢٢	٤١	٤	١٦	٣٥

The sevenfold square

Its base is one hundred and sixty-eight, and its benefits are many: for memory, for intelligence, for the acquiring of the sciences, for elevation, uprightness, might, prestige, acceptance, and the obtaining of what is hoped for. Whoever engraves it upon a tablet of yellow copper while the Moon is in the sign of Cancer, or Mercury in Virgo, and fumigates it with aloeswood, and mentions His names, exalted be He, Hādī, ʿAlīm, Qawī (هادي عليم قوي), one thousand two hundred and twenty-five times, and hangs it upon a boy, that boy will become the most retentive of the people of his time and will not forget anything he has memorized. And if he hangs it upon a pregnant woman, she will be safe from every evil in herself and in her child, and her child will attain a great degree of distinction. And if he places it in a vessel and pours water over it and gives it to drink to a woman who is much given to jealousy, she will grow calm, her character will become good, and her malice will depart. And if the man whose wife hates him hangs it upon his waist and lies with her, she will love him with a great love and will turn toward him with every one of her limbs. And whoever puts it into a fragrant oil and anoints his body from it, then presents himself before whomever he wishes of women and of men, they will hold him in awe and will fulfil his needs, whatever they may be.

On the Eightfold Square and Its Properties

As for the eightfold square, the form of its arrangement is thus:

٨	٥٨	٥٩	٥	٤	٦٢	٦٣	١
٤٩	١٥	١٤	٥٢	٥٣	١١	١٠	٥٦
٤١	٢٣	٢٢	٤٤	٤٥	١٩	١٨	٤٨
٣٣	٣٤	٣٥	٢٩	٢٨	٣٨	٣٩	٥٢
٤٠	٢٦	٢٧	٣٧	٣٦	٣٠	٣١	٣٣
١٧	٤٧	٤٦	٢٠	٢١	٤٣	٤٢	٢٤
٩	٥٥	٥٤	١٢	١٣	٥١	٥	١٦
٦٤	٢	٣	٦١	٢٥	٩	٧	٥٧

The eightfold square

Its base is two hundred and fifty-two, and its benefits are many: for the removal of all the diseases that befall human beings and beasts. Whoever writes it in a glazed vessel with saffron, rosewater and musk, and washes it off with fresh water or with rosewater, and gives it to drink to one who has a fever, the fever will leave him. And if one who has the itch upon his body is anointed with it, he will be cured. And if a man of ill character drinks it, his state will be bettered and his folly will depart. And if it is given to drink to a she-camel that bolts, she will grow quiet and settled. And whoever writes it upon a sheet and writes around it His name, exalted be He, Ḥamīd (حميد), sixty-four times, and wraps it in a rag from the trace of a woman who keeps ill company with her husband, and then places it in a clean chest, that woman will become of the best condition, she will not cross her husband thereafter, and her companionship with him will be bettered. And whoever writes it and writes around it His name, exalted be He, Ḥayy (حي), eighteen times, and carries it level with his heart, his heart will be quickened with the light of faith and of gnosis, and he will become one of the friends of God Most High.

And whoever writes it and writes around it the names of God, exalted be He, Ḥakam, Ḥakīm, Ḥalīm, Ḥannān, Ḥasīb, Ḥamīd, Ḥaqq, Ḥaqq, Ḥafīẓ, Ḥayy (حكم حكيم حليم حنان حسيب حميد حق حق حفيظ حي), thirty-one times, and then mentions them over it a thousand times and carries it with him, he will be accepted by everyone who sees him, his word will become effective, his countenance will be beloved, and he will not approach anyone with a need but that it is fulfilled for him. And whoever engraves it upon a tablet of iron and hangs it in the place from which a runaway has fled, he will return to it in haste and will not tarry beyond the length of the road. And if he places it in the storehouses of grain, they will be safe from weevil and from blight. And whoever writes it in the first hour of the day of Wednesday, and fumigates it with musk and ambergris, and carries it, his strength will increase, and however far he walks he will not grow weary nor ever thirst. And if he places it upon the side in which there is a stabbing pain, it will vanish at once; and if he sets it upon the head of one sick with headache, it will leave him.

On the Ninefold Square and Its Properties

As for the ninefold square, the form of its arrangement is thus:

٢٧	٨٧	٢٩	٧٠	٢١	٦٢	١٣	٥٤	٥
[illegible]	٣٨	٧٩	٣٠	٧١	٢٢	٦٣	١٤	٤٦
٤٧	٧	٣٩	٨٠	٣١	٧٢	١٣	٥٥	١٥
١٦	٤٨	٨	٤٠	٨١	٣٢	٦٤	٢٤	٥٦
٥٧	١٧	٤٩	٩	٤١	٧٣	٣٣	٦٥	٢٥
٢٦	٥٨	١٨	٥٠	١	٤٢	٧٤	٣٤	٦٦
٦٧	٢٧	٥٩	١٠	٥١	٢	٤٣	٧٥	٣٥
٣٦	٦٨	١٩	٦٠	١١	٥٢	٣	٤٤	٧٦
٧٧	٢٨	٦٩	٢٠	٦١	١٢	٤	٤	٤٥

The ninefold square

Its base is three hundred and sixty, and its benefits are many: love and acceptance, the increase of might and of prestige, victory over enemies, the fulfilling of needs, reconciliation between adversaries, and the departure of diseases of the soul and of the body, the taming of beasts, and the subduing of the obstinate. Whoever engraves it upon a tablet of silver weighing nine dirhams, and fumigates it with mastic, benzoin and ambergris, and recites Sūrat al-Anʿām over it nine times, and carries it with him, will attain everything we have mentioned. He will meet no one who does not hold him in awe, honour him, and fulfil his need. And if he goes down into the sea with it at the time of its raging, it will grow calm. And if he hangs it in a place of trade, the customers will hurry to it from every quarter. And if he hangs it upon a girl left unwed, the suitors will hasten to her from every side, and she will acquire might, acceptance and beauty, and no one will see her without loving her.

The Method of Drawing the Minds of All Creation

And whoever wishes that everyone who sees him should love him, and to draw to himself the minds of all creation, and that their worlds be made subject to him, let him write it in the manner that follows, in the first hour of the Moon on Monday while the Moon is increasing in light, or in one of the hours of the Moon upon any day, though the first hour mentioned is the better. Let him fumigate it with a sweet incense, then hand it to the seeker, that he may carry it. After that the practitioner places his hand upon the head of the seeker, and recites the names and the verses that encircle the square forty-one times, and says:

O spiritual powers of the minds, come here, by the right of Abū al-Qāsim, the Messenger.

Yā rūḥānīyat al-ʿuqūl, (...) ilā hunā bi-ḥaqq Abī al-Qāsim al-rasūl

يا روحانية العقول (...) إلى هنا بحق أبي القاسم الرسول

And when that is completed, his purpose is accomplished for him and he attains the end he sought.

On the Amulet of the Washerwoman

Some of the authors have mentioned that the great imam and famous gnostic known as Ibn al-Ḥājib wrote it for one of the chiefs of the tribes; he carried it, and he rose in the height of his rank and surpassed his neighbours, until he came to possess most of their lands.

It is mentioned also that Hārūn al-Rashīd had a black slave-girl who attained a great portion of might, standing and acceptance. When she died and the washerwoman came to wash her, she found an amulet upon her head, and took it and carried it; and she became of dazzling freshness and surpassing beauty, and everyone who saw her loved her, though she had been a grey-haired old woman. So the suitors hurried to her, and a man of the notables married her; and when she died they opened this amulet and found in it this blessed square, and they named it the Amulet of the Washerwoman (ḥirz al-mughassila).

It is mentioned also that a youth in his adolescence sought the blessed amulet; and when he obtained it and carried it he attained abundant fortune and dazzling might, until he became one of the men of the state to whom the final word returns and upon whom reliance is placed in affairs. In sum, its worth is great and its merit immense, and whoever carries it has no need of any other, and its form is as follows:

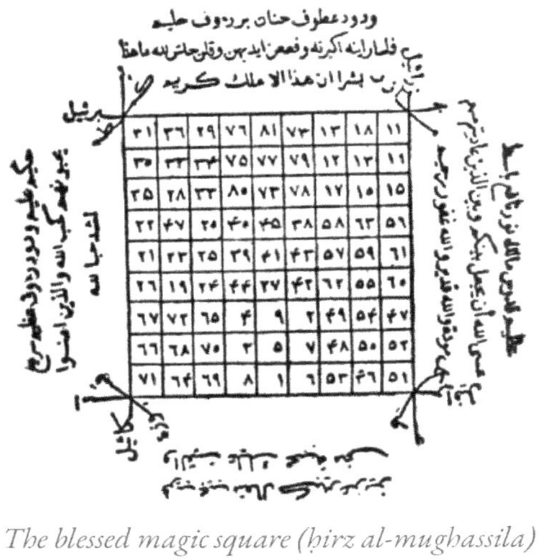

The blessed magic square (ḥirz al-mughassila)

Its Use for Disclosure in a Dream

And whoever writes it in this manner upon a sheet of paper, and does not write with it what surrounds it of the names, the verses, the angels and the heads, then places it beneath his pillow, and recites Sūrat al-Ḍuḥā seven times, and Sūrat al-Qadr seven times, and Sūrat al-Zalzala seven times, then says:

Take charge, O Taqwābīl, O servant of this blessed square, and inform me in this sleep of mine concerning such-and-such.

Tawakkal yā Taqwābīl yā khādim hādhā al-wafq al-mubārak wa-akhbirnī fī manāmī hādhā ʿan kadhā wa-kadhā

توكل يا تقوابيل يا خادم هذا الوفق المبارك وأخبرني في منامي هذا عن كذا وكذا

and he names his need. May God bless you. Then let him sleep upon this pillow, and he will see what he sought to be informed about, and his case will be disclosed to him. So know its worth. May God guide us and you to that in which lie good and right guidance.

As for the tenfold magic square, its form and composition are as follows:

١٠	٩	٩٣	٩٤	٥	٩٦	٩٧	٩٨	٢	١
١١	١٩	١٨	٨٤	٨١	٨٦	٨٧	١٣	١٢	٩٥
١٧	٢٢	٢٨	٢٧	٧٥	٧٦	٢٤	٢٣	٧٩	٨٠
٦١	٦٢	٣٣	٣٧	٣٦	٣٥	٣٤	٦٨	٦٩	٧٥
٥٠	٥٢	٥٣	٤٤	٤٦	٤٥	٥٧	٥٨	٥٩	٤١
٦٠	٤٩	٤٣	٥٤	٥٦	٥٥	٤٧	٤٨	٤٢	٥١
٤٠	٣٢	٦٣	٦٧	٦١	٦٥	٦٤	٣٨	٣٩	٣١
٢١	٨٢	٧٨	٧٧	٧٦	٢٥	٧٤	٧٣	٢٩	٣٠
٨١	٨٩	٨٨	٧١	١٥	١٢	١٤	٨٣	٨٣	٢٠
١٠٠	٩٩	٨	٤	٩٥	٦	٧	٣	٩٢	٩١

The tenfold square

Its basis is four hundred and ninety-five. Among its properties: if it is written in the exaltation of Venus upon an unfired potsherd, in the name of whomever you desire, and you cast it into the fire, that person will be seized with a violent panting from the intensity of love. And among them: it is of benefit for the repelling of poisons, and that is done by engraving it at the time when Jupiter enters its exaltation, while the Moon beholds it from a trine or a sextile, upon a tablet of any metal, on condition that the engraving be clear. Then you seal with it ten disks of any bread, and the poisoned man eats them one after another, and he will be cured of that.

And among them, for the fulfilling of needs, the attaining of aims, safety from things hateful, the expanding of breasts, the dispelling of sorrows, and everything a man seeks of good or of evil: you take a tablet made of six metals — gold, silver, lead, copper, iron and tin — on condition that the weights be equal, and that its casting be while the Sun is in the sign of Aquarius. Then you pour it out in the sign of Pisces, and engrave it in the ten signs, at the rate of ten cells in each sign, on condition that the lord of each sign be fortunate, not retrograde, and free of the malefics. When its working is complete, keep it by you, for it is a mighty treasure. In this measure there is sufficiency. God is the granter of success in what is right, and to Him are the return and all aims.

The Third Purpose: A Mention of Some of the Secrets of the Names, the Verses, the Invocations, the Oaths, and the Employments (al-Maqṣad al-Thālith fī Dhikr Shay' min Asrār al-Asmā' wa-l-Āyāt wa-l-Daʿawāt wa-l-Aqsām wa-l-Istikhdāmāt)

This section contains three chapters:

- Chapter One: On the secrets of the names.
- Chapter Two: On the secrets of the verses.
- Chapter Three: On the invocations, the oaths, and the employments.

Section on the Properties of the Name of the Essence (Faṣl fī Khawāṣṣ Ism al-Dhāt)

Among them, for the easing of provision: recite the Name of the Essence five thousand times every day, and not a week will pass over you but that provision comes to you from every side.

And among them: whoever wishes to call upon God by the Greatest Name, let him draw the square that follows while the Moon is in al-Sharaṭayn, and build upon it the Name of the Essence in this manner, Allāh (الله), sixty-six times, and let him ask for what he desires; it will be answered for him at once. And this is the form of the square, as you see:

٣٤	اف	١١
١٤	•لا:	٦٠
٦٣	٨	٤٠

The threefold square

And among them, for love: write the following wafq in rue-water with a pen upon paper, and hang it on a pomegranate twig or a palm frond, and recite over it the Noble Name 4356 times in an empty place, in a state of purity, while you fumigate, and charge the servant, for he will not disobey. And this is the form of the wafq, as you see:

٣	٦٢	١
٦١	يوكل يا كهيل وهيا كل ويا هلال بكذا وكذا بسر الاسم الاعظم	٥
٦	٤	٦٠

The wafq for love

The Rite for Every Matter of Good or Ill

And among them, for the fulfilling of every matter you desire, whether of good or of evil: recite the Name of Majesty with the vocative yāʾ 66 times, then say:

In the name of God, the Merciful, the Compassionate. Praise belongs to God, Lord of the worlds, and may God bless our master Muḥammad and his family and his Companions and grant them peace. O Most Merciful of the merciful (twice); O Merciful One, O Compassionate One (three times); O best of those who are asked, O Answerer of the prayer of the distressed, O God of the worlds, to You I have brought down my need and You know it best, so fulfil it. O God, You are its keeper and the keeper of every need, so fulfil it by the grace of "In the name of God, the Merciful, the Compassionate": whatever mercy God opens to men, none can withhold.

Bismi Allāhi al-Raḥmāni al-Raḥīm. Al-ḥamdu li-Llāhi rabbi al-ʿālamīn, wa-ṣallā Allāhu ʿalā sayyidinā Muḥammadin wa-ʿalā ālihi wa-ṣaḥbihi wa-sallam. Yā arḥama al-rāḥimīn ٢, yā Raḥmān yā Raḥīm ٣, yā khayra al-mas'ūlīn, yā mujība da'wati al-muḍṭarrīn, yā ilāha al-'ālamīn, bika anzaltu ḥājatī wa-anta a'lamu bihā fa-iqḍihā. Allāhumma anta lahā wa-li-kulli ḥājatin fa-iqḍihā bi-faḍli Bismi Allāhi al-Raḥmāni al-Raḥīm: mā yaftaḥi Allāhu li-l-nāsi min raḥmatin fa-lā mumsika lahā.

بسم الله الرحمن الرحيم الحمد لله رب العالمين وصلى الله على سيدنا محمد وعلى آله وصحبه وسلم يا أرحم الراحمين ٢ يا رحمن يا رحيم ٣ يا خير المسئولين يا مجيب دعوة المضطرين يا إله العالمين بك أنزلت حاجتي وأنت أعلم بها فاقضها اللهم أنت لها ولكل حاجة فاقضها بفضل بسم الله الرحمن الرحيم ما يفتح الله للناس من رحمة فلا ممسك لها

Recite this ten times.

And among them for that also: recite the Noble Name 4256 times, and at every 66 recitations read the supplication once, and your need will be fulfilled, whatever it may be. It is that you say:

O God, I ask You by the majesty of divinity, by the secrets of lordship, by the might of everlastingness, by the right of Your exalted Essence that is far above modality and likeness, by the right of Your angels, the people of the essential attributes, and by the sanctity of him whom the lights envelop with the secrets that are within him, that You fulfil my need, such-and-such, or from You. O God, O God, O God; the Holy, the Holy, the Holy; lift from me the veils of darkness, and show me by Your light what

You have shown to Your servants, the people of pure hearts. O You who have clothed the hearts of the knowers in the light of divinity, so that the angels cannot raise their heads before the force of omnipotence. O You who said in the decisive text of His mighty Book and His pre-eternal words: God is the Light of the heavens and the earth. The parable of His light is as if there were a niche, in which there is a lamp, the lamp is in glass, the glass as it were a brilliant star, kindled from a blessed tree, an olive neither of the East nor of the West, whose oil would almost glow though no fire touched it: light upon light. God guides to His light whom He wills, and God sets forth parables for men, and God is Knower of all things.

Allāhumma innī as'aluka bi-ʿaẓamati al-ulūhīya, wa-bi-asrāri al-rubūbīya, wa-bi-ʿizzati al-sarmadīya, wa-bi-ḥaqqi dhātika al-ʿalīya al-mutanazzih ʿani al-kayfīya wa-l-shabahīya, wa-bi-ḥaqqi malāʾikatika ahli al-ṣifāti al-jawharīya, wa-bi-ḥurmati alladhī taghshāhu al-anwāru bimā fīhi mina al-asrār, illā mā qaḍayta ḥājatī min kadhā wa-kadhā aw minka. Yā Allāh yā Allāh yā Allāh, al-Quddūs al-Quddūs al-Quddūs, irfaʿ ʿannī ḥujuba al-ẓulumāt, wa-arinī bi-nūrika mā aẓhartahu li-ʿibādika ahli al-qulūbi al-ṭāhirāt. Yā man kasā qulūba al-ʿārifīna bi-nūri al-ulūhīya, fa-lan tastaṭīʿa al-malāʾikatu rafʿa ruʾūsihim min saṭwati al-jabarūt. Yā man qāla fī muḥkami kitābihi al-ʿazīz wa-kalimātihi al-azalīya: Allāhu nūru al-samāwāti wa-l-arḍ, mathalu nūrihi ka-mishkātin fīhā miṣbāḥ, al-miṣbāḥu fī zujāja, al-zujājatu ka-annahā kawkabun durrīyun yūqadu min shajaratin mubārakatin zaytūnatin lā sharqīyatin wa-lā gharbīyatin yakādu zaytuhā yuḍī'u wa-law lam tamsas'hu nār, nūrun 'alā nūr, yahdī Allāhu li-nūrihi man yashā', wa-yaḍribu Allāhu al-amthāla li-l-nās, wa-Allāhu bi-kulli shay'in 'alīm.

اللهم إني أسألك بعظمة الألوهية وبأسرار الربوبية وبعزة السرمدية وبحق ذاتك العلية المتنزه عن الكيفية والشبهية وبحق ملائكتك أهل الصفات الجوهرية وبحرمة الذي تغشاه الأنوار بما فيه من الأسرار إلا ما قضيت حاجتي من كذا وكذا أو منك يا الله يا الله يا الله القدوس القدوس القدوس ارفع عني حجب الظلمات وأرني بنورك ما أظهرته لعبادك أهل القلوب الطاهرات يا من كسى قلوب العارفين بنور الألوهية فلن تستطيع الملائكة رفع رؤوسهم من سطوة الجبروت يا من قال في محكم كتابه العزيز وكلماته الأزلية الله نور السماوات والأرض مثل نوره كمشكاة فيها مصباح المصباح في زجاجة الزجاجة كأنها كوكب دري يوقد من شجرة مباركة زيتونة لا شرقية ولا غربية يكاد زيتها يضيء ولو لم تمسسه نار نور على نور يهدي الله لنوره من يشاء ويضرب الله الأمثال للناس والله بكل شيء عليم

Section on the Properties of the Beautiful Names (Faṣl fī Khawāṣṣ al-Asmā' al-Ḥusnā)

Whoever desires some matter, let him purify himself and pray two cycles to God Most High, and let him draw the following wafq at a favourable time, with a sweet fragrance. Let him ask God Most High for forgiveness one hundred times, and invoke blessings upon the Prophet, may God bless him and grant him peace, as much as is easy for him. Then let him recite the Beautiful Names over it 99 times, asking his need at the end of each recitation, and let him seal with blessings upon the Prophet, may God bless him and grant him peace. He will see what gladdens him.

And this is the form of the wafq, as you see:

غفار	مصور	بارئ	متعال	سلام	قدوس	ملك	رحيم	رحمن	الله
مجيد	حليم	مغني	مانع	محصي	قيوم	حفيظ	مميت	معز	واحد
متكبر	باسط	نافع	رءوف	شهيد	واسع	عليم	محيي	خافض	حي
مبدئ	حسيب	مقيت	مالك الملك	بصير	فتاح	قهار	ضار	ودود	مقتدر
بديع	حكيم	ظاهر	مميت	باعث	آخر	جامع	باقي	واجد	هادي
وكيل	جليل	معيد	رازق	شكور	رقيب	قابض	عظيم	وال	وهاب
منتقم	رافع	صمد	قوي	كبير	مؤخر	كريم	حميد	ولي	وارث
مجيب	غني	بر	رشيد	مهيمن	مقسط	صبور	عدل	أول	مذل
تواب	ذو الجلال والاكرام	باطن	متين	جبار	عزيز	مؤمن	أحد	غفور	خالق
محمد	عفو	حكيم	نور	خبير	سميع	لطيف	علي	ماجد	قادر

The wafq of the Beautiful Names

So be diligent with it, for it is the greatest comprehensive magic square, the shining and radiant light, and the all-encompassing secret.

The Method of Matching One's Name by Abjad

And it has come down from some of the learned men possessed of secrets and blessings that whoever wishes to call upon God Most High by the Greatest Name should take the number of his own name by abjad reckoning and look to see which of the Beautiful Names of God Most High agrees with it, whether one name, or two names, or three only. For example, one whose name is Hilāl is matched, among the names of God Most High, by Wakīl; one whose name is ʿAlī is matched, among the names of God, by ʿAlī; and one whose name is Muḥammad is matched, among the names of God, by Bāsiṭ and Wadūd. Then he mentions the names, setting the noble formula before them, in this manner, for example:

There is no god but God, the Trustee, for one whose name is Hilāl; there is no god but God, the Exalted, for one whose name is ʿAlī; there is no god but God, the Expander, the Loving, for one whose name is Muḥammad.

Lā ilāha illā Allāh al-Wakīl li-man ismuhu Hilāl; lā ilāha illā Allāh al-ʿAlī li-man kāna ismuhu ʿAlī; lā ilāha illā Allāh al-Bāsiṭ al-Wadūd li-man kāna ismuhu Muḥammad.

لا إله إلا الله الوكيل لمن اسمه هلال، لا إله إلا الله العلي لمن كان اسمه علي، لا إله إلا الله الباسط الودود لمن كان اسمه محمد

He repeats this formula according to the number of his own name. Then, after this remembrance, he recites Sūrat Alam Nashraḥ in the same manner; then he sends blessings upon the Prophet, may God bless him and grant him peace, in the same manner; then he asks for his need, and it is granted by the permission of God Most High.

The Table of the Beautiful Names and Their Numbers

And this is a table setting forth the numbers of the Beautiful Names of God, as you see:

عدده	الإسم		عدده	الإسم	
٢١٣	بارىء	١٣	٦٦	الله	١
٣٣٦	مصور	١٤	٢٩٨	رحمن	٢
١٢٨١	غفار	١٥	٢٥٨	رحيم	٣
٣٠٦	قهار	١٦	٩٠	ملك	٤
١٤	وهاب	١٧	١٧٠	قدوس	٥
٣٠٨	رزاق	١٨	١٣١	سلام	٦
٤٨٩	فتاح	١٩	١٢٦	مؤمن	٧
١٥٠	عليم	٢٠	١٤٥	مهيمن	٨
٩٠٣	قابض	٢١	٩٤	عزيز	٩
٧٢	باسط	٢٢	٢٠٦	جبار	١٠
١٤٨١	خافض	٢٣	٦٦٢	متكبر	١١
٣٥١	رافع	٢٤	٧٢١	خالق	١٢

The numbers of the Beautiful Names, entries 1 to 24

No.	Name	Number	No.	Name	Number
1	Allāh	66	13	Bāri’	213
2	Raḥmān	298	14	Muṣawwir	336
3	Raḥīm	258	15	Ghaffār	1281
4	Malik	90	16	Qahhār	306
5	Quddūs	170	17	Wahhāb	14
6	Salām	131	18	Razzāq	308
7	Mu’min	126	19	Fattāḥ	489
8	Muhaymin	145	20	‘Alīm	150
9	‘Azīz	94	21	Qābiḍ	903

No.	Name	Number	No.	Name	Number
10	Jabbār	206	22	Bāsiṭ	72
11	Mutakabbir	662	23	Khāfiḍ	1481
12	Khāliq	721	24	Rāfiʿ	251

	الإسم	عدده		الإسم	عدده
٢٥	معز	١١٧	٤٧	حكيم	٧٨
٢٦	مذل	٧٧٠	٤٨	ودود	٢٠
٢٧	سميع	١٨٠	٤٩	مجيد	٥٧
٢٨	بصير	٣٠٢	٥٠	باعث	٥٧٣
٢٩	حكم	٦٨	٥١	شهيد	٣١٩
٣٠	عدل	١٠٤	٥٢	حق	١٠٨
٣١	لطيف	١٢٩	٥٣	وكيل	٦٦
٣٢	خبير	٨١	٥٤	قوى	١١٦
٣٣	حليم	٨٨	٥٥	متين	٥٠٠
٣٤	عظيم	١٠٢٠	٥٦	ولى	٤٦
٣٥	غفور	١٢٨٦	٥٧	حميد	٧٢
٣٦	شكور	٥٢٦	٥٨	محصى	١٤٨
٣٧	على	١١٠	٥٩	مبدىء	٥٦
٣٨	كبير	٢٣٢	٦٠	معيد	١٢٤
٣٩	حفيظ	٩٩٨	٦١	محيى	٦٨
٤٠	مقيت	٥٥٠	٦٢	مميت	٤٩٠
٤١	حسيب	٨٠	٦٣	حى	١٨
٤٢	جليل	٨٣	٦٤	قيوم	١٥٦
٤٣	كريم	٢٧٠	٦٥	واجد	١٤
٤٤	رقيب	٣١٢	٦٦	ماجد	٤٨
٤٥	مجيب	٥٥	٦٧	واحد	١٩
٤٦	واسع	١٣٧	٦٨	صمد	١٢٤

The numbers of the Beautiful Names, entries 25 to 68

No.	Name	Number	No.	Name	Number
25	Muʿizz	117	47	Ḥakīm	78
26	Mudhill	770	48	Wadūd	20
27	Samīʿ	180	49	Majīd	57
28	Baṣīr	302	50	Bāʿith	573
29	Ḥakam	68	51	Shahīd	319
30	ʿAdl	104	52	Ḥaqq	108
31	Laṭīf	129	53	Wakīl	66
32	Khabīr	81	54	Qawī	116

No.	Name	Number	No.	Name	Number
33	Ḥalīm	88	55	Matīn	500
34	ʿAẓīm	1020	56	Walī	46
35	Ghafūr	1286	57	Ḥamīd	72
36	Shakūr	526	58	Muḥṣī	148
37	ʿAlī	110	59	Mubdiʾ	56
38	Kabīr	232	60	Muʿīd	124
39	Ḥafīẓ	998	61	Muḥyī	68
40	Muqīt	550	62	Mumīt	490
41	Ḥasīb	80	63	Ḥayy	18
42	Jalīl	83	64	Qayyūm	156
43	Karīm	270	65	Wājid	14
44	Raqīb	312	66	Mājid	48
45	Mujīb	55	67	Wāḥid	19
46	Wāsiʿ	137	68	Ṣamad	134

عدده	الإسم		عدده	الإسم	
١١٠	ذو الجلال والإكرام	٨٥	٣٠٥	قادر	٦٩
١٠٩	مقسط	٨٦	٧٤٤	مقدر	٧٠
١١٤	جامع	٨٧	١٨١	متقدم	٧١
١٠٦٠	غنى	٨٨	٨٨٦	مؤخر	٧٢
١١٠٠	مغنى	٨٩	٣٧	أول	٧٣
١٦١	مانع	٩٠	٨٠١	آخر	٧٤
١٠٠١	ضار	٩١	١١٦	ظاهر	٧٥
٢٠١	نافع	٩٢	٦٢	باطن	٧٦
٢٥٦	نور	٩٣	٤٧	وال	٧٧
٢٠	هادى	٩٤	٥٤١	متعال	٧٨
٨٦	بديع	٩٥	٢٠٢	بر	٧٩
١١٣	باقى	٩٦	٤٠٩	تواب	٨٠
٧٠٧	وارث	٩٧	٣٦٠	منتقم	٨١
٢٩٨	رشيد	٩٨	١٥٦	عفو	٨٢
	صبور	٩٩	٢٨٦	رءوف	٨٣
٣٢٨٣٨	الجملة		٢١٢	مالك الملك	٨٤

The numbers of the Beautiful Names, entries 69 to 99

No.	Name	Number	No.	Name	Number
69	Qādir	305	85	Dhū al-Jalāl wa-l-Ikrām	110
70	Muqtadir	744	86	Muqsiṭ	909
71	Muqaddim	181	87	Jāmiʿ	114
72	Mu'akhkhir	886	88	Ghanī	1060
73	Awwal	37	89	Mughnī	1100
74	Ākhir	801	90	Māniʿ	161
75	Ẓāhir	116	91	Ḍārr	1001
76	Bāṭin	62	92	Nāfiʿ	201
77	Wāl	47	93	Nūr	256
78	Mutaʿāl	541	94	Hādī	20
79	Barr	202	95	Badīʿ	86
80	Tawwāb	409	96	Bāqī	113
81	Muntaqim	360	97	Wārith	707
82	ʿAfūw	156	98	Rashīd	298
83	Ra'ūf	286	99	Ṣabūr	—
84	Mālik al-Mulk	212		Total	32828

A Benefit for the Fulfilling of Needs and the Relief of Distress (Fā'ida li-Qaḍā' al-Ḥawā'ij wa-Tafrīj al-Kurūb)

When you have prayed the dawn prayer, say while you are seated:

In the name of God, the Merciful, the Compassionate.

Bismi Allāh al-Raḥmān al-Raḥīm

بسم الله الرحمن الرحيم

Say it one hundred times. Then say:

There is no power and no strength save in God, the High, the Mighty. O Ancient One, O Everlasting One, O Single One, O Odd One, O One, O Eternal Refuge, O Living One, O Self-Subsisting One, O Possessor of Majesty and Honour.

Lā ḥawla wa-lā quwwata illā bi-llāh al-ʿAlī al-ʿAẓīm, yā Qadīm, yā Dāʾim, yā Fard, yā Witr, yā Aḥad, yā Ṣamad, yā Ḥayy, yā Qayyūm, yā Dhā al-Jalāl wa-l-Ikrām

لا حول ولا قوة إلا بالله العلي العظيم يا قديم يا دائم يا فرد يا وتر يا أحد
يا صمد يا حي يا قيوم يا ذا الجلال والإكرام

Say it one hundred times also. Then ask your need, and it will be answered for you.

A Benefit from the Precious Treasures, for Matters of Moment (Fāʾida min al-Dhakhāʾir al-Nafīsa li-l-Muhimmāt)

Whoever is visited by distress, or by a hard matter, or by straitness, or by fear of an enemy, an unjust ruler, a thief, a night-prowler or a highwayman, and wishes to drive that away swiftly, let him rise and pray; and when he has finished the prayer, let him say the name, facing the qibla, one thousand five hundred and eleven times, and ask for what he wants, and it will be answered for him swiftly and beyond all doubt. So withhold it from one who is not worthy of it.

An Important Benefit for the Accomplishing of Every Matter You Desire (Fā'ida Muhimma li-Qaḍā' Kull Amr Turīd)

You say:

O Swift One.

Yā Sarī'

يا سريع

Say it seventy thousand times, and at the head of every hundred say:

Answer, O Khandūsh, and you, O Lakān, by the right of the Name whose beginning is Ān and whose end is Ān, Ajlūthā Jalūsh; and take charge of such-and-such. Quickly, in haste, this very hour.

Ajib yā Khandūsh wa-anta yā Lakān bi-ḥaqq al-ism alladhī awwaluhu Ān wa-ākhiruhu Ān, Ajlūthā Jalūsh, wa-tawakkalū bi-kadhā wa-kadhā, al-waḥā al-'ajal al-sā'a

أجب يا خندوش وأنت يا لكان بحق الاسم الذي أوله آن وآخره آن أجلوثا جلوش وتوكلوا بكذا وكذا الوحا العجل الساعة

A Benefit for Love and for the Fulfilling of Needs (Fā'ida li-l-Maḥabba wa-Qaḍā' al-Ḥawā'ij)

You write this name:

O Merciful One to every crier for help and every stricken one, their succour and their refuge.

Yā Raḥīm kull ṣarīkh wa-makrūb wa-ghiyāthahu wa-ma'ādhahu

يا رحيم كل صريخ ومكروب وغياثه ومعاذه

Write it upon a paper with musk, saffron and rosewater, and recite the name over it a thousand times; then wash it off with clean water and give it to the one desired to drink. He will love the seeker with a vehement love, and will strive in his service and fulfil his need, whatever it may be.

A Benefit for the Binding of Tongues (Fāʾida li-ʿAqd al-Alsina)

You take the name of the seeker, the name of the one sought, and the need, thus, for example: Muḥammad seeks the binding of the tongue of Aḥmad (محمد يطلب عقد لسان أحمد). You spread them out into their letters and mingle them with the letters of His two names, exalted be He, Laṭīf and Ṣamad (لطيف صمد), and break them down until the zimām comes out. Then you take the numbers of all that has come out with you from the letters as a single sum, and write that sum upon a small paper, and recite the two names over it by that number. Then let the seeker carry it, and he will see what gladdens him.

A Benefit for the Fulfilling of Needs (Fāʾida li-Qaḍāʾ al-Ḥawāʾij)

You say, one hundred times:

O Great One above every great one, O Hearing One, O Seeing One, O You who have no partner and no minister, O Creator of the sun and of the shining moon, O Succourer of whoever seeks succour and refuge in You, O Mender of the broken bone, O Subduer of every stubborn tyrant: I ask You by the right of these eight names, written upon the horn of the sun, that You bring about for me such-and-such.

Yā Kabīran fawqa kull kabīr, yā Samīʿ, yā Baṣīr, yā man lā sharīka lahu wa-lā wazīr, yā Khāliq al-shams wa-l-qamar al-munīr, yā Mughīth man kāna bika mustaghīthan wa-mustajīran, yā Jābir al-ʿaẓm al-kasīr, yā Qāmiʿ kull jabbār ʿanīd, as'aluka bi-ḥaqq hādhihi al-asmā' al-thamāniya al-maktūba ʿalā qarn al-shams an tajʿala lī kadhā wa-kadhā

يا كبيرا فوق كل كبير يا سميع يا بصير يا من لا شريك له ولا وزير يا خالق الشمس والقمر المنير يا مغيث من كان بك مستغيثا ومستجيرا يا جابر العظم الكسير يا قامع كل جبار عنيد أسألك بحق هذه الأسماء الثمانية المكتوبة على قرن الشمس أن تجعل لي كذا وكذا

A Benefit for the Fulfilling of Needs of All Their Kinds (Fā'ida li-Qaḍā' al-Ḥawā'ij bi-Kāffat Anwāʿihā)

You write the wafq that follows in the fifth hour of the day of Thursday, and write around it:

In the name of God, the Merciful, the Compassionate, and by Him We seek help, and there is no power and no strength except with God the Supreme. And may God bless our master Muḥammad and his family and companions, and may He grant them peace. O God, O You who set low the necks of kings, so that they stand in fear of His sovereignty; O You who are alone in might and majesty, so that all His creation trembles in awe of Him; O You who gather the crumbled bones, so that on that Day they are raised up; O You who honoured His friends with obedience, so that they are safe from the greatest terror. There is no god but He. O God, Your knowledge encompasses it as a thing inscribed, and God encompasses them from behind. In truth We sent it down, and in truth it came down. Enter upon them by the gate; and when you have entered it, you will be victorious. And put your trust in God, if you are believers. All-glorious, All-holy, Lord of the angels and the Spirit. Take charge, O you who obey the names of God the Most High, of the binding of a tongue, or of love, or of the subjugation of so-and-so, with no power and no strength except with God.

Bismi Allāh al-Raḥmān al-Raḥīm wa-bihi Nastaʿīnu wa-lā ḥawla wa-lā quwwata illā bi-Allāh al-ʿAẓīm, wa-ṣallā Allāhu ʿalā sayyidinā Muḥammad wa-ʿalā ālihi wa-ṣaḥbihi wa-sallam. Allāhumma yā man waḍaʿa riqāba al-mulūk fa-hum min sulṭānihi khāʾifūn, yā man tafarrada bi-l-ʿizzati wa-l-ʿaẓamati fa-jamīʿu khalqihi min khīfatihi wajilūn, yā man yaḥshuru al-ʿiẓāma al-dāthirāti fa-hum yawmaʾidhin yubʿathūn, yā man aʿazza awliyāʾahu bi-l-ṭāʿati fa-hum min al-fazaʿ al-akbar āminūn. Lā ilāha illā (...) yā Allāh, muḥīṭun bihi ʿilmuka ka-masṭūr, wa-Allāhu min warāʾihim muḥīṭ, wa-bi-l-ḥaqqi anzalnāhu wa-bi-l-ḥaqqi nazal, udkhulū ʿalayhim al-bāb fa-idhā dakhaltumūhu fa-innakum ghālibūn, wa-ʿalā Allāh fa-tawakkalū in kuntum muʾminīn. Subbūḥun quddūs, rabb al-malāʾikati wa-l-rūḥ. Tawakkal ayyuhā al-muṭīʿ li-asmāʾ Allāh Taʿālā bi-ʿaqd lisān aw maḥabba aw ikhḍāʿ fulān, bi-lā ḥawla wa-lā quwwata illā bi-Allāh.

بسم الله الرحمن الرحيم وبه نستعين ولا حول ولا قوة إلا بالله العظيم وصلى الله على سيدنا محمد وعلى آله وصحبه وسلم. اللهم يا من وضع رقاب الملوك فهم من سلطانه خائفون، يا من تفرد بالعزة والعظمة فجميع خلقه من خيفته وجلون، يا من يحشر العظام الداثرات فهم يومئذ يبعثون، يا من أعز أولياءه بالطاعة فهم من الفزع الأكبر آمنون. لا إله إلا (...) يا الله محيط به علمك كمسطور والله من ورائهم محيط وبالحق أنزلناه وبالحق نزل ادخلوا عليهم الباب فإذا دخلتموه فإنكم غالبون وعلى الله فتوكلوا إن كنتم مؤمنين سبوح قدوس رب الملائكة والروح توكل أيها المطيع لأسماء الله تعالى بعقد لسان أو محبة أو إخضاع فلان بلا حول ولا قوة إلا بالله

Let the letters be written joined together, except for "there is no power and no strength except with God" at the end of the prayer, which you write with its letters separated. Then fumigate it with mastic and benzoin, and recite the prayer over it until it turns. Then seal it with wax and carry it, and you will see what gladdens you. And this is the form of the wafq, as you see:

٣٠١	٣٠٤	٣٠٧	٢٩٤
٣٠٦	٢٩٥	٣٠٠	٣٠٥
٢٩٦	٣٠٩	٣٠٢	٢٩٩
٣٠٣	٢٩٨	٢٩٧	٣٠٨

The fourfold wafq

A Splendid Benefit for Fulfilling Every Need and Attaining Every Desire (Fā'ida Jalīla li-Qaḍā' Kull Ḥāja wa-Nayl Kull Marghūb)

Whoever knows this benefit will have no need of any other.

Whoever watches for the moon to enter the mansion of al-Sharaṭayn should pray two cycles with the Fātiḥa and with His words, may He be exalted:

He is the First and the Last, the Outward and the Inward, and He has knowledge of all things.

Huwa al-Awwal wa-l-Ākhir wa-l-Ẓāhir wa-l-Bāṭin wa-huwa bi-kulli shay'in 'alīm.

هو الأول والآخر والظاهر والباطن وهو بكل شيء عليم

Then let him say:

O God (66 times), O First (37 times), O Last (1001).

Yā Allāh 66 marra, yā Awwal 37 marra, yā Ākhir 1001.

يا الله ٦٦ مرة يا أول ٣٧ مرة يا آخر ١٠٠١

Then, if he asks God for something, He grants him what he asked.

Whoever watches for its entry into the mansion of al-Buṭayn should pray two cycles with the Fātiḥa and with His words, may He be exalted:

Originator of the heavens and the earth. How should He have a child, when He has no consort? He created everything, and He has knowledge of all things.

Badīʿu al-samāwāti wa-l-arḍi annā yakūnu lahu waladun wa-lam takun lahu ṣāḥiba, wa-khalaqa kulla shay'in wa-huwa bi-kulli shay'in ʿalīm.

بديع السموات والأرض أنى يكون له ولد ولم تكن له صاحبة وخلق كل شيء وهو بكل شيء عليم

And let him say:

O Benevolent One, O Originator (288 times).

Yā Barr, yā Badīʿ 288 marra.

يا بر يا بديع ٢٨٨ مرة

Then let him ask God the Most High for the attainment of his object, for the winning of happiness, and for the opening of doors, and God grants him what he seeks.

Whoever watches for its entry into the mansion of al-Thurayyā should pray two cycles with the Fātiḥa and Sūrat al-Mulk, and say:

O Majestic One, O Gatherer (207 times).

Yā Jalīl, yā Jāmiʿ 207 marra.

يا جليل يا جامع ٢٠٧ مرة

Then let him ask God the Most High for his need, and he obtains it.

Whoever watches for its entry into the mansion of al-Dabarān should pray two cycles with the Fātiḥa and with His words, may He be exalted:

He is the First and the Last, the Outward and the Inward, and He has knowledge of all things.

Huwa al-Awwal wa-l-Ākhir wa-l-Ẓāhir wa-l-Bāṭin wa-huwa bi-kulli shay'in 'alīm.

هو الأول والآخر والظاهر والباطن وهو بكل شيء عليم

And let him say:

O Everlasting One (55 times), O Judge (65 times).

Yā Dā'im 55 marra, yā Dayyān 65 marra.

يا دائم ٥٥ مرة يا ديان ٦٥ مرة

Then let him ask God the Most High for blessing in his provision and his wealth, and for safety in his homeland, and he is given what he asked.

Whoever watches for its entry into the mansion of al-Haqʿa should pray two cycles with the Fātiḥa and with His words, may He be exalted:

He is the First and the Last, the Outward and the Inward, and He has knowledge of all things.

Huwa al-Awwal wa-l-Ākhir wa-l-Ẓāhir wa-l-Bāṭin wa-huwa bi-kulli shay'in 'alīm.

هو الأول والآخر والظاهر والباطن وهو بكل شيء عليم

And let him say:

O He (11 times), O Guide (20 times), O Destroyer (95 times).

Yā Huwa 11 marra, yā Hādī 20 marra, yā Muhlik 95 marra.

يا هو ١١ مرة يا هادي ٢٠ مرة يا مهلك ٩٥ مرة

Then let him ask God for success and victory, and he attains them both.

Whoever watches for its entry into the mansion of al-Han'a should pray two cycles with the Fātiḥa and the Verse of the Throne, and then say:

O Protector (46 times), O Trustee (66 times), O Loving One (20 times).

Yā Walī 46 marra, yā Wakīl 66 marra, yā Wadūd 20 marra.

يا ولي ٤٦ مرة يا وكيل ٦٦ مرة يا ودود ٢٠ مرة

Then let him seek from God the Most High gentleness and well-being and the easing of what is hard, and he attains his purpose.

Whoever watches for its entry into the mansion of al-Dhirā' should pray two cycles with the Fātiḥa and with His words, may He be exalted:

Have you considered what you sow? Is it you who cause it to grow, or are We the growers?

A-fa-ra'aytum mā taḥruthūn, a-antum tazra'ūnahu am naḥnu al-zāri'ūn.

أفرأيتم ما تحرثون أأنتم تزرعونه أم نحن الزارعون

Then let him say:

O Pure One (27 times).

Yā Zakī 27 marra.

يا زكي ٢٧ مرة

His worry and his grief depart from him, and he attains gladness and joy.

Whoever watches for its entry into the mansion of al-Nathra should pray two cycles with the Fātiḥa and the beginning of Sūrat Āl ʿImrān, up to His words, may He be exalted:

Truly God does not fail the appointed promise.

Inna Allāha lā yukhlifu al-mīʿād.

إن الله لا يخلف الميعاد

Then let him say:

O Living One (18 times), O Self-Subsisting One (156 times), O Praiseworthy One (62 times), O Wise One (78 times), O Compassionate One (109 times), O Forbearing One (68 times), O Preserver (998 times), O Forbearing One (68 times).

Yā Ḥayy 18 marra, yā Qayyūm 156 marra, yā Ḥamīd 62 marra, yā Ḥakīm 78 marra, yā Ḥannān 109 marra, yā Ḥalīm 68 marra, yā Ḥafīẓ 998 marra, yā Ḥalīm 68 marra.

يا حي ١٨ مرة يا قيوم ١٥٦ مرة يا حميد ٦٢ مرة يا حكيم ٧٨ مرة يا حنان ١٠٩ مرة يا حليم ٦٨ مرة يا حفيظ ٩٩٨ مرة يا حليم ٦٨ مرة

He obtains the good of this world and of the next.

He attains an abundant share of standing, acceptance and might, and he rises to the highest offices.

The Lunar Mansions from al-Ṭarfa to al-Naʿāʾim

And whoever observes the Moon's alighting in the mansion of al-Ṭarfa, and prays two rakʿas with the Fātiḥa and with His saying, exalted be He:

We have not sent down the Qurʾān upon you that you should be wretched, but only as a reminder to him who fears.

Mā anzalnā ʿalayka al-Qurʾāna li-tashqā illā tadhkiratan li-man yakhshā

ما أنزلنا عليك القرآن لتشقى إلا تذكرة لمن يخشى

then let him say:

O Pure One, 315 times; O Purifier, 254 times.

Yā Ṭāhir 315, yā Muṭahhir 254 marra.

يا طاهر ٣١٥ يا مطهر ٢٥٤ مرة

His character is made good, and acts of obedience are made beloved to him.

And whoever observes its alighting in the mansion of al-Jabha, and prays two rakʿas with the Fātiḥa and with His saying, exalted be He:

By the wise Qur'ān, indeed you are among the messengers, upon a straight path, a revelation of the Mighty, the Most Merciful.

Wa-l-Qur'āni al-ḥakīm innaka la-mina al-mursalīn ʿalā ṣirāṭin mustaqīm tanzīla al-ʿAzīzi al-Raḥīm

والقرآن الحكيم إنك لمن المرسلين على صراط مستقيم تنزيل العزيز الرحيم

then let him say:

O Facilitator, make it easy, 120 times.

Yā Muyassir yassir 120 marra.

يا ميسر يسر ١٢٠ مرة

He attains what he seeks.

And whoever observes its alighting in the mansion of al-Zubra, and prays two rakʿas with the Fātiḥa and with His saying, exalted be He:

His command, when He wills a thing, is only to say to it: Be, and it is.

Innamā amruhu idhā arāda shay'an an yaqūla lahu kun fa-yakūn

إنما أمره إذا أراد شيئا أن يقول له كن فيكون

then let him say:

O Sufficient One, 111 times.

Yā Kāfī 111.

يا كافي ١١١

He is safe from all that he fears.

And whoever observes its alighting in the mansion of al-Ṣarfa, and prays two rakʿas with the Fātiḥa and with His saying, exalted be He:

He is gracious to His servants; He provides sustenance for whom He wills, and He is the Strong, the Mighty.

Laṭīfun bi-ʿibādihi yarzuqu man yashāʾu wa-huwa al-Qawīyu al-ʿAzīz

لطيف بعباده يرزق من يشاء وهو القوي العزيز

then let him say:

O Gracious One, 129 times.

Yā al-Laṭīf 129.

يا اللطيف ١٢٩

His worry and his grief depart, and his need is fulfilled.

And whoever observes its alighting in the mansion of al-ʿAwwāʾ, and prays two rakʿas with the Fātiḥa and with His saying, exalted be He:

O God, Master of the dominion, You grant dominion to whom You will and remove dominion from whom You will; You exalt whom You will and You abase whom You will. In Your hand is the good; indeed You have power over all things.

Allāhumma Mālika al-mulki tuʾtī al-mulka man tashāʾu wa-tanziʿu al-mulka mimman tashāʾu wa-tuʿizzu man tashāʾu wa-

tudhillu man tashā'u bi-yadika al-khayru innaka 'alā kulli shay'in qadīr

اللهم مالك الملك تؤتي الملك من تشاء وتنزع الملك ممن تشاء وتعز من تشاء وتذل من تشاء بيدك الخير إنك على كل شيء قدير

then let him say:

O Sovereign, 90 times; O Glorious One, 75 times.

Yā Mālik 90, yā Majīd 75 marra.

يا مالك ٩٠ يا مجيد ٧٥ مرة

He gains perfect health and the continuance of blessing.

And whoever observes its alighting in the mansion of al-Simāk, and prays two rakʿas with the Fātiḥa and with His saying, exalted be He:

Our Lord, pour out upon us patience, make our feet firm, and give us victory over the unbelieving people.

Rabbanā afrigh 'alaynā ṣabran wa-thabbit aqdāmanā wa-unṣurnā 'alā al-qawmi al-kāfirīn

ربنا أفرغ علينا صبرا وثبت أقدامنا وانصرنا على القوم الكافرين

then let him say:

O Light, 256 times.

Yā Nūr 256 marra.

يا نور ٢٥٦ مرة

He attains an abundant share of good fortune among his brethren.

And whoever observes its alighting in the mansion of al-Ghafr, and prays two rakʿas with the Fātiḥa and with His saying, exalted be He:

Peace, a word from a Merciful Lord.

Salāmun qawlan min Rabbin Raḥīm

سلام قولا من رب رحيم

then let him say:

O Peace, 131 times; O All-Hearing, 180 times.

Yā Salām 131 marra, yā Samīʿ 180 marra.

يا سلام ١٣١ مرة يا سميع ١٨٠ مرة

He is safe from all that he fears in this world and in the hereafter.

And whoever observes its alighting in the mansion of al-Zubānā, and prays two rakʿas with the Fātiḥa and with His saying, exalted be He:

And God created you and what you do.

Wa-Allāhu khalaqakum wa-mā taʿmalūn

والله خلقكم وما تعملون

then let him say:

O All-Knowing, 100 times; O Magnificent, 1520 times.

Yā ʿAlīm 100 marra, yā ʿAẓīm 1520 marra.

يا عليم ١٠٠ مرة يا عظيم ١٥٢٠ مرة

He attains success and guidance.

And whoever observes its alighting in the mansion of al-Iklīl, and prays two rakʿas with the Fātiḥa and with His saying, exalted be He:

With Him are the keys of the unseen; none knows them but He. He knows what is in the land and the sea. Not a leaf falls but He knows it, nor is there a grain in the darknesses of the earth, nor anything moist or dry, but it is in a clear book.

Wa-ʿindahu mafātiḥu al-ghaybi lā yaʿlamuhā illā huwa wa-yaʿlamu mā fī al-barri wa-l-baḥri wa-mā tasquṭu min waraqatin illā yaʿlamuhā wa-lā ḥabbatin fī ẓulumāti al-arḍi wa-lā raṭbin wa-lā yābisin illā fī kitābin mubīn

وعنده مفاتح الغيب لا يعلمها إلا هو ويعلم ما في البر والبحر وما تسقط من ورقة إلا يعلمها ولا حبة في ظلمات الأرض ولا رطب ولا يابس إلا في كتاب مبين

then let him say:

O Opener, 489 times.

Yā Fattāḥ 489 marra.

يا فتاح ٤٨٩ مرة

His provision is increased, and he attains his desire.

And whoever observes its alighting in the mansion of al-Qalb, and prays two rakʿas with the Fātiḥa and with His saying, exalted be He:

And We sent down from the sky blessed water, and We brought forth with it gardens and the grain of the harvest.

Wa-anzalnā mina al-samā'i mā'an mubārakan fa-anbatnā bihi jannātin wa-ḥabba al-ḥaṣīd

وأنزلنا من السماء ماء مباركا فأنبتنا به جنات وحب الحصيد

then let him say:

O Truthful One, O Eternal Refuge, 329 times.

Yā Ṣādiq, yā Ṣamad 329 marra.

يا صادق يا صمد ٣٢٩ مرة

and let him invoke blessing upon the Prophet, may God bless him and grant him peace, 110 times. He attains leadership over his peers.

And whoever observes its alighting in the mansion of al-Shawla, and prays two rakʿas with the Fātiḥa and with His saying, exalted be He:

And pardon us, and forgive us, and have mercy upon us. You are our Protector, so give us victory over the unbelieving people.

Wa-ʿfu ʿannā wa-ighfir lanā wa-irḥamnā anta mawlānā fa-unṣurnā ʿalā al-qawmi al-kāfirīn

واعف عنا واغفر لنا وارحمنا أنت مولانا فانصرنا على القوم الكافرين

and with His saying, exalted be He:

And it was incumbent upon Us to give victory to the believers.

Wa-kāna ḥaqqan ʿalaynā naṣru al-muʾminīn

وكان حقا علينا نصر المؤمنين

then let him say:

O Self-Subsisting, 156 times; O All-Powerful, 314 times; O Subduer, 206 times.

Yā Qayyūm 156 marra, yā Qadīr 314 marra, yā Qahhār 206 marra.

يا قيوم ١٥٦ مرة يا قدير ٣١٤ مرة يا قهار ٢٠٦ مرة

God fulfils his need and grants him victory over his enemies.

And whoever observes its alighting in the mansion of al-Naʿāʾim, and prays two rakʿas with the Fātiḥa and with His saying, exalted be He:

Our Lord, You encompass all things in mercy and knowledge.

Rabbanā wasiʿta kulla shayʾin raḥmatan wa-ʿilman

ربنا وسعت كل شيء رحمة وعلما

and His saying:

As for him, if he be of those brought near, then there is rest and fragrance and a garden of bliss.

Fa-ammā in kāna mina al-muqarrabīna fa-rawḥun wa-rayḥānun wa-jannatu naʿīm

فأما إن كان من المقربين فروح وريحان وجنة نعيم

then let him say:

O Most Gracious, O Most Merciful, 200 times.

Yā Raḥmān, yā Raḥīm 200 marra.

يا رحمن يا رحيم ٢٠٠ مرة

He attains whatever good he desires of this world and of the hereafter.

The Lunar Mansions from al-Balda to al-Rishāʾ

And whoever observes its alighting in the mansion of al-Balda, and prays two rakʿas with the Fātiḥa and with His saying, exalted be He:

And such is the seizing of your Lord when He seizes the townships while they are doing wrong; truly His seizing is painful and severe.

Wa-kadhālika akhdhu Rabbika idhā akhadha al-qurā wa-hiya ẓālima, inna akhdhahu alīmun shadīd

وكذلك أخذ ربك إذا أخذ القرى وهي ظالمة إن أخذه أليم شديد

then let him say:

O Witness, O Severe One, 500 times.

Yā Shahīd, yā Shadīd 500 marra.

يا شهيد يا شديد ٥٠٠ مرة

And if he intends against his enemy any harm that has passed through his mind, it befalls him then and there. So let him fear God.

And whoever observes its alighting in the mansion of al-Dhābiḥ, and prays two rakʿas with the Fātiḥa and with His saying, exalted be He:

Then He turned to them, that they might turn in repentance; truly God is the Ever-Relenting, the Merciful.

Thumma tāba ʿalayhim li-yatūbū, inna Allāha huwa al-Tawwābu al-Raḥīm

ثم تاب عليهم ليتوبوا إن الله هو التواب الرحيم

then let him say:

O Ever-Relenting One, 400 times.

Yā Tawwāb 400 marra.

يا تواب ٤٠٠ مرة

He is kept safe from every hateful thing in religion, in this world and in the hereafter.

And whoever observes its alighting in the mansion of Saʿd Bulaʿ, and prays two rakʿas with the Fātiḥa and with His saying, exalted be He:

Our Lord, pour out upon us patience, make our feet firm, and give us victory over the unbelieving people.

Rabbanā afrigh ʿalaynā ṣabran wa-thabbit aqdāmanā wa-unṣurnā ʿalā al-qawmi al-kāfirīn

ربنا أفرغ علينا صبرا وثبت أقدامنا وانصرنا على القوم الكافرين

and His saying:

God makes firm those who believe with the firm word in the life of this world and in the hereafter.

Yuthabbitu Allāhu alladhīna āmanū bi-l-qawli al-thābiti fī al-ḥayāti al-dunyā wa-fī al-ākhira

يثبت الله الذين آمنوا بالقول الثابت في الحياة الدنيا وفي الآخرة

then let him say:

O Establisher (500 times).

Yā Muthabbit 500 marra.

يا مثبت ٥٠٠ مرة

He is made firm in his affairs, and he is held in awe.

And whoever observes its alighting in the mansion of Saʿd al-Suʿūd, and prays two rakʿas with the Fātiḥa and with His saying, exalted be He:

Say: O God, Master of sovereignty — the verse.

Qul Allāhumma Mālika al-mulk, al-āya

قل اللهم مالك الملك الآية

then let him say:

O All-Aware, O Creator, 600 times.

Yā Khabīr, yā Khāliq 600 marra.

يا خبير يا خالق ٦٠٠ مرة

His word is carried out and his standing is raised high.

And whoever observes its alighting in the mansion of Saʿd al-Akhbiya, and prays two rakʿas with the Fātiḥa and with His saying, exalted be He:

O you who believe, remember God with much remembrance, and glorify Him morning and evening.

Yā ayyuhā alladhīna āmanū udhkurū Allāha dhikran kathīran wa-sabbiḥūhu bukratan wa-aṣīlā

يا أيها الذين آمنوا اذكروا الله ذكرا كثيرا وسبحوه بكرة وأصيلا

then let him say:

O Possessor of Bounty, 700 times.

Yā Dhā al-Ṭawl 700 marra.

يا ذا الطول ٧٠٠ مرة

His supplication is answered and his word is carried out.

And whoever observes its alighting in the mansion of al-Fargh al-Muqaddam, and prays two rakʿas with the Fātiḥa and with His saying, exalted be He:

And God leads the wrongdoers astray, and God does what He wills.

Wa-yuḍillu Allāhu al-ẓālimīn wa-yafʿalu Allāhu mā yashā'

ويضل الله الظالمين ويفعل الله ما يشاء

then let him say:

O Harmer, 800 times.

Yā Ḍārr 800 marra.

يا ضار ٨٠٠ مرة

And if he intends evil against an oppressor, what he has concealed within himself befalls that oppressor at once.

And whoever observes its alighting in the mansion of al-Fargh al-Mu'akhkhar, and prays two rakʿas with the Fātiḥa and with His saying, exalted be He:

Behold, the curse of God is upon the wrongdoers, who turn others from the way of God and seek to make it crooked, and who disbelieve in the hereafter.

Alā laʿnatu Allāhi ʿalā al-ẓālimīn, alladhīna yaṣuddūna ʿan sabīli Allāhi wa-yabghūnahā ʿiwajan wa-hum bi-l-ākhirati hum kāfirūn

ألا لعنة الله على الظالمين الذين يصدون عن سبيل الله ويبغونها عوجا وهم بالآخرة هم كافرون

then let him say:

O Manifest One, 900 times.

Yā Ẓāhir 900 marra.

يا ظاهر ٩٠٠ مرة

He overcomes his adversary and prevails over him.

And whoever observes its alighting in the mansion of al-Rishā', and prays two rakʿas with the Fātiḥa and with His saying, exalted be He:

Did He not find you an orphan and shelter you, and find you astray and guide you, and find you in need and enrich you?

A-lam yajidka yatīman fa-āwā, wa-wajadaka ḍāllan fa-hadā, wa-wajadaka ʿāʾilan fa-aghnā

ألم يجدك يتيما فآوى ووجدك ضالا فهدى ووجدك عائلا فأغنى

then let him say:

O Rich One, O Overcomer, a thousand times.

Yā Ghanī, yā Ghālib alf marra.

يا غني يا غالب ألف مرة

His need is fulfilled, his word is carried out, his standing is raised high, and his condition is set right.

A Benefit for Might and Awe (Fāʾidat al-ʿIzz wa-l-Hayba)

Write this magic square as you see it, and carry it.

ز	ى	ز	ع
١٩	٤٨	١	٣
٦٧	٨	١٣	٦
١	١٨	٥٣	١٦

The fourfold square of might and awe

And keep constantly to the remembrance of the Name after every prayer, thus:

O Mighty One, 41 times.

Yā ʿAzīz 41 marra.

يا عزيز ٤١ مرة

and after it, the invocation that follows, three times, which is that you say:

Lord, station me in the station of might, of perfection, of splendour and of majesty, so that I find no atom and no subtle thing but that there has covered it, from Your might, that which shields it from abasement before any other than You, until I behold the abasement of all besides me. Grant me through You support by a subtle measure of dread, by which every rebellious devil and every obstinate tyrant is humbled before me; and let me remain in the abasement of servanthood, the tongue of acknowledgement spread out and the tongue of pretension withheld. Truly You are the Compeller, the Supremely Great, the Subduer. And say: Praise belongs to God, who has taken no son, who has no partner in sovereignty, and who has no protector out of weakness; and magnify Him greatly.

Rabbi awqifnī mawqifa al-ʿizzi wa-l-kamāli wa-l-bahjati wa-l-jalāli ḥattā lā ajida dharratan wa-lā daqīqatan illā wa-qad ghashiyahā min ʿizzika mā yamnaʿuhā min al-dhulli li-ghayrika ḥattā ushāhida dhulla man siwāya, li-tarzuqanī bika muʾayyadan bi-daqīqatin min al-ruʿbi yakhḍaʿu lī bihā kullu shayṭānin marīdin wa-jabbārin ʿanīdin, wa-abqā ʿalā dhulli al-ʿubūdiyyati fī (...) yabsuṭu lisāna al-iʿtirāfi wa-yaqbiḍu lisāna al-daʿwā, innaka anta al-Jabbāru al-Mutakabbiru al-Qahhār. Wa-qul al-ḥamdu li-llāhi alladhī lam yattakhidh waladan wa-lam yakun lahu sharīkun fī al-mulki wa-lam yakun lahu waliyyun min al-dhulli wa-kabbirhu takbīrā

رب أوقفني موقف العز والكمال والبهجة والجلال حتى لا أجد ذرة ولا دقيقة إلا وقد غشيها من عزك ما يمنعها من الذل لغيرك حتى أشاهد ذل من سواي لترزقني بك مؤيدا بدقيقة من الرعب يخضع لي بها كل شيطان مريد وجبار عنيد وأبقى على ذل العبودية في (...) يبسط لسان الاعتراف ويقبض لسان الدعوى إنك أنت الجبار المتكبر القهار وقل الحمد لله الذي لم يتخذ ولدا ولم يكن له شريك في الملك ولم يكن له ولي من الذل وكبره تكبيرا

Section on the Manner of Operating with the Greatest Name of God (Faṣl fī Kayfiyyat al-Taṣarruf bi-Ism Allāh al-Aʿẓam)

Barbarous names: Aham Saqak Ḥalaʿ Yaṣ

أهم سقك حلع يص

It serves for every matter the seeker desires, whether of good or of ill.

Know that this Name is called the Key, and that its numbers are 11, 111 and 1111; and it has, together with a noble name, requisites of its own, and by the joining of these three the object sought is accomplished. So when you wish to operate with it, you recite it by one of the three numbers, and after it you recite the Fātiḥa three times, and then the noble Name 75 times if you are reciting it by its lesser number, and 100 times if you are reciting it by its middle number, and ten thousand if you are reciting it by its great number; then seal it with al-Falaq three times.

And this is the form of the intention; you say:

O God, I ask You by the sanctity of Your Essence, by the praise of Your attributes, by the majesty of Your name, by the light of Your face, by the breadth of Your generosity, by the carrying out of Your judgement, and by the fulfilment of Your covenant, that You subject to me the spirituality of this noble name, that it may be a help to me in the accomplishing of my need and the answering of my call. O God, let there be no need of mine in which You have good pleasure and in which there is good for us but that You accomplish it, O Lord of the worlds. And may God bless our master Muḥammad and his family and his Companions, and grant them peace.

Allāhumma innī as'aluka bi-ḥurmat dhātika wa-thanā' ṣifātika wa-jalāl ismika wa-nūr wajhika wa-wāsi' karamika wa-infādh ḥukmika wa-wafā' 'ahdika an tusakhkhira lī rūḥāniyyat hādhā al-ism al-sharīf yakūnu lī 'awnan 'alā qaḍā' ḥājatī wa-ijābat da'watī. Allāhumma lā takūnu lī ḥājatun wa-laka fīhā riḍā' wa-lanā fīhā ṣalāḥ illā qaḍaytahā yā Rabb al-'ālamīn, wa-ṣallā Allāh 'alā sayyidinā Muḥammad wa-'alā ālihi wa-ṣaḥbihi wa-sallam.

اللهم إني أسألك بحرمة ذاتك وثناء صفاتك وجلال اسمك ونور وجهك وواسع كرمك وإنفاذ حكمك ووفاء عهدك أن تسخر لي روحانية هذا الإسم الشريف يكون لي عونا على قضاء حاجتي وإجابة دعوتي اللهم لا

تكون لي حاجة ولك فيها رضاء ولنا فيها صلاح إلا قضيتها يا رب العالمين وصلى الله على سيدنا محمد وعلى آله وصحبه وسلم

And this is the form of the noble name; you say:

O God, I ask You, O Kahaj, Kahkahaj, Kalūḥ, Makahīj, Basṭāṭ, Malīḥad, Mahlahā, Sahlā, Warwara, yā Hū, Hū, Kabā, Sir, Ṭalah, Ṭahṭiyāl, Mahṭabrūlah. It is Your mighty, supreme name, which, when You are called upon by it, You answer, and when You are asked by it, You give. I ask You to bless our master Muḥammad and his family and his Companions and to grant them peace, and to accomplish for me my need, which is such-and-such.

Allāhumma innī as'aluka yā Kahaj Kahkahaj Kalūḥ Makahīj Basṭāṭ Malīḥad Mahlahā Sahlā Warwara yā Hū Hū Kabā (...) Sir Ṭalah Ṭahṭiyāl Mahṭabrūlah, wa-huwa ismuka al-ʿaẓīm al-aʿẓam alladhī idh duʿīta bihi ajabta wa-idhā su'ilta bihi aʿṭayta. As'aluka an tuṣalliya ʿalā sayyidinā Muḥammad wa-ʿalā ālihi wa-ṣaḥbihi wa-tusallim wa-taqḍiya lī ḥājatī wa-hiya kadhā wa-kadhā.

اللهم إني أسألك يا كهج كهكهج كلوح مكهيج بسطاط مليحد مهلها سهلى وروة يا هو هو كبا (...) سر طله طهطيال مهطبروله وهو اسمك العظيم الأعظم الذي إذ دعيت به أجبت وإذا سئلت به أعطيت أسألك أن تصلي على سيدنا محمد وعلى آله وصحبه وتسلم وتقضي لي حاجتي وهي كذا وكذا

And this is the form; you say:

My Lord, I ask You for a spiritual reinforcement by which the strength of my formal and particular powers is made strong, until I subdue, by the power of my soul's signal, every overpowering soul, so that its subtle parts are made hateful, in a retribution by which its powers are brought down, and there remains in the universe no possessor of spirit but that the abode of subjugation has brought about its manifestation. O Severe in Assault, O Subduer, I ask You by that which You deposited with ʿAzrāʾīl of the power of Your subduing names, whereby the souls swore to him by that subduing power, that You clothe me in this secret in this hour, so that by it I may soften every hardship and humble by it every obstinate tyrant, by the right of Your greatest name, which, when You are called upon by it, You answer, and when You are asked by it, You give. Truly You have power over all things.

Rabbi as'aluka madadan rūḥāniyyan taqwā bihi quwwat quwāya al-shakliyya wa-l-juz'iyya ḥattā aqhara bi-quwwat ishārat nafsī kulla nafsin qāhira fa-yubghaḍa raqā'iquhā intiqāman yasquṭu bihi quwāhā fa-lā yabqā fī al-kawn dhū rūḥin illā wa-dār al-qahr aḥdatha ẓuhūrahu, yā Shadīd al-baṭsh yā Qahhār, as'aluka bi-mā awdaʿtahu ʿAzrā'īl min quwwat asmā'ika al-qahriyya fa-aqsamat lahu al-nufūs bi-l-qahriyya an taksūnī hādhā al-sirr fī hādhihi al-sāʿa ḥattā ulayyina bihi kulla ṣaʿb wa-udhilla bihi kulla jabbārin ʿanīd bi-ḥaqq ismika al-aʿẓam alladhī idhā duʿīta bihi ajabta wa-idhā su'ilta bihi aʿṭayta innaka ʿalā kulli shay'in qadīr.

رب أسألك مددا روحانيا تقوى به قوة قواي الشكلية والجزئية حتى أقهر بقوة إشارة نفسي كل نفس قاهرة فيبغض رقائقها انتقاما يسقط به قواها فلا يبقى في الكون ذو روح إلا ودار القهر أحدث ظهوره يا شديد البطش يا قهار أسألك بما أودعته عزرائيل من قوة أسمائك القهرية فأقسمت له النفوس بالقهرية أن تكسوني هذا السر في هذه الساعة حتى ألين به كل صعب وأذل به كل جبار عنيد بحق إسمك الأعظم الذي إذا دعيت به أجبت وإذا سئلت به أعطيت إنك على كل شيء قدير

The Properties of the Greatest Name

Then know that this majestic name has many benefits, and its properties are beyond reckoning. Among them is that whoever recites it over food or drink eleven times and gives it to whomever he wishes, the one who eats of it or drinks of it will love him with an intense love.

And whoever recites it eleven times at a lawsuit will overcome his adversary and prevail over him.

And whoever recites it eleven times in the face of his enemy will subdue him and be victorious over him.

And whoever recites it eleven times over dust and scatters it in the face of an attacking army, that army will be routed.

And whoever recites it twenty-one times after every prayer for a period of eleven days, intending thereby that harm should fall upon his enemy, that will come about.

And whoever finds some matter among his affairs hard going should pray two cycles; then, after the salutation, he recites Qul huwa Allāhu aḥad three times and al-Fātiḥa once, and supplicates with the supplication that follows, and recites the name 1111 times; then he asks God for his need, and he will attain it.

And whoever wishes to see the Prophet, may God bless him and grant him peace, in his sleep should recite the name eleven times and the supplication seven times, and then sleep; he will see him, may God bless him and grant him peace.

And whoever wishes to be safe from the evil of highwaymen and thieves should pray two cycles, then recite the name 1111 times and supplicate with the supplication, and then set out upon his journey; he will be safe and at ease, and will return safe and having gained.

And whoever wishes to make peace between those who are estranged should pray two cycles and recite after them the name 1111 times and the supplication eleven times, and then say:

I have bound your tongues from foul speech, and your hands from the doing of evil, and your hearts from the harbouring of harm, and I have cast among you affection and love.

ʿAqadtu alsinatakum ʿan badhīʾ al-qawl wa-aydiyakum ʿan fiʿl al-sūʾ wa-qulūbakum ʿan iḍmār al-adhā wa-alqaytu baynakum al-ulfa wa-l-mawadda.

عقدت ألسنتكم عن بذيء القول وأيديكم عن فعل السوء وقلوبكم عن إضمار الأذى وألقيت بينكم الألفة والمودة

The Rite for Safety from Harm and for Increase

And whoever writes the wafq that follows, and writes the supplication around it, and carries it with him, will be safe from all harms. No sorcery will reach him, and no injury from man, jinn, beast, or vermin, by permission of God Most High.

And whoever places it in a purse of dirhams, they will never grow few.

And whoever places it among grain, no harm will befall it, nor weevil, nor anything of the vermin.

And whoever places it in the midst of a planting, its fruits will be good and its blessing will increase.

And whoever hangs it in his house, no thief, no wrongdoer, and no envier will enter it.

And this is the form of the wafq, as you see:

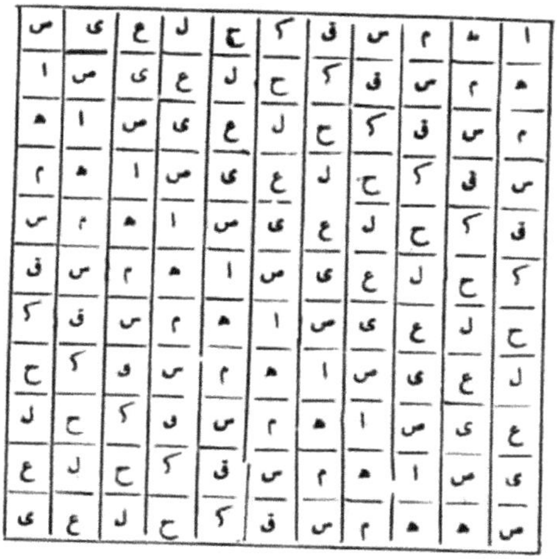

The eleven-by-eleven letter wafq

And this is the form of the supplication. You say:

In the name of God, the Most Gracious, the Most Merciful. May God bless our master Muḥammad and his family and his Companions, and grant them peace. O God, I ask You by the alif of Your divinity, O God; by the hāʾ of guidance, O Guide; by the mīm of sovereignty, O King; by the sīn of safekeeping, O Peace;

by the qāf of subjugation, O Subduer; by the kāf of sufficiency, O Sufficient One; by the ḥāʾ of forbearance, O Forbearing One; by the lām of kindness, O Subtle One; by the ʿayn of knowledge, O Knowing One; by the yāʾ of good fortune, O Possessor of Bounty; and by the ṣād of eternal self-sufficiency, O Eternal Refuge. O God, O One, O Unique, O Sufficient One, O Guarantor, You are the God of whoever is in the heavens and whoever is on the earth, and You are the Guide. O Guide, guide me to the even path. O Faithful One, O Guardian, O Peace, keep me safe from the afflictions of this world and the Hereafter. O Subduer, subdue my enemy and make me one who subdues and is not subdued, and suffice me against the evil of what You have decreed. O Guarantor, O Sufficient One, suffice me against harm by what You will and however You will; truly You have power over whatever You will. O Forbearing One, O Knowing One, O Subtle One, be gentle with me in all affairs, and teach me from Your presence a knowledge that brings benefit in this world and the Hereafter. And pardon me, O God, O Guide, O King, O Peace, O Subduer, O Sufficient One, O Forbearing One, O Subtle One, O Knowing One, O Eternal Refuge. And praise belongs to God, Lord of the worlds. May God bless our master Muḥammad and his family and his Companions, and grant them peace.

Bismi Allāh al-Raḥmān al-Raḥīm, wa-ṣallā Allāh ʿalā sayyidinā Muḥammad wa-ʿalā ālihi wa-ṣaḥbihi wa-sallam. Allāhumma innī asʾaluka bi-alif ulūhiyyatika yā Allāh, wa-bi-hāʾ al-hidāya yā Hādī, wa-bi-mīm al-mulk yā Malik, wa-bi-sīn al-salāma yā

Salām, wa-bi-qāf al-qahr yā Qāhir, wa-bi-kāf al-kifāya yā Kāfī, wa-bi-ḥā' al-ḥilm yā Ḥalīm, wa-bi-lām al-luṭf yā Laṭīf, wa-bi-'ayn al-'ilm yā 'Alīm, wa-yā' al-yumn yā Dhā al-mann, wa-bi-ṣād al-ṣamadāniyya yā Ṣamad, yā Allāh yā Wāḥid yā Aḥad yā Kāfī yā Kafīl, anta ilāhu man fī al-samāwāt wa-man fī al-arḍ wa-anta al-Hādī, yā Hādī ihdinī ilā sawā' al-sabīl, yā Mu'min yā Muhaymin yā Salām sallimnī min āfāt al-dunyā wa-l-ākhira, yā Qāhir iqhar 'aduwwī wa-j'alnī qāhiran ghayra maqhūr, wa-ikfi sharra mā qaḍayta yā Kar(...) yā Kafīl yā Kāfī ikfi al-sū' bi-mā shi'ta wa-kayfa shi'ta innaka 'alā mā tashā'u qadīr, yā Ḥalīm yā 'Alīm yā Laṭīf ulṭuf bī fī al-umūr wa-'allimnī min ladunka 'ilman tantafi'u bihi fī al-dunyā wa-l-ākhira, wa-'fu 'annī yā Allāh yā Hādī yā Malik yā Salām yā Qāhir yā Kāfī yā Ḥalīm yā Laṭīf yā 'Alīm yā Ṣamad, wa-l-ḥamdu li-llāh Rabb al-'ālamīn, wa-ṣallā Allāh 'alā sayyidinā Muḥammad wa-'alā ālihi wa-ṣaḥbihi wa-sallam.

بسم الله الرحمن الرحيم وصلى الله على سيدنا محمد وعلى آله وصحبه وسلم. اللهم إني أسألك بألف ألوهيتك يا الله، وبهاء الهداية يا هادي، وبميم الملك يا ملك، وبسين السلامة يا سلام، وبقاف القهر يا قاهر، وبكاف الكفاية يا كافي، وبحاء الحلم يا حليم، وبلام اللطف يا لطيف، وبعين العلم يا عليم، وياء اليمن يا ذا المن، وبصاد الصمدانية يا صمد يا الله يا واحد يا أحد يا كافي يا كفيل، أنت إله من في السموات ومن في الأرض وأنت الهادي يا هادي اهدني إلى سواء السبيل يا مؤمن يا مهيمن يا سلام سلمني من آفات الدنيا والآخرة، يا قاهر اقهر عدوي واجعلني قاهرا غير مقهور واكفي شر ما قضيت يا كر(...) يا كفيل يا

كافي اكفني السوء بما شئت وكيف شئت إنك على ما تشاء قدير، يا حليم يا عليم يا لطيف الطف بي في الأمور وعلمني من لدنك علما تنتفع به في الدنيا والآخرة، واعف عني يا الله يا هادي يا ملك يا سلام يا قاهر يا كافي يا حليم يا لطيف يا عليم يا صمد والحمد لله رب العالمين، وصلى الله على سيدنا محمد وعلى آله وصحبه وسلم.

A Benefit for Blessing in Grains, Crops and the Like (Fā'ida li-Baraka fī al-Ḥubūb wa-l-Zurūʿ wa-Naḥwihā)

Write the following names on a piece of paper on Monday at sunrise, fold it, and set it in the middle of the ṣāʿ measure that holds the grain. Then recite the names over it a thousand times. Afterwards, when you intend to measure out from it for sowing, recite the names forty times and then take from it. God will bless it and its yield with a manifest blessing, and you will see of good and increase what gladdens you. These are the names:

O God, O Lord, O Most Gracious, O Most Merciful, O King, O Preserver, O Most Holy, O Strong One, O Severe One, O Possessor of Enduring Strength. O God, bless our master Muḥammad and his family, and grant them peace and benediction, with a perfect blessing whose perfection has no end, just as Your own perfection has no end.

Yā Allāh, yā Rabb, yā Raḥmān, yā Raḥīm, yā Malik, yā Ḥafīẓ, yā Quddūs, yā Qawī, yā Shadīd, yā Dhā al-quwwa al-matīn. Allāhumma ṣalli wa-sallim wa-bārik ʿalā sayyidinā Muḥammad wa-ʿalā ālihi ṣalātan kāmilatan lā nihāyata li-kamālihā kamā lā nihāyata li-kamālik.

يا الله يا رب يا رحمن يا رحيم يا ملك يا حفيظ يا قدوس يا قوي يا شديد يا ذا القوة المتين. اللهم صل وسلم وبارك على سيدنا محمد وعلى آله صلاة كاملة لا نهاية لكمالها كما لا نهاية لكمالك.

A Benefit Concerning the Discipline of His Two Names Most High, Living and Self-Subsisting, for the Fulfilment of Every Need and the Attainment of Every Desire (Fāʾida fī Riyāḍat Ismayhi Taʿālā Ḥayy Qayyūm li-Qaḍāʾ Kull Ḥāja wa-Nayl Kull Marghūb)

Fast for twenty-one days in complete discipline, and after every prayer recite a thousand times:

O Living One, O Self-Subsisting One.

Yā Ḥayy yā Qayyūm.

يا حي يا قيوم

Enter your retreat on Sunday, at the head of the second week or the third. On the fifth of its days a light, a splendour and a radiance will appear to you, and it will not cease to take form until it becomes a companionable angel, fair of aspect, with a crown of light upon his head. He will greet you with eloquence, so return the greeting to him with courtesy and humility. Then he will say to you: What has driven you to occupy yourself with this Greatest Name? Say to him: I want you as a brother in God Most High. He will say to you: And I am indeed an excellent brother; stretch out your hand. You will have with you a green palm-strip on which the Throne Verse is written. Give it to him, and keep your hand closed upon the words "God, there is no god but He, the Living, the Self-Subsisting" and "the Most High, the Most Great", while it lies beneath the grip of his hand. When he has taken hold of it, that is the covenant between you and him. Say to him: Give me a sign by which I may know it.

He will give you a jewel, or a ring, or a bezel-stone; and when you rub it he will present himself before you, visibly, at any time except the time of the Friday prayer. The incense for the whole period of the discipline is male frankincense. Let your breaking of the fast be upon raisins and good oil only, and you are to carry the wafq that follows, with the Throne Verse and the closing verses of Sūrat al-Ḥashr written around it.

And this is the form of the wafq, as you see:

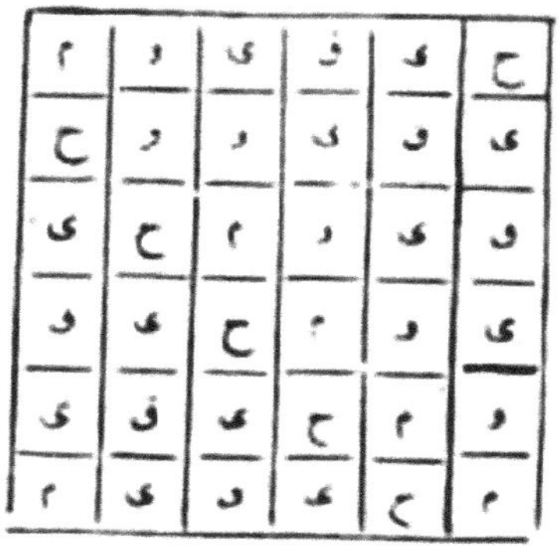

The six-by-six letter wafq

Section on the Invocation of His Name, Exalted is He, al-Laṭīf (Faṣl fī Dhikr Daʿwat Ismihi Taʿālā al-Laṭīf)

You fast for it seven days in complete discipline, and you recite the name after every prayer 129 times, and after it you read the invocation that follows once. And every night you recite the name 6641 times and read the invocation after it four times. Then the servants will come to you, and make a covenant with you, and take you as a brother, and accomplish for you everything you desire, and give you such provision as will be a full sufficiency for you, so long as you keep to their covenant.

And this is the invocation; you say:

In the name of God, the Merciful, the Compassionate. O God, I ask You and seek to draw near to You by Your Name al-Laṭīf, the Subtle, whose kindness has embraced the people of the heavens and the people of the earth; You were gentle with the unborn in the wombs of their mothers, and You encompassed all created things in knowledge. I ask You by the secret and by the secrets, by the light and by the lights, O You whom no sight reaches, while He reaches all sight, and He is the Subtle, the Aware, whose command, when He desires a thing, is only to say to it "Be," and it is. Subject to me the servants of Your blessed Name al-Laṭīf; truly my Lord is subtle toward whatever He wills, and He is the Knowing, the Wise. O God, O Subduer of the heavens and of the seven earths, and of whoever is within them and whoever is upon them, subject to me the servants of Your blessed Name al-Laṭīf by the secret of the secret of Your Name the Subtle, the Bringer into Being. Have you not seen that God sends down water from the sky, and the earth becomes green? Truly God is Subtle, Aware. O God, O Lord of lords, Nurturer of all created things by the subtlety of His lordship, hasten for me the flowing of Your kindness through my whole affair and through all that I desire. O

You who are not absent, that I should wait for You, nor far away. Hidden is Your hidden kindness; hidden is Your hidden kindness. And let my concern, my right guidance and my heart be between two fingers of the fingers of Your kindness, until I witness the subtlety of kindness from every quarter upon which the sign has fallen or which it has expressed, until I am drowned in the seas of kindness, rejoicing in the sweetness of the sea's subtlety, immersed in lights that shone upon a radiance from the flashes of His light, in His secret, and His secret in His creation. Does He not know what He created, and He is the Subtle, the Aware? O You who know in sum and have no need of detail, Your generosity dispenses with speaking and Your knowledge dispenses with asking. Hope is cut off from all but You, expectations have failed except in You, and the roads are closed except the road to You. O Subtle One of all kindness, give me understanding of Your secrets, and clothe me in the garments of Your lights, and pour upon me from the bounties of the subtleties of the knowledges of the stillness of Your hidden kindness, until there remains in the universe nothing moving, silent or speaking, outward or inward, that is not made subject to me by the secret of Your Name al-Laṭīf. "O my son, though it be but the weight of a grain of mustard seed, and though it be in a rock, or in the heavens, or in the earth, God will bring it forth; truly God is Subtle, Aware." O Uncoverer of harms and of secrets, O Light of lights, I ask You by Your greatest Name, al-Laṭīf, that You subject to me by Your kindness everyone in the universe, in my service and compliant with my will, and that You strengthen me with the servant of Your Name al-Laṭīf, with the highest honour and the most faithful secret. "And remember what is recited in your houses of the signs of God and the wisdom; truly God is Subtle, Aware." I ask You by these names and these verses, and by the secrets that You deposited in Your hidden kingdom, that You subject to me the servants of Your blessed, subtle Name and all Your creation, and that You make plain to me what is beneath Your earth and what is above it of the circulating blessings and provisions and of the good things that travel through Your land and Your sea. God is subtle toward His servants; He provides for whom He wills, and He is the Strong, the Mighty. O God, I ask You by the hidden, stored secret in the attributes of Your subtle Name, the guarded, the blessed, the pure, by which, when You are called, You answer, and when You are asked, You give, that You subject to me a spiritual support from the servants of Your subtle Name, with compassion, with the plain disclosure of unveiling in sleep and in waking, in travel and at home, and with tidings of what I hold within me, outwardly and inwardly. Seat me upon its banner, purify me upon its carpet, keep me upon its signs, and make me understand out of Your knowledge, for You have power over everything. O God, I ask You: O Lahyūsh, O Ṭahyūsh, O Būsh, O Fahyūsh. I ask You, O God, by the right of these names and secrets that You cast into the heart of Your prophet Muḥammad, may God bless him and grant him peace, with which You clothed him from the majesty of Your kindness and by which You guided him through the purity of Your holiness, that You subject to me the spiritual beings of the servants of Your blessed, subtle Name, the upper and the lower, so that they may be a help to me in what I desire, which is such-and-such. Answer, O ʿAbd al-Laṭīf; and you, O Shuʿāʿ, and you, O Shaʿḍūḍ, by the right of what you know of the secret of this subtle Name, of the nobility of its supreme knowledge and the mention of its majesty. And remember what is recited in your houses of the signs of God and the wisdom; truly God is Subtle, Aware. Fulfil my need, comply with what pleases me, aid me with obedience to the service of God and of the Messenger, and enrich me from the wealth of God that is among God's creation. By Your right, O God, O Subtle One: O God, I ask You by the lām of Your kindness, by the ṭāʾ of Your bounty, by the yāʾ of Your wakefulness, and by the fāʾ of Your singularity. I ask You to subject to me by them a secret from Your secret, a light from Your light, a kindness from Your kindness, and an awe from Your awe; to subject to me by them all Your creation, to make their hearts yield to me in fellowship and affection, and to deposit my love in their hearts as a secret, a light, and a joy. Answer, O ʿAbd al-Laṭīf.

Bismi Allāh al-Raḥmān al-Raḥīm. Allāhumma innī as'aluka wa-atawassalu ilayka bi-ismika al-Laṭīf alladhī wasiʿa luṭfuhu ahl al-samāwāt wa-ahl al-arḍ, wa-laṭufta bi-l-ajinna fī buṭūn ummahātihā, wa-aḥaṭta bi-l-kā'ināt ʿilman. As'aluka bi-l-sirr wa-bi-l-asrār wa-l-nūr wa-l-anwār, yā man lā tudrikuhu al-abṣār wa-huwa yudriku al-abṣār wa-huwa al-Laṭīf al-Khabīr, innamā amruhu idhā arāda shay'an an yaqūla lahu kun fa-yakūn. Sakhkhir lī khuddām ismika al-Laṭīf al-mubārak, inna rabbī laṭīfun li-mā yashā' innahu huwa al-'Alīm al-Ḥakīm. Allāhumma yā musakhkhir al-samāwāt wa-l-arḍ al-sab' wa-man fīhinna wa-man 'alayhinna, sakhkhir lī khuddām ismika al-Laṭīf al-mubārak bi-sirr sirr ismika al-Laṭīf al-Mukawwin. A-lam tara anna Allāha anzala min al-samā' mā'an fa-tuṣbiḥu al-arḍu mukhḍarratan inna Allāha Laṭīfun Khabīr. Allāhumma yā Rabb al-arbāb, murabbī al-kā'ināt bi-laṭīf rubūbiyyatihi, asri' lī sarayān luṭfika fī sha'nī wa-murādī kullihi, yā man laysa bi-ghā'ib fa-antaẓirahu wa-lā ba'īd (...), al-khafī luṭfuka al-khafī, al-khafī luṭfuka al-khafī, wa-hammī rushdī wa-qalbī bayna iṣba'ayn min aṣābi' luṭfika, ḥattā ashhada laṭīf al-luṭf min kull jiha waqa'at al-ishāra 'alayhā aw 'abbarat 'anhā, ḥattā aghraqa fī biḥār al-luṭf mubtahijan bi-ḥalāwat daqq al-baḥr, munghamisan fī anwār ashraqat 'alā ḍaw' min bawāriq nūrihi fī sirrihi wa-sirrihi fī khalqihi. A-lā ya'lamu man khalaqa wa-huwa al-Laṭīf al-Khabīr. Yā 'āliman bi-l-jumla wa-ghaniyyan 'an al-tafṣīl, kafā karamuka 'an al-maqāl wa-kafā 'ilmuka 'an al-su'āl. Inqaṭa'a al-rajā' illā minka, wa-khābat al-āmāl illā fīka, wa-insaddat al-ṭuruq illā ilayka. Yā Laṭīf al-luṭf, fahhimnī fahm asrārika, wa-albisnī malābis anwārika, wa-afiḍ 'alayya min 'awārif laṭā'if ma'ārif sakīnat luṭfika al-khafī, ḥattā lā yakūna fī al-kawn shay'un mutaḥarrikun ṣāmitun aw nāṭiqun ẓāhirun aw bāṭinun illā sukhkhira lī bi-sirr ismika al-Laṭīf. Yā bunayya innahā in taku mithqāl ḥabba min khardal fa-takun fī ṣakhra aw fī al-samāwāt aw fī al-arḍ ya'ti bihā Allāh inna Allāha Laṭīfun Khabīr. Yā Kāshif al-aḍrār wa-l-asrār, yā Nūr al-anwār, as'aluka bi-ismika al-a'ẓam al-Laṭīf an tusakhkhira lī bi-luṭfika kull man fī al-kawn bi-khidmatī mumtathilan ṭawʿī, wa-tuʾayyidanī bi-khādim ismika al-Laṭīf bi-l-sharaf al-aʿlā wa-l-sirr al-awfā. Wa-udhkurna mā yutlā fī buyūtikunna min āyāt Allāh wa-l-ḥikma inna Allāha kāna Laṭīfan Khabīran. Asʾaluka bi-hādhihi al-asmāʾ wa-l-āyāt, wa-l-asrār allatī awdaʿtahā fī mulkika al-maknūn an tusakhkhira lī khuddāma ismika al-Laṭīf al-mubārak wa-jamīʿa khalqika wa-bayyin lī mā taḥta arḍika wa-mā fawqahā min al-barakāt wa-l-arzāq al-dāʾira wa-l-khayrāt al-sāʾira bi-mā fī barrika wa-baḥrika Allāhu Laṭīfun bi-ʿibādihi yarzuqu man yashāʾu wa-huwa al-Qawiyyu al-ʿAzīz. Allāhumma innī asʾaluka bi-l-sirr al-maknūn al-makhzūn fī nuʿūt ismika al-Laṭīf al-maṣūn al-mubārak al-ṭāhir alladhī idhā duʿīta bihi ajabta wa-idhā suʾilta bihi aʿṭayta an tusakhkhira lī madadan rūḥāniyyan min khuddām ismika al-Laṭīf bi-l-raʾfa wa-bayān al-mukāshafa fī al-nawm wa-l-yaqaẓa wa-l-safar wa-l-ḥaḍar wa-akhbār mā aḍmartu ʿalayhi ẓāhiran wa-bāṭinan. Wa-ajlisnī ʿalā liwāʾihi wa-ṭahhirnī ʿalā bisāṭihi wa-abqinī ʿalā ʿalāmātihi wa-fahhimnī min ʿilmika innaka ʿalā kulli shayʾin qadīr. Allāhumma innī asʾaluka yā Lahyūsh wa-yā Ṭahyūsh wa-yā Būsh wa-yā Fahyūsh. Asʾaluka Allāhumma bi-ḥaqq hādhihi al-asmāʾ wa-l-asrār allatī alqaytahā fī qalb nabiyyika Muḥammad ṣallā Allāhu ʿalayhi wa-sallam wa-kasawtahu min jalāl luṭfika wa-hadaytahu bi-ṭahārat qudsika an tusakhkhira lī rūḥāniyyat khuddām ismika al-Laṭīf al-mubārak al-ʿulwiyya wa-l-sufliyya yakūnūna ʿawnan lī ʿalā mā urīdu wa-huwa kadhā wa-kadhā. Ajib yā ʿAbd al-Laṭīf, wa-anta yā Shuʿāʿ wa-anta yā Shaʿḍūḍ, bi-ḥaqq mā taʿrifūnahu min sirr hādhā al-ism al-Laṭīf wa-sharīf ʿilmihi al-aʿẓam wa-dhikr jalālihi. Wa-udhkurna mā yutlā fī buyūtikunna min āyāti Allāh wa-l-ḥikma inna Allāha kāna Laṭīfan khabīran. Iqḍū ḥājatī wa-imtathilū marḍātī wa-asʿifūnī bi-l-ṭāʿa li-khidmat Allāh wa-l-Rasūl wa-athnūnī min māl Allāh alladhī maʿa khalq Allāh. Bi-ḥaqqika yā Allāh yā Laṭīf, Allāhumma mā innī as'aluka bi-lām luṭfika wa-ṭā' ṭawlika wa-yā' yaqaẓatika wa-fā' fardāniyyatika. As'aluka an tusakhkhira lī bihā sirran min sirrika wa-nūran min nūrika wa-luṭfan min luṭfika wa-haybatan min haybatika, tusakhkhiru lī bihā jamīʿa khalqika wa-tukhḍiʿu lī qulūbahum bi-l-ulfa wa-l-mawadda wa-tūdiʿu fī qulūbihim maḥabbatī sirran wa-nūran wa-bahja. Ajib yā ʿAbd al-Laṭīf.

بسم الله الرحمن الرحيم اللهم إني أسألك وأتوسل إليك باسمك اللطيف الذي وسع لطفه أهل السموات وأهل الأرض ولطفت بالأجنة في بطون أمهاتها وأحطت بالكائنات علما أسألك بالسر وبالأسرار والنور والأنوار يا من لا تدركه الأبصار وهو يدرك الأبصار وهو اللطيف الخبير إنما أمره إذا أراد شيئا أن يقول له كن فيكون سخر لي خدام اسمك اللطيف المبارك إن ربي لطيف لما يشاء إنه هو العليم الحكيم اللهم يا مسخر السموات والأرض السبع ومن فيهن ومن عليهن سخر لي خدام اسمك اللطيف المبارك بسر سر اسمك اللطيف المكون ألم تر أن الله أنزل من السماء ماء فتصبح الأرض مخضرة إن الله لطيف خبير اللهم يا رب الأرباب مربي الكائنات بلطيف ربوبيته أسرع لي سريان لطفك في شأني ومرادي كله يا من ليس بغائب فأنتظره ولا بعيد (...) الخفي لطفك الخفي الخفي لطفك الخفي وهمي رشدي وقلبي بين أصبعين من أصابع

لطفك حتى أشهد لطيف اللطف من كل جهة وقعت الإشارة عليها أو عبرت عنها حتى أغرق في بحار اللطف مبتهجا بحلاوة دق البحر منغمسا في أنوار أشرقت على ضوء من بوارق نوره في سره وسره في خلقه ألا يعلم من خلق وهو اللطيف الخبير يا عالما بالجملة وغنيا عن التفصيل كفى كرمك عن المقال وكفى علمك عن السؤال انقطع الرجاء إلا منك وخابت الآمال إلا فيك وانسدت الطرق إلا إليك يا لطيف اللطف فهمني فهم أسرارك وألبسني ملابس أنوارك وأفض علي من عوارف لطائف معارف سكينة لطفك الخفي حتى لا يكون في الكون شيء متحرك صامت أو ناطق ظاهر أو باطن إلا سخر لي بسر اسمك اللطيف يا بني إنها إن تك مثقال حبة من خردل فتكن في صخرة أو في السماوات أو في الأرض يأت بها الله إن الله لطيف خبير يا كاشف الأضرار والأسرار يا نور الأنوار أسألك باسمك الأعظم اللطيف أن تسخر لي بلطفك كل من في الكون بخدمتي ممتثلا طوعي وتؤيدني بخادم اسمك اللطيف بالشرف الأعلى والسر الأوفى واذكرن ما يتلى في بيوتكن من آيات الله والحكمة إن الله كان لطيفا خبيرا أسألك بهذه الأسماء والآيات والأسرار التي أودعتها في ملكك المكنون أن تسخر لي خدام اسمك اللطيف المبارك وجميع خلقك وبين لي ما تحت أرضك وما فوقها من البركات والأرزاق الدائرة والخيرات السائرة بما في برك وبحرك الله لطيف بعباده يرزق من يشاء وهو القوي العزيز اللهم إني أسألك بالسر المكنون المخزون في نعوت اسمك اللطيف المصون المبارك الطاهر الذي إذا دعيت به أجبت وإذا سئلت به أعطيت أن تسخر لي مددا روحانيا من خدام اسمك اللطيف بالرأفة وبيان المكاشفة في النوم واليقظة والسفر

والحضر وأخبار ما أضمرت عليه ظاهرا وباطنا وأجلسني على لوائه
وطهرني على بساطه وأبقني على علاماته وفهمني من علمك إنك على
كل شيء قدير اللهم إني أسألك يا لهيوش ويا طهيوش ويا بوش ويا
فهيوش أسألك اللهم بحق هذه الأسماء والأسرار التي ألقيتها في قلب
نبيك محمد صلى الله عليه وسلم وكسيته من جلال لطفك وهديته
بطهارة قدسك أن تسخر لي روحانية خدام اسمك اللطيف المبارك
العلوية والسفلية يكونون عونا لي على ما أريد وهو كذا وكذا أجب يا عبد
اللطيف وأنت يا شعاع وأنت يا شعضوض بحق ما تعرفونه من سر هذا
الاسم اللطيف وشريف علمه الأعظم وذكر جلاله واذكرن ما يتلى في
بيوتكن من آيات الله والحكمة إن الله كان لطيفا خبيرا اقضوا حاجتي
وامتثلوا مرضاتي واسعفوني بالطاعة لخدمة الله والرسول وأثنوني من مال
الله الذي مع خلق الله بحقك يا الله يا لطيف اللهم ما إني أسألك بلام
لطفك وطاء طولك وياء يقظتك وفاء فردانيتك أسألك أن تسخر لي بها
سرا من سرك ونورا من نورك ولطفا من لطفك وهيبة من هيبتك تسخر لي
بها جميع خلقك وتخضع لي قلوبهم بالألفة والمودة وتودع في قلوبهم
محبتي سرا ونورا وبهجة أجب يا عبد اللطيف

Barbarous names: Yā ʿAbd al-Ṭālib, Yā ʿAbd al-Bāriʾ, Yā ʿAbd al-Fattāḥ, Yā Shuʿāʿ, Yā Nūr, Yā Ṣāliḥ, Yā Shaʿḍūḍ, Yā Ḥaqbāl

يا عبد الطالب ويا عبد البارئ ويا عبد الفتاح ويا شعاع ويا نور ويا صالح
ويا شعضوض ويا حقبال

O noble angels of God, come to my aid. O assemblies of the spiritual spirits, hasten with what I desire of you, in obedience to

Him and to His names, by the blessing of our master Muḥammad, may God bless him and grant him peace. Praise belongs to God, Lord of the worlds, and may God bless our master Muḥammad and his family and his companions, and grant them peace.

yā malāʾikat Allāh al-kirām asʿifūnī, yā maʿāshir al-arwāḥ al-rūḥāniyya wa-asriʿū bi-mā urīduhu minkum bi-l-ṭāʿa lahu wa-li-asmāʾihi bi-barakat sayyidinā Muḥammad ṣallā Allāhu ʿalayhi wa-sallam. Wa-l-ḥamdu li-Llāh Rabb al-ʿālamīn wa-ṣallā Allāhu ʿalā sayyidinā Muḥammad wa-ʿalā ālihi wa-ṣaḥbihi wa-sallam.

يا ملائكة الله الكرام أسعفوني يا معاشر الأرواح الروحانية وأسرعوا بما أريده منكم بالطاعة له ولأسمائه ببركة سيدنا محمد صلى الله عليه وسلم والحمد لله رب العالمين وصلى الله على سيدنا محمد وعلى آله وصحبه وسلم

Its incense is anything of pleasant fragrance.

Section on the Operation with His Name, Exalted is He, Wadūd, for Every Matter (Faṣl fī al-Taṣrīf bi-Ismihi Taʿālā Wadūd li-Kull Amr)

This is done by saying:

God is greatest.

Allāhu akbar

الله أكبر

ten times, and:

In the name of God, the Most Gracious, the Most Merciful.

Bismi Allāh al-Raḥmān al-Raḥīm

بسم الله الرحمن الرحيم

one hundred times, and:

Single, Living, Self-Subsisting, Judge, Just, Most Holy.

Fard Ḥayy Qayyūm Ḥakam ʿAdl Quddūs

فرد حي قيوم حكم عدل قدوس

one hundred times. Then you recite a verse suited to what you seek, the number of whose letters is nineteen, one hundred times. Then you invoke:

O Loving One.

Yā Wadūd

يا ودود

twelve thousand times. Then you say:

O Loving One, You are the one who brought forth the secret of love and affection in the hearts of the secrets. You are the one who perfected the essences of the seekers with the light of lights, who manifested Yourself in the abiding might and in the light that stands over the created orders, who brought the human being into view, created the bodily forms, and joined them to the spirits. I ask You by the secret of the flowing of Your love through Your prophets and Your friends that You cast the love of such-

and-such into the heart of such-and-such, just as You cast the revelation upon the heart of Your prophet Muḥammad, may God bless him and grant him peace. There is neither power nor strength save through God, the High, the Magnificent.

Yā Wadūd, anta alladhī aṭlaʿta sirra al-maḥabba wa-l-mawadda fī qulūb al-asrār, wa-anta alladhī akmalta dhawāt al-ṭālibīn bi-nūr al-anwār, wa-tajallayta bi-l-ʿizz al-dāʾim wa-l-nūr al-qāʾim ʿalā al-akwān, wa-aẓharta al-insān wa-khalaqta al-ashbāḥ wa-allafta baynahā wa-bayna al-arwāḥ. Asʾaluka bi-sirr sarayān wuddika fī anbiyāʾika wa-awliyāʾika an tulqiya maḥabbata kadhā fī qalb kadhā kamā alqayta al-waḥya ʿalā qalb nabiyyika Muḥammad ṣallā Allāhu ʿalayhi wa-sallam bi-ḥaqq (...) wa-lā ḥawla wa-lā quwwata illā bi-Llāh al-ʿAlī al-ʿAẓīm.

يا ودود أنت الذي أطلعت سر المحبة والمودة في قلوب الأسرار وأنت الذي أكملت ذوات الطالبين بنور الأنوار وتجليت بالعز الدائم والنور القائم على الأكوان وأظهرت الإنسان وخلقت الأشباح وألفت بينها وبين الأرواح أسألك بسر سريان ودك في أنبيائك وأوليائك أن تلقي محبة كذا في قلب كذا كما ألقيت الوحي على قلب نبيك محمد صلى الله عليه وسلم بحق (...) ولا حول ولا قوة إلا بالله العلي العظيم

And say once after every thousand:

May God bless our master Muḥammad and his family and his companions, and grant them peace.

wa-ṣallā Allāhu ʿalā sayyidinā Muḥammad wa-ʿalā ālihi wa-ṣaḥbihi wa-sallam

وصلى الله على سيدنا محمد وعلى آله وصحبه وسلم

The best of times is the last third of the night, and the incense is the wood of al-ishrāq. Whoever wishes to bring about harmony between two disputants should say:

O Loving One.

Yā Wadūd

يا ودود

four hundred times, then the invocation once, and it will come about. And whoever says:

O Loving One.

Yā Wadūd

يا ودود

twenty thousand times, reciting the invocation after every thousand while fumigating with jāwī and intending reconciliation between two disputants, it comes about at once.

A Benefit for Binding a Woman from Any Man Other Than Her Husband (Fāʾida li-ʿAqd al-Marʾa ʿan Ghayr Zawjihā)

Whoever writes in the square that follows, and places the name of his wife in its empty cells; then let him lie with her, and after that no one other than he will lie with her. This is its form, as you see:

The sixfold letter square

Section on Employing His Exalted Name Khabīr, for Seeking Guidance and for Disclosing in a Dream What a Person Desires (Faṣl fī al-Taṣrīf bi-Ismihi Taʿālā Khabīr li-l-Istikhāra wa-Kashf mā Yurīduhu al-Insān fī al-Manām)

Shaykh Abū al-ʿAbbās al-Būnī said: as for His exalted name Khabīr, whoever sets it in an eightfold figure by the numerical taksīr arrangement, and writes around it in a circle:

Exalted in degrees, Possessor of the Throne, He casts the Spirit of His command upon whomever He wills of His servants, that he may warn of the Day of Meeting, the Day when they come forth.

Rafīʿ al-darajāt dhū al-ʿarsh yulqī al-rūḥa min amrihi ʿalā man yashāʾu min ʿibādihi li-yundhira yawma al-talāq, yawma hum bārizūn

رفيع الدرجات ذو العرش يلقي الروح من أمره على من يشاء من عباده لينذر يوم التلاق يوم هم بارزون

and then places it beneath his head and sleeps while reciting these names:

O All-Aware, O Guide, O Manifest.

Yā Khabīr, yā Hādī, yā Mubīn

يا خبير يا هادي يا مبين

until he falls asleep, holding in his mind the thing he desires, he will see it in his sleep, made plain and clear. This is the form of the eightfold figure, as you see:

٢٠٠	١٠	٢	٦٠٠	٢٠٠	١٠	٢	٦٠٠
٢	٦٠٠	٢٠٠	١٠	٢	٦٠٠	٢٠٠	١٠
٢٠٠	١٠	٢	٦٠٠	٢٠	١٠	٢	٦٠٠
٢	٦٠٠	٢٠٠	١٠	٢	٢	٢٠٠	١٠
١٠	٢	٦٠٠	٢٠٠	٠	٦٠٠	٦٠٠	٢٠٠
٦٠٠	٢٠	١٠	٢	٦٠٠	٢٠٠	١٠	٢
١٠	٢	٦٠٠	٢٠٠	١٠	٢	٦	٢٠٠
٦٠٠	٢٠٠	١٠	٢	٦٠٠	٢٠٠	١٠	٢

The eightfold wafq of the name Khabīr

Section on Employing His Exalted Name Jabbār (Faṣl fī Taṣrīf Ismihi Taʿālā Jabbār)

For the destruction of a tyrant or a thief: whoever desires that should rise in the depth of the darkening night, perform the ablution amply, and pray two rakʿas, in the first the Opening of the Book and Sūrat Nūn, and in the second the Opening of the Book and al-Ḥāqqa. Then let him stand upon his feet and recite the name, which is Jabbār, 824 times, and let him do that for three nights. At the head of every hundred recitations of the name he says:

O Compeller, O All-Powerful, seize so-and-so the tyrant.

Yā Jabbār, yā Qadīr, khudh fulānan al-ẓālim

يا جبار يا قدير خذ فلانا الظالم

and he mentions whatever kinds of affliction he wishes. Guard it well, and do not invoke it against any but an obstinate tyrant, for the three nights will not pass before you see of God's doing what tongues are unable to describe. It is best that the work be done at the end of the Arab month, and that it begin on the night of Wednesday, so that the sealing falls on the night of Friday.

A Noble Benefit for the Subjugation of Princes and Rulers (Fā'ida Jalīla li-Taskhīr al-Umarā' wa-l-Ḥukkām)

You say:

O Loving One, 400 times; O Subjugator, 900 times.

Yā Wadūd 400 marra, yā Musakhkhir 900 marra.

يا ودود ٤٠٠ مرة يا مسخر ٩٠٠ مرة

then, 100 times:

Have you not seen that God has subjected to you whatever is in the earth, and the ships that run upon the sea by His command? And He holds back the sky lest it fall upon the earth, save by His leave. Indeed God is Gentle and Merciful to mankind.

A-lam tara anna Allāha sakhkhara lakum mā fī al-arḍi wa-l-fulka tajrī fī al-baḥri bi-amrihi wa-yumsiku al-samā'a an taqa'a

ʿalā al-arḍi illā bi-idhnihi inna Allāha bi-l-nāsi la-ra'ūfun raḥīm

ألم تر أن الله سخر لكم ما في الأرض والفلك تجري في البحر بأمره ويمسك السماء أن تقع على الأرض إلا بإذنه إن الله بالناس لرؤوف رحيم

Then recite the oath that follows 41 times, and send blessings upon the Prophet, may God bless him and grant him peace, at the beginning and at the end. This is the form of the oath. You say:

In the name of God, the Most Gracious, the Most Merciful. By the name

Bismi Allāh al-Raḥmān al-Raḥīm, bi-ism

بسم الله الرحمن الرحيم باسم

Barbarous names: Qāhir Jalīl Hālikh Dalkh Dalkhī Hamlūkhī Hamlūkhīm

قاهر جليل هالخ دلخ دلخي هملوخي هملوخيم

Answer, O master, by Him before whom necks are humbled, before whom the towering heights have fallen prostrate, and before whom faces are bowed low. He is God, the Living, the Self-Subsisting, Owner of the heavens and the earth and their Sustainer. I ask You, by the right of these names and these verses, to subject to me the spirit of such-and-such, so that it may be obedient to my hand and may fulfil my need.

Ajib ayyuhā al-sayyid Ṭamṭa(...)āl bi-lladhī dhallat lahu al-riqāb wa-kharra lahu al-shumm al-bādhikhāt wa-ʿanat al-wujūh, wa-huwa Allāh al-Ḥayy al-Qayyūm mālik al-samawāt wa-l-arḍ wa-

qayyūmuhā. As'aluka bi-ḥaqq hādhihi al-asmā' wa-hādhihi al-āyāt an tusakhkhira lī rūḥāniyyat kadhā wa-kadhā ḥattā yakūna ṭaw'a yadī wa-yaqḍiya ḥājatī.

أجب أيها السيد طمطه(...)ال بالذي ذلت له الرقاب وخر له الشم الباذخات وعنت الوجوه وهو الله الحي القيوم مالك السموات والأرض وقيومها أسألك بحق هذه الأسماء وهذه الآيات أن تسخر لي روحانية كذا وكذا حتى يكون طوع يدي ويقضي حاجتي

It is good that the recitation take place during the days when the light of the moon is increasing. In this measure there is sufficiency. God is the granter of success to what is right, and to Him are the return and the final resort.

Chapter Two: On Mentioning a Selection of the Special Properties of Some Qur'ānic Verses (al-Bāb al-Thānī fī Dhikr Nubdha min Khawāṣṣ Ba'ḍ al-Āyāt al-Qur'āniyya)

Section on Operating with the Basmala for Every Matter the Seeker Desires (Faṣl fī al-Taṣrīf bi-l-Basmala fī Kull Amr Yurīduhu al-Ṭālib)

This is done by reciting the basmala 786 times. Then after that you say:

O God, I ask You by the greatness of "In the name of God, the Most Gracious, the Most Merciful"; and I ask You by the majesty of In the name of God, the Most Gracious, the Most Merciful; and I ask You by the perfection of In the name of God, the Most Gracious, the Most Merciful; and I ask You by the beauty of In the name of God, the Most Gracious, the Most Merciful; and I ask You by the sublimity of In the name of God, the Most Gracious, the Most Merciful; and I ask You by the splendour of In the name of God, the Most Gracious, the Most Merciful; and I ask You by the praise of In the name of God, the Most Gracious, the Most Merciful; and I ask You by the bounties of In the name of God, the Most Gracious, the Most Merciful; and I ask You by the radiance of In the name of God, the Most Gracious, the Most Merciful; and I ask You by the light of In the name of God, the Most Gracious, the Most Merciful; and I ask You by the excellences of In the name of God, the Most Gracious, the Most Merciful; and I ask You by the power of In the name of God, the Most Gracious, the Most Merciful; and I ask You by the disposing of In the name of God, the Most Gracious, the Most Merciful; and I ask You by the special properties of In the name of God, the Most Gracious, the Most Merciful; and I ask You by the station of In the name of God, the Most Gracious, the Most Merciful; and I ask You by the subtleties of In the name of God, the Most Gracious, the Most Merciful; and I ask You by the strength of In the name of God, the Most Gracious, the Most Merciful; and I ask You by the awe of In the name of God, the Most Gracious, the Most Merciful; and I ask You by the granting of success of In the name of God, the Most Gracious, the Most Merciful; and I ask You by Your exaltedness in In the name of God, the Most Gracious, the Most Merciful; and I ask You by the kindnesses of In the name of God, the Most Gracious, the Most Merciful; and I ask You by the beginning of In the name of God, the Most Gracious, the Most Merciful; and I ask You by the ending of In the name of God, the Most Gracious, the Most Merciful; and I ask You by the supplying of In the name of God, the Most Gracious, the Most Merciful; and I ask You by the encompassing of In the name of God, the Most Gracious, the Most Merciful, that You admit me into its shelter, and nourish me from its supply, and provide for me from its rain. My God, cast to me the key of permission, which is the cave of the sciences of gnosis, so that I may speak at every beginning by Your name, the Originator, the Everlasting, the Maker, the Raiser, the Expander, the Hidden, by which every inscribed writ has been opened. You are the Originator of everything and its Maker. To You be praise, O Maker, at every beginning, and to You be thanks, O Everlasting, at every ending. You are the Raiser of every good, the Inward of the inward, the Attainer of the signs of all affairs, the Expander of the provisions of the worlds. Bless me, O God, among those who come after, as You blessed our master Abraham; truly it is from You and unto You. And by In the name of God, the Most Gracious, the Most Merciful, do for me such-and-such.

Allāhumma innī as'aluka bi-ʿaẓamati Bismi Allāh al-Raḥmān al-Raḥīm, wa-as'aluka bi-jalāli Bismi Allāh al-Raḥmān al-Raḥīm, wa-as'aluka bi-kamāli Bismi Allāh al-Raḥmān al-Raḥīm, wa-as'aluka bi-jamāli Bismi Allāh al-Raḥmān al-Raḥīm, wa-as'aluka bi-sanā'i Bismi Allāh al-Raḥmān al-Raḥīm, wa-as'aluka bi-bahā'i Bismi Allāh al-Raḥmān al-Raḥīm, wa-as'aluka bi-thanā'i Bismi Allāh al-Raḥmān al-Raḥīm, wa-as'aluka bi-ālā'i Bismi Allāh al-Raḥmān al-Raḥīm, wa-as'aluka bi-ḍiyāʾi Bismi Allāh al-Raḥmān al-Raḥīm, wa-asʾaluka bi-nūri Bismi Allāh al-Raḥmān al-Raḥīm, wa-asʾaluka bi-faḍāʾili Bismi Allāh al-Raḥmān al-Raḥīm, wa-asʾaluka bi-qudrati Bismi Allāh al-Raḥmān al-Raḥīm, wa-asʾaluka bi-taṣrīfi Bismi Allāh al-Raḥmān al-Raḥīm, wa-asʾaluka bi-khaṣāʾiṣi Bismi Allāh al-Raḥmān al-Raḥīm, wa-asʾaluka bi-maqāmi Bismi Allāh al-Raḥmān al-Raḥīm, wa-asʾaluka bi-laṭāʾifi Bismi Allāh al-Raḥmān al-Raḥīm, wa-asʾaluka bi-quwwati Bismi Allāh al-Raḥmān al-Raḥīm, wa-asʾaluka bi-haybati Bismi Allāh al-Raḥmān al-Raḥīm, wa-asʾaluka bi-tawfīqi Bismi Allāh al-Raḥmān al-Raḥīm, wa-asʾaluka bi-ʿuluwwika Bismi Allāh al-Raḥmān al-Raḥīm, wa-asʾaluka bi-ʿurūfi Bismi Allāh al-Raḥmān al-Raḥīm, wa-asʾaluka bi-ibtidāʾi Bismi Allāh al-Raḥmān al-Raḥīm, wa-asʾaluka bi-intihāʾi Bismi Allāh al-Raḥmān al-Raḥīm, wa-asʾaluka bi-imdādi Bismi Allāh al-Raḥmān al-Raḥīm, wa-asʾaluka bi-iḥāṭati Bismi Allāh al-Raḥmān al-Raḥīm an tudkhilanī fī kanafihā wa-tughdhinī min madadihā wa-tarzuqanī bi-ghaythihā. Ilāhī, alqi ilayya miftāḥ al-idhn alladhī huwa kahf al-maʿārif ḥattā anṭiqa fī kull bidāya bi-ismika al-Badīʿ al-Bāqī al-Bārī al-Bāʿith al-Bāsiṭ al-Bāṭin alladhī infataḥat bihi kull raqīm masṭūr. Wa-anta bi-lā huwa, fa-anta badīʿ kull shayʾ wa-bāriʾuhu. Laka al-ḥamd yā Bāriʾ ʿalā kull bidāya wa-laka al-shukr yā Bāqī ʿalā kull nihāya. Anta al-Bāʿith li-kull khayr, bāṭin al-bāṭin, bāligh āyāt al-umūr kullihā, bāsiṭ arzāq al-ʿālamīn. Bārik Allāhumma ʿalayya fī al-ākhirīn kamā bārakta ʿalā sayyidinā Ibrāhīm, innahu minka wa-ilayka.

Wa-innahu Bismi Allāh al-Raḥmān al-Raḥīm wa-an taf'ala lī kadhā wa-kadhā.

اللهم إني أسألك بعظمة بسم الله الرحمن الرحيم وأسألك بجلال بسم الله الرحمن الرحيم وأسألك بكمال بسم الله الرحمن الرحيم وأسألك بجمال بسم الله الرحمن الرحيم وأسألك بسناء بسم الله الرحمن الرحيم وأسألك ببهاء بسم الله الرحمن الرحيم وأسألك بثناء بسم الله الرحمن الرحيم وأسألك بآلاء بسم الله الرحمن الرحيم وأسألك بضياء بسم الله الرحمن الرحيم وأسألك بنور بسم الله الرحمن الرحيم وأسألك بفضائل بسم الله الرحمن الرحيم وأسألك بقدرة بسم الله الرحمن الرحيم وأسألك بتصريف بسم الله الرحمن الرحيم وأسألك بخصائص بسم الله الرحمن الرحيم وأسألك بمقام بسم الله الرحمن الرحيم وأسألك بلطائف بسم الله الرحمن الرحيم وأسألك بقوة بسم الله الرحمن الرحيم وأسألك بهيبة بسم الله الرحمن الرحيم وأسألك بتوفيق بسم الله الرحمن الرحيم وأسألك بعلوك بسم الله الرحمن الرحيم وأسألك بعروف بسم الله الرحمن الرحيم وأسألك بابتداء بسم الله الرحمن الرحيم وأسألك بانتهاء بسم الله الرحمن الرحيم وأسألك بإمداد بسم الله الرحمن الرحيم وأسألك بإحاطة بسم الله الرحمن الرحيم أن تدخلني في كنفها وتغذني من مددها وترزقني بغيثها إلهي ألق إلي مفتاح الإذن الذي هو كهف المعارف حتى أنطق في كل بداية باسمك البديع الباقي الباري الباعث الباسط الباطن الذي انفتحت به كل رقيم مسطور وأنت بلا هو فأنت بديع كل شيء وبارئه لك الحمد يا بارئ على كل بداية ولك الشكر يا باقي على كل نهاية أنت الباعث لكل خير باطن الباطن بالغ آيات الأمور كلها باسط أرزاق العالمين بارك

اللهم علي في الآخرين كما باركت على سيدنا إبراهيم إنه منك وإليك
وإنه بسم الله الرحمن الرحيم وأن تفعل لي كذا وكذا

It is also proper, once you have finished, to entreat Him by saying:

My God, I ask You by the rank of our master Muḥammad, may God bless him and grant him peace, to do for me such-and-such, and to cast to me the key of permission.

Ilāhī as'aluka bi-jāhi sayyidinā Muḥammad ṣallā Allāh ʿalayhi wa-sallam an taʿmala lī kadhā wa-kadhā wa-an tulqiya ilayya miftāḥ al-idhn.

إلهي أسألك بجاه سيدنا محمد صلى الله عليه وسلم أن تعمل لي كذا
وكذا وأن تلقي إلي مفتاح الإذن

A Benefit for Sending the Unseen Caller (Fāʾida li-Irsāl al-Hātif)

You take a sheet of paper and write the basmala upon it 19 times, with the charge after each time, in saffron and rose water. Then you place it in a small Persian case and stop its mouth with wax, and bind it about its middle with a thread of red silk, and hang it on a branch of a sour pomegranate, and fumigate it with benzoin. Recite the basmala over it 786 times, and then perform the operation with Sūrat al-Zalzala and the end of Sūrat al-Jumuʿa. The sign of the response is the turning of the case; and when it has turned, the incense and the recitation of the operation must be stopped.

A Benefit for Relieving Distress (Fā'ida li-Tafrīj al-Kurūb)

You say, without counting:

O Mighty One, You are the Mighty. A distress has grieved me that is made light by Your mighty name, by the virtue of the words In the name of God, the Most Gracious, the Most Merciful.

Yā ʿAẓīm, anta al-ʿAẓīm. Qad hammanī karbun yahūnu bi-ismika al-ʿaẓīm, bi-faḍli Bismi Allāh al-Raḥmān al-Raḥīm.

يا عظيم أنت العظيم قد همني كرب يهون باسمك العظيم بفضل بسم الله الرحمن الرحيم

A Benefit for Love (Fā'idat al-Maḥabba)

Recite the basmala 781 times over any sweet thing and feed it to the one desired, and you will see a wonder from the increase of love.

Section on Employing the Blessed Helper Rayḥān, Servant of the King al-Ukhayḍir and of Sūrat al-Fātiḥa (Faṣl fī Istikhdām al-ʿAwn al-Mubārak Rayḥān Khādim al-Malik al-Ukhayḍir Khādim Sūrat al-Fātiḥa)

He does everything the seeker desires, whether good or evil, so long as it accords with the resplendent Law. You recite the noble Sūrat al-Fātiḥa a thousand times, and after each time you say:

Barbarous names: Baṭhash ٢ Mashāsh ٢ Kashāwūsh ٢ Qaṭmūsh ٢ Anhamat ٢ ʿAlūsh ٢ ʿAkhlūsh ʿAlūsh ٢

بطهش ٢ مشاش ٢ كشاوش ٢ قطموش ٢ أنهمت ٢ علوش ٢ عخلوش علوش ٢

Answer, O Rayḥān, and do for me such-and-such, by the right of the noble Fātiḥa, the Mother of the Qurʾān, and by the right of the King who holds you by the forelock. Answer! Blessing be in you and upon you, by the right of the Single, the Compeller, al-Takrūr, the Firm, the Supporter, the All-Aware, the Astute. Quickly (twice), in haste (twice), this very hour (twice).

Ajib yā Rayḥān wa-afʿal lī kadhā wa-kadhā bi-ḥaqq al-Fātiḥa al-sharīfa Umm al-Qurʾān, wa-bi-ḥaqq al-Malik al-ākhidh bi-nāṣiyatika. Ajib, bārik fīka wa-ʿalayka, bi-ḥaqq al-Fard al-Jabbār al-Takrūr al-Thābit al-Ẓahīr al-Khabīr al-Dhakī, al-waḥā ٢ al-ʿajal ٢ al-sāʿa ٢.

أجب يا ريحان وافعل لي كذا وكذا بحق الفاتحة الشريفة أم القرآن وبحق
الملك الآخذ بناصيتك أجب بارك فيك وعليك بحق الفرد الجبار
التكرور الثابت الظهير الخبير الذكي الوحا ٢ العجل ٢ الساعة ٢

The incense throughout the recitation is benzoin and coriander.

A Benefit for Performing a Scrying Mirror with the Noble Sūrat al-Fātiḥa (Fāʾida fī ʿAmal Mandal bi-Sūrat al-Fātiḥa al-Sharīfa)

Write the following seal on the back of a mirror and fumigate it with male frankincense and coriander. Place the mirror upon a chair and look into it, on condition that you do not see your own reflection in it, and recite Sūrat al-Fātiḥa in full 313 times. At every hundred you say:

Come, O servant of this surah, and lift the veil between me and you, until I see you with my eye and address you with my tongue.

Aḥḍir yā khādim hādhihi al-sūra, wa-akshif al-ḥijāb baynī wa-baynak, ḥattā arāka bi-ʿaynī wa-ukhāṭibaka bi-lisānī.

أحضر يا خادم هذه السورة واكشف الحجاب بيني وبينك حتى أراك بعيني وأخاطبك بلساني

When the count is complete, a man of Maghribi appearance will show himself to you in the mirror, and you say to him:

Peace be upon you, and the mercy of God.

Al-salāmu ʿalaykum wa-raḥmatu Allāh.

السلام عليكم ورحمة الله

Then mention your need to him, and he will tell you of it without concealment, without equivocation and without doubt. This is the form of the seal, as you see:

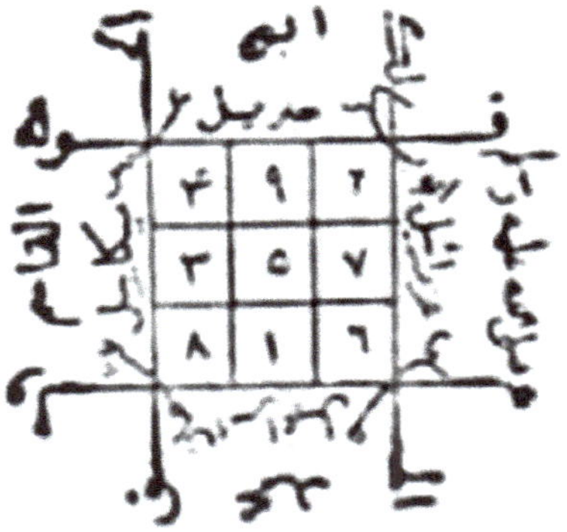

The seal of the scrying mirror of Sūrat al-Fātiḥa

It is stipulated, before performing this mandal, that you first recite the Fātiḥa and dedicate its reward to the four caliphs, to the Presence of the Prophet, may God bless him and grant him peace, and to the noble companions of the turn, saying:

O companions of the turn, I have taken permission from you, and by your authorization and your leave I say: In the name of God, the Most Gracious, the Most Merciful. Praise be to God, Lord of the worlds.

Yā aṣḥāb al-nawba, akhadhtu al-idhn minkum, wa-bi-ijāzatikum wa-bi-idhnikum aqūlu: Bismi Allāh al-Raḥmān al-Raḥīm, al-ḥamdu li-Llāhi Rabb al-ʿālamīn.

يا أصحاب النوبة أخذت الإذن منكم وبإجازتكم وبإذنكم أقول بسم الله الرحمن الرحيم الحمد لله رب العالمين

A Benefit for Love and Attraction (Fā'idat al-Maḥabba wa-l-Jalb)

Write the following talisman, together with the names of the seeker and the one desired, upon the palm of the seeker, and conjure over it with the Fātiḥa 75 times. When the palm has become blurred, bid him lick it with his tongue; otherwise the recitation is repeated until that occurs. Whenever it occurs, the need is fulfilled without doubt. This is the form of the talisman, as you see:

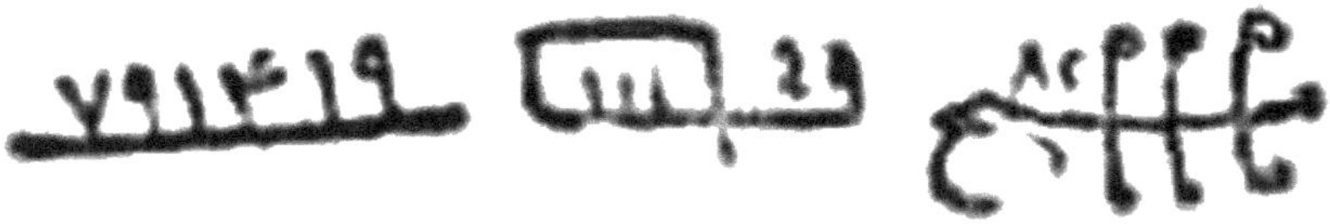

The talisman for love and attraction

A Benefit for Stirring and Love (Fā'ida li-Tahyīj wa-l-Maḥabba)

Take 21 sheets of paper and write this talisman upon each one of them:

The talisman for stirring and love

Place in each sheet a pebble of male frankincense and throw it into the fire, reciting Sūrat al-Fātiḥa over it until its smoke is cut off. Then throw in the second and do with it in the same way, and so on to the completion of the twenty-one sheets, and you will see what gladdens you. It is stipulated that the work be done on the night of Sunday, Monday or Tuesday, while the moon is waxing bright.

A Benefit for the Talisman of Obedience (Fāʾida fī Bayān Ṭilasm al-Ṭāʿa)

Whoever wishes to be magnified in the eyes of his wife, and that she love him with so intense a love that she cannot leave him or contrive any matter against him, let him write the following talisman upon the egg of a black hen, without any mark upon it. Then let him place it in a vessel over a gentle fire, recite the Fātiḥa 288 times and the following invocation seven times while fumigating with male frankincense, coriander and mastic. The sign of response is that the egg cracks. This is the form of the talisman, as you see:

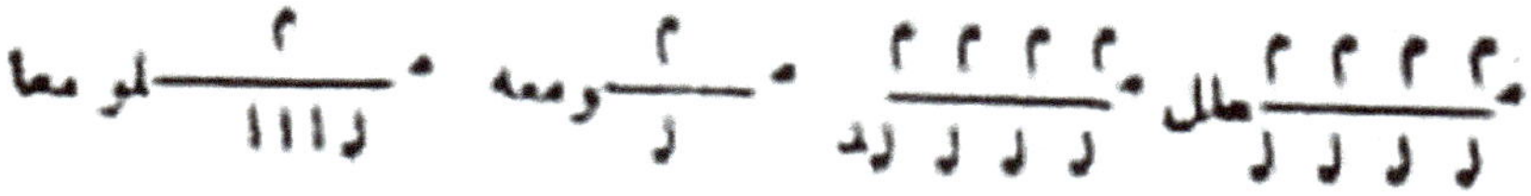

The talisman of obedience

Take charge, O servants of these names, of casting the love of so-and-so into the heart of so-and-so.

Tawakkalū yā khuddām hādhihi al-asmāʾ bi-ilqāʾ maḥabbat kadhā fī qalb kadhā.

توكلوا يا خدام هذه الأسماء بإلقاء محبة كذا في قلب كذا

And this is the invocation; you say:

In the name of God, the Most Gracious, the Most Merciful. Praise belongs to God, Lord of the worlds, with a praise that is a satisfaction to Him and, for me, well-pleasing in the sight of the Lord of the worlds. The Most Gracious, the Most Merciful, who spread out the regions and singled out Moses the Interlocutor by

the Reviver of the bones when they are decayed; for these two are two mighty names, a healing for every ailing sickness, a road to the gardens of bliss and a deliverance from the torment of hellfire. Master of the Day of Judgement, who has in His dominion no partner, no contender and no helper. O God, cast the love of so-and-so into the heart of so-and-so. You alone do we worship, by open acknowledgement, and we confess our shortcoming, and we bear witness that there is no god but God alone, without partner, the King, the Manifest Truth; and we bear witness that Muḥammad is the Messenger of God, whom He sent as a bearer of glad tidings and a warner to all creatures together and as a mercy to the believers. For God Most High is the Bringer of all beings into being, the Knower of what is hidden in the breast, who wraps the night over the day for all the worlds and turns them toward the near and the far among the differing races. You alone do we ask for help: by You, for the casting of so-and-so into the heart of so-and-so. O God, O Owner of the kings of all the worlds together, there is no god but You; glory be to You, I was among the wrongdoers. My Lord, deliver me and reach me with Your mercy, O Most Merciful of the merciful, and deliver me from what I fear and guard against. Cast the love of so-and-so into the heart of so-and-so, guide her heart to him and give him mastery over her forelock. Guide us upon the straight path, the path of those upon whom You have bestowed favour, not of those who incur wrath, nor of those who go astray.

Bismi Allāh al-Raḥmān al-Raḥīm. Al-ḥamdu li-Llāhi rabb al-ʿālamīn, ḥamdan yakūnu lahu riḍan wa-lī marḍiyyan ʿinda rabb al-ʿālamīn. Al-Raḥmān al-Raḥīm alladhī daḥā al-aqālīm wa-ikhtaṣṣa Mūsā al-Kalīm bi-muḥyī al-ʿiẓām wa-hiya ramīm, fa-humā ismān ʿaẓīmān shifāʾ li-kull dāʾ saqīm, wa-ṭarīq ilā jannāt al-naʿīm wa-najāh min ʿadhāb al-jaḥīm. Mālik yawm al-dīn, laysa lahu fī al-mulk sharīk wa-lā munāziʿ wa-lā muʿīn. Allāhumma alqi maḥabbat kadhā fī qalb kadhā. Iyyāka naʿbudu bi-l-iqrār, wa-naʿtarifu bi-l-taqṣīr, wa-nashhadu an lā ilāha illā Allāh waḥdahu lā sharīka lahu al-malik al-ḥaqq al-mubīn, wa-nashhadu anna Muḥammadan rasūl Allāh alladhī arsalahu bashīran wa-nadhīran ilā kāffat al-khalāʾiq ajmaʿīn wa-raḥmatan li-l-muʾminīn. Fa-inna Allāh taʿālā mukawwin al-akwān wa-ʿālim khafiyyāt al-aḍmār wa-mukawwir al-layl ʿalā al-nahār jamīʿan li-kull al-ʿālamīn wa-muwajjihuhum ilā al-aqrabīn wa-l-abʿadīn min al-ajnās al-mukhtalifīn. Wa-iyyāka nastaʿīn bika ʿalā ilqāʾ kadhā fī qalb kadhā. Allāhumma yā mālik mulūk al-ʿawālim kullihā ajmaʿīn, lā ilāha illā anta subḥānaka innī kuntu min al-ẓālimīn. Rabbi najjinī wa-adriknī bi-raḥmatika yā arḥam al-rāḥimīn wa-najjinī mimmā akhāfu wa-aḥdhar, wa-alqi maḥabbat kadhā fī qalb kadhā wa-ihdi lahu qalbahā wa-makkinhu min nāṣiyatihā. Ihdinā al-ṣirāṭ al-mustaqīm ṣirāṭ alladhīna anʿamta ʿalayhim ghayr al-maghḍūb ʿalayhim wa-lā al-ḍāllīn.

بسم الله الرحمن الرحيم (الحمد لله رب العالمين) حمدا يكون له رضا ولي مرضيا عند رب العالمين (الرحمن الرحيم) الذي دحا الأقاليم واختص موسى الكليم بمحيي العظام وهي رميم فهما اسمان عظيمان شفاء لكل داء سقيم وطريق إلى جنات النعيم ونجاة من عذاب الجحيم

(مالك يوم الدين) ليس له في الملك شريك ولا منازع ولا معين اللهم ألق محبة كذا في قلب كذا (إياك نعبد) بالإقرار ونعترف بالتقصير ونشهد أن لا إله إلا الله وحده لا شريك له الملك الحق المبين ونشهد أن محمدا رسول الله الذي أرسله بشيرا ونذيرا إلى كافة الخلائق أجمعين ورحمة للمؤمنين فإن الله تعالى مكون الأكوان وعالم خفيات الأضمار ومكور الليل على النهار جميعا لكل العالمين وموجههم إلى الأقربين والأبعدين من الأجناس المختلفين (وإياك نستعين) بك على إلقاء كذا في قلب كذا اللهم يا مالك ملوك العوالم كلها أجمعين لا إله إلا أنت سبحانك إني كنت من الظالمين رب نجني وأدركني برحمتك يا أرحم الراحمين ونجني مما أخاف وأحذر وألق محبة كذا في قلب كذا واهد له قلبها ومكنه من ناصيتها (اهدنا الصراط المستقيم صراط الذين أنعمت عليهم غير المغضوب عليهم ولا الضالين)

A Benefit for Fulfilling Every Desire and Attaining Every Request (Fāʾida li-Qaḍāʾ Kull Marghūb wa-Nayl Kull Maṭlūb)

You recite the Fātiḥa eighteen times after the dawn, the noon, the afternoon and the sunset prayers, and twenty-eight times after the night prayer, so that the hundred is completed, on condition that each time be within a single breath and wholly sound in its letters, free of mispronunciation and error. Then after that you say three times:

In the name of God, the Most Gracious, the Most Merciful. May God bless our master Muḥammad and his family and his Companions, and grant them peace. O Ghanā, Kafī, Barānday,

Khudāy, Būḥā: that is God, the Lord of the worlds. O God, I ask You by Sūrat al-Fātiḥa, and by the secret that Sūrat al-Fātiḥa has enfolded, to bless our master Muḥammad and his family and his Companions and to grant them peace, and to do for me such-and-such. And may God bless our master Muḥammad and his family and his Companions, and grant them peace.

Bismi Allāh al-Raḥmān al-Raḥīm. Wa-ṣallā Allāh ʿalā sayyidinā Muḥammad wa-ʿalā ālihi wa-ṣaḥbihi wa-sallam. Yā (...) Ghanā Kafī Barānday Khudāy Būḥā, dhālika Allāh rabb al-ʿālamīn. Allāhumma innī as'aluka bi-sūrat al-Fātiḥa wa-bi-l-sirr alladhī inṭawat ʿalayhi sūrat al-Fātiḥa an tuṣalliya wa-tusallima ʿalā sayyidinā Muḥammad wa-ʿalā ālihi wa-ṣaḥbihi wa-an tafʿala lī kadhā wa-kadhā. Wa-ṣallā Allāh ʿalā sayyidinā Muḥammad wa-ʿalā ālihi wa-ṣaḥbihi wa-sallam.

بسم الله الرحمن الرحيم وصلى الله على سيدنا محمد وعلى آله وصحبه وسلم يا (...) غنا كفي برانداي خداي بوحا ذلك الله رب العالمين اللهم إني أسألك بسورة الفاتحة وبالسر الذي انطوت عليه سورة الفاتحة أن تصلي وتسلم على سيدنا محمد وعلى آله وصحبه وأن تفعل لي كذا وكذا وصلى الله على سيدنا محمد وعلى آله وصحبه وسلم

Section on Operating with the Noble Verse of the Throne, for Fulfilling Needs and Attaining Desires (Faṣl fī al-Taṣarruf bi-Āyat al-Kursī al-Sharīfa li-Qaḍā' al-Ḥājāt wa-Nayl al-Raghabāt)

You recite the Verse of the Throne three times, then you say one hundred times:

God, the Living, the Self-Subsisting, the Exalted, the Magnificent.

Allāh al-Ḥayy al-Qayyūm al-'Alī al-'Aẓīm.

الله الحي القيوم العلي العظيم

Then you recite the following invocation once. If the matter is very weighty, recite the Perfecting Prayer:

O God, bless our master Muḥammad and the family of our master Muḥammad, to the number of God's perfection and as befits His perfection.

Allāhumma ṣalli 'alā sayyidinā Muḥammad wa-'alā āl sayyidinā Muḥammad 'adada kamāl Allāh wa-kamā yalīqu bi-kamālihi.

اللهم صل على سيدنا محمد وعلى آل سيدنا محمد عدد كمال الله وكما يليق بكماله

Recite it one hundred times, then the noble verse one thousand times, and after it the invocation ten times, then the Perfecting Prayer one hundred times. And this is the invocation; you say:

In the name of God, the Most Gracious, the Most Merciful. O God, I ask You, O Ancient, O Everlasting, O Single, O Odd, O

One, O Eternally Besought, O Self-Subsisting, O Originator of the heavens and the earth, O Possessor of majesty and honour. I ask You for the ascent through the holy stations that lead to the Presence of Divinity by the lights of the holy perfections upheld by You through the support of pre-eternal providence. God, there is no god but He, who is alone in oneness in pre-eternity and singular in unity in everlastingness. Yours are the radiances of singularity, the dominion of lordship, the greatness of divinity and the holy attributes. The Living, the Self-Subsisting, the inmost reality of whose greatness the learned and the knowers are powerless to grasp. Glory be to your Lord, the Lord of might, above what they describe. Neither slumber nor sleep overtakes Him. Your affirmation of Your oneness is the sound affirmation, free of change, of veiling and of separation, and of otherness. So by the right of the might of everlastingness and of oneness, and of its mirror within its self-disclosure, and of the gathering of its gathering within its very source — that which minds do not grasp, nor unveilings, nor lights, nor secrets. To Him belongs whatever is in the heavens and whatever is on the earth. Grant me, out of that self-disclosure, the subjection of the angelic spirit that stands in service beneath that most holy and lofty secret, the encompassing of the Qur'ānic words that comprehends the affairs of Your merciful names, attended in that by a secret through which hearts are led with the submission of a love that longing accompanies. O You who are He, and not I. Who is there that shall intercede with Him except by His leave? I ask You, O God, by every name — I draw my supply from You, by You, for You, that I may be wrought upon by the secret of the greatness of universal existence — that You bring near from Yourself a subtle filament from the filaments of Your greatness, by which everything may be wrought for me in the knowledge of Your unseen that encompasses the reality of every witnessed thing, so that I may be enabled to do all that I desire, an enabling indeed, and may dispose of it throughout all existence by the universal permission that runs through every existent thing. He knows what lies before them and what lies behind them. And that You refine me in the presence of Your beloved ones by the lights of Your beauty, Your perfection and the perfection of that, and that a tongue be loosed upon me with the speech of the presence of Your intimate address: courtesy with You, receiving from You, passing away in You and abiding by You, there being nothing apart from You. They encompass nothing of His knowledge except what He wills. Grant me, O God, the treasury that gathers Your secrets, made ready by Your leave for whomever You will, as a supply from the presence of Your witnessing. Shine upon me, out of Your divine secrets, that by which the reality of human nature is made complete. Make me, by the mercy of the realm of mercy, a witness to the majesty of the realm of might. Enrich me with the longing of the realm of longing in place of the dread of the realm of dread, and do not disappoint me by the sight of the kingdom so that I am kept from the contemplation of the dominion. His Throne embraces the heavens and the earth. His command lies between the kāf and the nūn, and when He decrees a matter He only says to it, Be, and it is. O You who have ordered the motes of existence and flooded them with bounty. O You whom no limits encompass. O You who are exalted above consort and offspring. I ask You, O Bountiful One, O Generous One, O Loving One, O You who in truth are worshipped — and the keeping of them does not weary Him — for the passing away in the presence of contemplation through the presence of witnessing, with the constancy of ascent to the utmost limit of that subsistence which leads toward witnessing; with the composing of the heart in the bliss of perfect reflection, and the repose of the spirit in tranquillity with You, without bewilderment. Separation has departed from it, the dot of the ghayn has been lifted from it, and within it the ghayn has been distinguished by the ʿayn. O You who exchanged the nūn of nearness for the yāʾ of servanthood among companions whom the watches of the lofty state have made scrupulous, and whom You joined to the secrets of divinity, so that nothing in them remained for any but You. And He is the Most High, the Magnificent. I ask You, O God, for the completeness of this gift, with nothing neglected and nothing forgotten, together with well-being from every affliction forever, so long as everlastingness endures. O You who are the Reminder to this human constitution: take me from this lower state to the summit of the exalted, purified and holy presence, in the company of the guide confirmed by nearness, where all things pass away in the witnessing of oneness and of unity. I adjure You by God to accept these well-pleasing petitions, by the lofty names, by the greatness within them in pre-eternity and in everlastingness, by the hidden secrets You have concealed within the inward unseen of oneness, and by the manifest lights You have brought forth in the outward of praise. Bless, O God, this Prophet crowned with the station of utmost perfection above all creation, and grant him the peace of special distinction in the presence of lordship: a blessing and a peace whose light is complete, which endures for us forever, whose reward is renewed and is never cut off eternally. God (three times). Indeed, He who imposed the Qurʾān upon you will bring you back to a place of return (three times). And may God bless our master Muḥammad, the unlettered Prophet, and his family and his companions, and grant them peace. Amen. And peace be upon the messengers, and praise belongs to God, Lord of the worlds.

Bismi Allāh al-Raḥmān al-Raḥīm. Allāhumma innī as'aluka yā Qadīm yā Dā'im yā Fard yā Witr yā Aḥad yā Ṣamad yā Qayyūm yā Badīʿ al-samāwāt wa-l-arḍ yā Dhā al-Jalāl wa-l-Ikrām. As'aluka al-ʿurūj fī al-maqāmāt al-qudsiyya al-mūṣila ilā ḥaḍrat al-ulūhiyya bi-anwār al-kamālāt al-qudsiyya al-mu'ayyada minka bi-ta'yīd al-ʿināya al-azaliyya. Allāh lā ilāha illā huwa alladhī tawaḥḥada bi-l-aḥadiyya fī al-azaliyya wa-tafarrada bi-l-waḥdāniyya fī al-abadiyya. Laka subuḥāt al-fardāniyya wa-mulk al-rubūbiyya wa-ʿaẓamat al-ulūhiyya wa-l-ṣifāt al-qudsiyya. Al-Ḥayy al-Qayyūm alladhī ʿajaza ʿan idrāk kunh ʿaẓamat dhātihi al-ʿālimūn wa-l-ʿārifūn. Subḥāna rabbika rabb al-ʿizza ʿammā yaṣifūn. Lā ta'khudhuhu sinatun wa-lā nawm. Tawḥīduka laka huwa al-tawḥīd al-sālim min al-taghayyur wa-l-ḥijāb wa-l-farq, wa-l-siwā', fa-bi-ḥaqqi ʿizzati al-

abadiyya wa-l-aḥadiyya wa-mir'ātihā fī tajallīhā wa-jam'i jam'ihā fī 'aynihā mimmā lā tudrikuhu al-'uqūl wa-lā al-kushūf wa-lā al-anwār wa-lā al-asrār (lahu mā fī al-samāwāti wa-mā fī al-arḍ) an tahaba lī min dhālika al-tajallī taskhīra al-rūḥ al-malakūtī al-qā'im fī khidma taḥta dhālika al-sirr al-aqdas al-rafī' iḥāṭati al-kalimāt al-Qur'āniyya al-mushtamil li-umūri asmā'ika al-raḥmāniyya maṣḥūban fī dhālika bi-sirrin tanqādu bihi ilā al-qulūb inqiyāda maḥabbatin taṣḥabuhā raghba. Yā man huwa wa-lā anā (man dhā alladhī yashfa'u 'indahu illā bi-idhnih) as'aluka Allāhumma bi-kulli ismin astamiddu minka bika laka fa-anfa'ilu bi-sirri 'aẓamati al-wujūd al-kullī an tudniya minka bi-raqīqatin min raqā'iqi 'aẓamatika li-yanfa'ila lī bihā kullu shay'in fī 'ilmi ghaybika al-muḥīṭ bi-ḥaqīqati kulli mashhūdin fa-atamakkana min fi'li kulli mā urīdu tamkīnan wa-ataṣarrafa bihi fī kulli al-wujūd bi-l-idhn al-kullī al-sārī fī kulli mawjūd (ya'lamu mā bayna aydīhim wa-mā khalfahum) wa-tuṣaffiya fī ḥaḍrati aḥbābika bi-anwāri jamālika wa-kamālika wa-kamāli dhālika wa-inṭalaqa lisānun 'alayya bi-kalāmi ḥaḍrati munājātika bi-l-adabi ma'aka wa-l-akhdhi minka wa-l-fanā'i fīka wa-l-baqā'i bika, lā shay'a dūnaka (wa-lā yuḥīṭūna bi-shay'in min 'ilmihi illā bi-mā shā') wa-a'ṭinī Allāhumma al-khizānata al-jāmi'ata li-asrārika al-mu'addata bi-idhnika man shi'ta imdādan min ḥaḍrati shuhūdika, wa-ashriq 'alayya min asrārika al-lāhūtiyya mā takmulu bihi ḥaqīqatu al-nāsūt wa-j'alnī bi-raḥmati al-raḥamūt shāhidan li-jalāli al-jabarūt wa-aghni bi-raghbati al-raghabūt min rahbati al-rahabūt wa-lā tukhayyibnī bi-mushāhadati al-mulk 'an muṭālaʿati al-malakūt (wasiʿa kursiyyuhu al-samāwāti wa-l-arḍ) wa-amruhu bayna al-kāf wa-l-nūn, wa-idhā qaḍā amran fa-innamā yaqūlu lahu kun fa-yakūn. Yā man dabbarta dharrāti al-wujūd wa-aghmartahā bi-l-jūd, yā man lā tuḥīṭu bihi al-ḥudūd, yā man tanazzaha ʿani al-ṣāḥiba wa-l-mawlūd, asʾaluka yā jawād yā karīm yā wadūd, yā man anta bi-l-ḥaqqi maʿbūd (wa-lā yaʾūduhu ḥifẓuhumā) al-fanāʾa fī ḥaḍrati al-mushāhada bi-ḥaḍrati al-shuhūd maʿa dawāmi al-irtiqāʾ ilā ghāyati al-baqāʾ al-mūṣil ilā naḥwi al-shuhūd maʿa taʾlīfi al-qalb bi-naʿīmi kamāli al-fikra wa-irtiyāḥi al-rūḥ maʿa al-ṭumaʾnīna bika bilā ḥayra. Dhahaba ʿanhā al-bayn wa-irtafaʿat ʿanhā nuqṭatu al-ghayn wa-farraqa fīhā al-ghayna bi-l-ʿayn. Yā man baddalta nūna al-ʿindiyya yāʾa al-ʿubūdiyya min aṣḥābin awraʿahum ānāʾu al-abiyya wa-wāṣaltahum bi-asrāri al-ulūhiyya fa-lam yabqa fīhim li-ghayrika baqiyya (wa-huwa al-ʿaliyyu al-ʿaẓīm) asʾaluka Allāhumma kamāla hādhihi al-ʿaṭiyya min ghayri muhmalatin wa-lā nasiyyatin maʿa al-ʿāfiya min kulli baliyyatin abadan mā dāma dawāmu al-abadiyya. Yā man huwa al-mudhakkir li-hādhihi al-nashʾa al-bashariyya khudhnī min hādhihi al-taḥtiyya ilā awji al-ḥaḍra al-ʿaliyya al-muṭahhara al-qudsiyya maʿa ṣuḥbati al-hādī al-muʾayyad bi-l-ʿindiyya ḥaythu yafnā kullu shayʾin bi-shuhūdi al-aḥadiyya wa-l-waḥdāniyya. Uqsimu bi-Llāhi ʿalayka fī qabūli hādhihi al-asʾila al-marḍiyya bi-l-asmāʾ al-ʿāliya bi-l-ʿaẓami minhā fī al-azaliyya wa-l-abadiyya wa-bimā abṭantahu min al-asrār al-khafiyya fī bāṭini ghaybi al-aḥadiyya wa-bimā aẓhartahu min al-anwār al-jaliyya fī ẓāhiri al-ḥamdiyya. Ṣalli Allāhumma ʿalā hādhā al-nabī al-

mutawwaj bi-maqāmi al-akmaliyya ʿalā sāʾiri al-bariyya wa-sallim ʿalayhi salāma al-khuṣūṣiyya fī ḥaḍrati al-rubūbiyya, ṣalātan wa-salāman yatimmu nūruhumā wa-yadūmu lanā abadan wa-yatajaddadu thawābuhumā wa-lā yanqaṭiʿu sarmadiyyan. Allāh ٣. Inna alladhī faraḍa ʿalayka al-Qurʾāna la-rādduka ilā maʿād ٣. Wa-ṣallā Allāhu ʿalā sayyidinā Muḥammad al-nabī al-ummī wa-ʿalā ālihi wa-ṣaḥbihi wa-sallam. Āmīn. Wa-salāmun ʿalā al-mursalīn wa-l-ḥamdu li-Llāhi rabbi al-ʿālamīn.

بسم الله الرحمن الرحيم اللهم إني أسألك يا قديم يا دائم يا فرد يا وتر يا أحد يا صمد يا قيوم يا بديع السموات والأرض يا ذا الجلال والإكرام أسألك العروج في المقامات القدسية الموصلة إلى حضرة الألوهية بأنوار الكمالات القدسية المؤيدة منك بتأييد العناية الأزلية (الله لا إله إلا هو) الذي توحد بالأحدية في الأزلية وتفرد بالوحدانية في الأبدية لك سبحات الفردانية وملك الربوبية وعظمة الألوهية والصفات القدسية (الحي القيوم) الذي عجز عن إدراك كنه عظمة ذاته العالمون والعارفون سبحان ربك رب العزة عما يصفون (لا تأخذه سنة ولا نوم) توحيدك لك هو التوحيد السالم من التغير والحجاب والفرق والسواء ، فبحق عزة الأبدية والأحدية ومرآتها في تجليها وجمع جمعها في عينها مما لا تدركه العقول ولا الكشوف ولا الأنوار ولا الأسرار (له ما في السماوات وما في الأرض) أن تهب لي من ذلك التجلي تسخير الروح الملكوتي القائم في خدمة تحت ذلك السر الأقدس الرفيع إحاطة الكلمات القرآنية المشتمل لأمور أسمائك الرحمانية مصحوبا في ذلك بسر تنقاد به إلى القلوب انقياد

محبة تصحبها رغبة يامن هو ولا أنا (من ذا الذي يشفع عنده إلا بإذنه) أسألك اللهم بكل اسم استمد منك بك لك فانفعل بسر عظمة الوجود الكلي أن تدني منك برقيقة من رقائق عظمتك لينفعل لي بها كل شيء في علم غيبك المحيط بحقيقة كل مشهود فأتمكن من فعل كل ما أريد تمكينا وأتصرف به في كل الوجود بالإذن الكلي الساري في كل موجود (يعلم ما بين أيديهم وما خلفهم) وتصفي في حضرة أحبابك بأنوار جمالك وكمالك وكمال ذلك وانطلق لسان علي بكلام حضرة مناجاتك بالأدب معك والأخذ منك والفناء فيك والبقاء بك لا شيء دونك (ولا يحيطون بشيء من علمه إلا بما شاء) وأعطني اللهم الخزانة الجامعة لأسرارك المعدة بإذنك من شئت إمدادا من حضرة شهودك ، وأشرق علي من أسرارك اللاهوتية ما تكمل به حقيقة الناسوت واجعلني برحمة الرحموت شاهدا لجلال الجبروت وأغني برغبة الرغبوت من رهبة الرهبوت ولا تخيبني بمشاهدة الملك عن مطالعة الملكوت (وسع كرسيه السماوات والأرض) وأمره بين الكاف والنون ، وإذا قضى أمرا فإنما يقول له كن فيكون ، يامن دبرت ذرات الوجود وأغمرتها بالجود يامن لا يحيط به الحدود يامن تنزه عن الصاحبة والمولود أسألك ياجواد يا كريم ياودود يامن أنت بالحق معبود (ولا يؤوده حفظهما) الفناء في حضرة المشاهدة بحضرة الشهود مع دوام الارتقاء إلى غاية البقاء الموصل إلى نحو الشهود مع تأليف القلب بنعيم كمال الفكرة وارتياح الروح مع الطمأنينة بك بلا حيرة ذهب عنها البين وارتفعت عنها نقطة الغين وفرق فيها الغين بالعين يامن بدلت نون العندية ياء العبودية من أصحاب أورعهم آناء الأبية وواصلتهم بأسرار الألوهية فلم يبق فيهم لغيرك بقية (وهو العلي العظيم)

أسألك اللهم كمال هذه العطية من غير مهملة ولا نسية مع العافية من كل بلية أبدا مادام دوام الأبدية يامن هو المذكر لهذه النشأة البشرية خذني من هذه التحتية إلى أوج الحضرة العلية المطهرة القدسية مع صحبة الهادي المؤيد بالعندية حيث يفنى كل شيء بشهود الأحدية والوحدانية أقسم بالله عليك في قبول هذه الأسئلة المرضية بالأسماء العالية بالعظم منها في الأزلية والأبدية وبما أبطنته من الأسرار الخفية في باطن غيب الأحدية وبما أظهرته من الأنوار الجلية في ظاهر الحمدية صل اللهم على هذا النبي المتوج بمقام الأكملية على سائر البرية وسلم عليه سلام الخصوصية في حضرة الربوبية صلاة وسلاما يتم نورهما ويدوم لنا أبدا ويتجدد ثوابهما ولا ينقطع سرمديا الله ٣ إن الذي فرض عليك القرآن لرادك إلى معاد ٣ وصلى الله على سيدنا محمد النبي الأمي وعلى آله وصحبه وسلم آمين وسلام على المرسلين والحمد لله رب العالمين

A Benefit for Love (Fāʾida li-l-Maḥabba)

Write the noble verse out in separated letters upon an unfired potsherd, and set it over the smoke of benzoin and male frankincense, near to the heat of the fire. Then adjure it with the verse seventy times each night for three nights, at the hour when people have grown quiet. When the term is complete, keep the potsherd in a clean box, and the thing desired will be obtained.

A Benefit for Every Aim, Good or Evil (Fāʾida li-Kull Gharaḍ min Khayr wa-Sharr)

Recite the noble verse 313 times while you are fumigating with white pepper if the work is for good, and with black pepper if the work is for evil. Perform the delegation at the head of the three and at every ten, and keep to that for seven consecutive days, with complete discipline and perfect purity, and the purpose will be attained by the permission of God Most High.

A Benefit Concerning Every Matter (Fāʾida fī Kull Amr)

Recite the Verse of the Throne 213 times along with this adjuration, which is that you say:

Barbarous names: Basrabāgh Kashībāgh Shalkhama Ṭalaʿ

بسرباغ كشيباغ شلخمة طلع

Attend, and may God bless you and be upon you, and do such-and-such.

Uḥḍurū, bāraka Allāh fīkum wa-ʿalaykum, wa-ifʿalū kadhā wa-kadhā.

احضروا بارك الله فيكم وعليكم وافعلوا كذا وكذا

The manner of their coming is that they descend in the form of green birds, four in number, their wings joined one to another. When they have come, command them by saying:

Depart to that which I have commanded you, and depart rewarded. May God bless you and be upon you, and may He reward you well on our behalf.

Inṣarifū ilā mā amartukum bihi wa-inṣarifū maʾjūrīn, bāraka Allāh fīkum wa-ʿalaykum wa-jazākum ʿannā khayran.

انصرفوا إلى ما أمرتكم به وانصرفوا مأجورين بارك الله فيكم وعليكم وجزاكم عنا خيرا

A Benefit for Consolation (Fā'ida li-l-Sulwa)

Write the Verse of the Throne five times in a glazed vessel with musk, saffron and rose water, and write the name of the beloved together with it, and set it out beneath the open sky. In the morning wash the writing away with rose water and give it to the lover to drink, for he will be consoled of his beloved; and if you repeat the work for three days, he will forget her and never remember her again.

A Benefit for Attraction (Fā'ida li-l-Jalb)

Write what follows on a paper and hang it on an eastern wall, and it is this:

In the name of God, the Most Gracious, the Most Merciful. God, there is no god but He, the Living, the Self-Subsisting. Neither drowsiness nor sleep overtakes Him. To Him belongs whatever is in the heavens and whatever is on the earth. Who is there that may intercede with Him except by His permission? He knows what is before them and what is behind them, and they encompass nothing of His knowledge except what He wills. His Footstool embraces the heavens and the earth, and their preservation does not weary Him, and He is the Most High, the Magnificent.

Bismi Allāh al-Raḥmān al-Raḥīm ۝ *Allāhu lā ilāha illā huwa al-Ḥayyu al-Qayyūm* ۝ *lā ta'khudhuhu sinatun wa-lā nawm* ۝ *lahu mā fī al-samāwāti wa-mā fī al-arḍi man dhā alladhī yashfa'u 'indahu illā bi-idhnihi ya'lamu* ۝ *mā bayna aydīhim*

ت wa-mā khalfahum ت wa-lā yuḥīṭūna bi-shay'in min ʿilmihi illā bimā shā'a wasiʿa kursiyyuhu al-samāwāti wa-l-arḍa wa-lā ya'ūduhu ḥifẓuhumā wa-huwa al-ʿAlī al-ʿAẓīm ت

بسم الله الرحمن الرحيم ت الله لا إله إلا هو الحي القيوم ت لا تأخذه سنة ولا نوم ت له ما في السموات وما في الأرض من ذا الذي يشفع عنده إلا بإذنه يعلم ت ما بين أيديهم ت وما خلفهم ت ولا يحيطون بشيء من علمه إلا بما شاء وسع كرسيه السموات والأرض ولا يؤوده حفظهما وهو العلي العظيم ت

Then write the seven figures that follow on a paper, and fumigate one paper of them each day. Take care, if the one sought comes before the burning of the papers is complete, not to burn what remains of them, for the one sought would perish from the intensity of the love. And if the paper is replaced with a trace of the one sought, the work is better. This is the form of the seven figures, as you see:

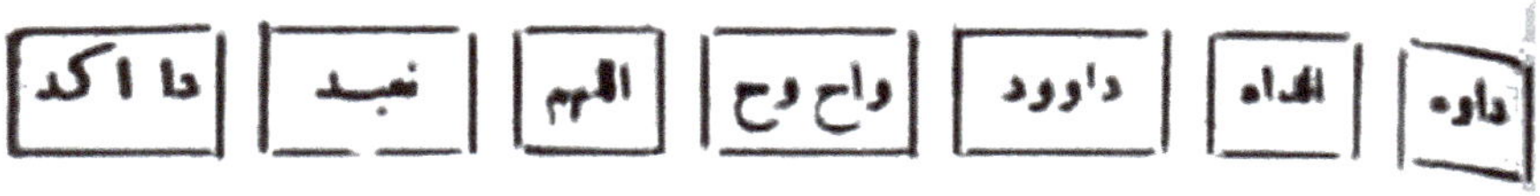

The seven figures

It is stipulated that with each of the seven papers you place something of mastic, male frankincense and benzoin, and that when you burn it you recite the verse to the number of the name of the one sought.

A Benefit for Love (Fāʾida li-l-Maḥabba)

Take three abrīmī (أبريمي) dates. On Friday, after the dawn prayer and before the sun rises, write upon the first with your saliva:

they love them

yuḥibbūnahum

يحبونهم

upon the second:

as God is loved

ka-ḥubb Allāh

كحب الله

and upon the third:

but those who believe are stronger in love for God

wa-lladhīna āmanū ashaddu ḥubban li-llāh

والذين آمنوا أشد حبا لله

Recite al-Fātiḥa over each one of them 41 times. Then gather the three together and recite over them:

O Badūḥ

Yā Badūḥ

يا بدوح

one thousand times, and breathe upon them with your own breath, and feed them to the one whose love you desire, for he will love you with an intense love.

The Manner of a Revealing Istikhāra (Ṣifat Istikhāra Kāshifa)

Take two papers and write upon the first, "Do it", and beneath it:

They make excuses to you when you return to them. Say: Do not make excuses; we shall never believe you. God has already informed us of your tidings. God will see your deed, and His Messenger; then you will be brought back to the Knower of the unseen and the seen, and He will inform you of what you used to do.

Ya'tadhirūna ilaykum idhā raja'tum ilayhim, qul lā ta'tadhirū lan nu'mina lakum qad nabba'anā Allāhu min akhbārikum wa-sa-yarā Allāhu 'amalakum wa-rasūluhu thumma turaddūna ilā 'ālimi al-ghaybi wa-l-shahādati fa-yunabbi'ukum bimā kuntum ta'malūn.

يعتذرون إليكم إذا رجعتم إليهم قل لا تعتذروا لن نؤمن لكم قد نبأنا الله من أخباركم وسيرى الله عملكم ورسوله ثم تردون إلى عالم الغيب والشهادة فينبئكم بما كنتم تعملون

and upon the second, “Do not do it”, and beneath it:

And say: Act, for God will see your deed, and His Messenger, and the believers; and you will be brought back to the Knower of the unseen and the seen, and He will inform you of what you used to do.

Wa-quli iʿmalū fa-sa-yarā Allāhu ʿamalakum wa-rasūluhu wa-l-mu'minūna wa-sa-turaddūna ilā ʿālimi al-ghaybi wa-l-shahādati fa-yunabbi'ukum bimā kuntum taʿmalūn.

وقل اعملوا فسيرى الله عملكم ورسوله والمؤمنون وستردون إلى عالم الغيب والشهادة فينبئكم بما كنتم تعملون

Then fold the two papers and put each one of them inside a piece of Meccan clay, then place them in a bowl containing water, and recite over them the words of God Most High:

And when you killed a soul and disputed over it, and God is the one who brings forth what you were concealing.

Wa-idh qataltum nafsan fa-iddāra'tum fīhā wa-Allāhu mukhrijun mā kuntum taktumūn.

وإذ قتلتم نفسا فادارأتم فيها والله مخرج ما كنتم تكتمون

twenty times. One of the two papers will rise to the surface of the water. If it is the first, go forward with your need, for it will be granted; and if it is the second, turn away from it, for it will not be granted.

A Benefit for the Crying of Children (Fā'ida li-Bukā' al-Aṭfāl)

Write it in an amulet and hang it upon him, and these are the verses:

In the name of God, the Most Gracious, the Most Merciful. Then We cast a cover over their ears in the cave for a number of years, and you would think them awake though they were asleep, and We turned them over, to the right and to the left. Do you perceive of them a single one, or hear of them the faintest sound? On that Day they will follow the Summoner in whom is no crookedness; voices will be hushed before the All-Merciful, and you will hear nothing but a murmur. This Day We seal their mouths, and their hands speak to Us, and their feet bear witness to what they used to earn. Do you then marvel at this discourse, and laugh and not weep, while you amuse yourselves? Ṭā Hā. We have not sent down the Qur'ān upon you that you should be wretched. Yā Sīn. By the wise Qur'ān. Ṣād. By the Qur'ān, possessor of the Reminder. Qāf. By the glorious Qur'ān. Nūn. By the pen and what they inscribe. God suffices us, and excellent is the Guardian; there is no power and no strength save in God, the Most High, the Most Great. And may God bless our master Muḥammad, and his family and his companions, and grant them peace.

Bismi Allāh al-Raḥmān al-Raḥīm. Fa-ḍarabnā 'alā ādhānihim fī al-kahfi sinīna 'adadā wa-taḥsabuhum ayqāẓan wa-hum ruqūd wa-nuqallibuhum dhāta al-yamīni wa-dhāta al-shimāl. Hal tuḥissu minhum min aḥadin aw tasma'u lahum rikzā.

Yawma'idhin yattabi'ūna al-dā'iya lā 'iwaja lahu, wa-khasha'ati al-aṣwātu li-l-Raḥmāni fa-lā tasma'u illā hamsā. Al-yawma nakhtimu 'alā afwāhihim wa-tukallimunā aydīhim wa-tashhadu arjuluhum bi-mā kānū yaksibūn. A-fa-min hādhā al-ḥadīthi ta'jabūn wa-taḍḥakūna wa-lā tabkūn wa-antum sāmidūn. Ṭā Hā, mā anzalnā 'alayka al-Qur'āna li-tashqā. Yā Sīn, wa-l-Qur'āni al-ḥakīm. Ṣād, wa-l-Qur'āni dhī al-dhikr. Qāf, wa-l-Qur'āni al-majīd. Nūn, wa-l-qalami wa-mā yasṭurūn. Wa-ḥasbunā Allāhu wa-ni'ma al-wakīl, wa-lā ḥawla wa-lā quwwata illā bi-Llāhi al-'Alīyi al-'Aẓīm, wa-ṣallā Allāhu 'alā sayyidinā Muḥammadin wa-'alā ālihi wa-ṣaḥbihi wa-sallam.

بسم الله الرحمن الرحيم فضربنا على آذانهم في الكهف سنين عددا وتحسبهم أيقاظا وهم رقود ونقلبهم ذات اليمين وذات الشمال . هل تحس منهم من أحد أو تسمع لهم ركزا . يومئذ يتبعون الداعي لا عوج له وخشعت الأصوات للرحمن فلا تسمع إلا همسا . اليوم نختم على أفواههم وتكلمنا أيديهم وتشهد أرجلهم بما كانوا يكسبون . أفمن هذا الحديث تعجبون وتضحكون ولا تبكون وأنتم سامدون . طه ما أنزلنا عليك القرآن لتشقى . يس والقرآن الحكيم . ص والقرآن ذي الذكر . ق والقرآن المجيد . ن والقلم وما يسطرون . وحسبنا الله ونعم الوكيل ولا حول ولا قوة إلا بالله العلي العظيم ، وصلى الله على سيدنا محمد وعلى آله وصحبه وسلم

A Benefit for Colic, Gripes, Smallpox, Leprosy and Vitiligo (Fāʾida li-l-Qawlanj wa-l-Maghṣ wa-l-Judarī wa-l-Judhām wa-l-Baraṣ)

Make a tablet of copper, engrave upon it the wafq that follows, and put that tablet into the water from which the sick person drinks; he will be healed by the permission of God Most High. This is the form of the wafq, as you see:

ه	ل	ا	ه	ل	ل	ا
ا	ه	ل	ل	ا	ه	ل
ل	ل	ا	ه	ل	ا	ه
ا	ه	ل	ا	ه	ل	ل
ل	ا	ه	ل	ل	ا	ه
ه	ل	ل	ا	ه	ل	ا
ل	ا	ه	ل	ا	ه	ل

The seven-by-seven letter wafq

Engrave upon its back the six verses of healing, which are:

And He will heal the breasts of a believing people, and take away the rage of their hearts. And a healing for what is in the breasts, and a guidance and a mercy for the believers. In it is healing for mankind. And We send down of the Qurʾān that which is a healing and a mercy for the believers. And when I am sick, it is He who heals me. Say: it is, for those who believe, a guidance and a healing.

Wa-yashfi ṣudūra qawmin muʾminīn wa-yudhhib ghayẓa qulūbihim. Wa-shifāʾun li-mā fī al-ṣudūri wa-hudan wa-

raḥmatun li-l-mu'minīn. Fīhi shifā'un li-l-nās. Wa-nunazzilu mina al-Qur'āni mā huwa shifā'un wa-raḥmatun li-l-mu'minīn. Wa-idhā mariḍtu fa-huwa yashfīn. Qul huwa li-lladhīna āmanū hudan wa-shifā'.

ويشف صدور قوم مؤمنين ويذهب غيظ قلوبهم ، وشفاء لما في الصدور وهدى ورحمة للمؤمنين ، فيه شفاء للناس ، وننزل من القرآن ما هو شفاء ورحمة للمؤمنين ، وإذا مرضت فهو يشفين ، قل هو للذين آمنوا هدى وشفاء

A Benefit for Fear, Terror, Anxiety, Grief, Madness, Inward and Outward Sickness, and All That Befalls the Human Body (Fā'ida li-l-Khawf wa-l-Fazaʿ wa-l-Hamm wa-l-Ghamm wa-l-Junūn wa-l-Maraḍ al-Bāṭin wa-l-Ẓāhir wa-Kull mā Yaḥduth fī Jism al-Insān)

It is written upon a sheet of paper and worn, or upon a vessel of glass and washed off with oil of rose and fine oil, or with sesame oil, and the person is anointed with it. This is what is written:

In the name of God, the Most Gracious, the Most Merciful. And may God bless our master Muḥammad, and his family and his companions, and grant them peace. Then He sent down upon you, after the grief, a security — a slumber overcoming a party of you, while another party was anxious for themselves, thinking of God what was not the truth, the thought of the Age of Ignorance. They say: have we any part in the matter? Say: the matter belongs entirely to God. They hide within themselves what they do not disclose to you. They say: had we had any part in the matter, we would not have been slain here. Say: had you been in your houses, those upon whom killing was written would have gone forth to the places where they lie slain — and that God might test what is in your breasts and purify what is in your hearts; and God knows what lies within the breasts. Muḥammad is the Messenger of God, and those who are with him are severe against the disbelievers, merciful among themselves. You see them bowing and prostrating, seeking bounty from God and good pleasure. Their mark is upon their faces from the trace of prostration. That is their likeness in the Torah; and their likeness in the Gospel is as a seed that puts forth its shoot and strengthens it, so that it grows stout and stands firm upon its stalk, delighting the sowers — that He may enrage the disbelievers by them. God has promised those of them who believe and do righteous deeds forgiveness and a great reward.

Bismi Allāh al-Raḥmān al-Raḥīm, wa-ṣallā Allāhu ʿalā sayyidinā Muḥammadin wa-ʿalā ālihi wa-ṣaḥbihi wa-sallam. Thumma anzala ʿalaykum min baʿdi al-ghammi amanatan nuʿāsan yaghshā ṭāʾifatan minkum, wa-ṭāʾifatun qad ahammathum anfusuhum yaẓunnūna bi-Llāhi ghayra al-ḥaqqi ẓanna al-jāhiliyya, yaqūlūna hal lanā mina al-amri min shayʾ, qul inna al-amra kullahu li-Llāh, yukhfūna fī anfusihim mā lā yubdūna lak, yaqūlūna law kāna lanā mina al-amri shayʾun mā qutilnā hāhunā, qul law kuntum fī buyūtikum la-baraza alladhīna kutiba ʿalayhimu al-qatlu ilā maḍājiʿihim, wa-li-yabtaliya Allāhu mā fī ṣudūrikum wa-li-yumaḥḥiṣa mā fī qulūbikum, wa-Allāhu ʿalīmun bi-dhāti al-ṣudūr. Muḥammadun rasūlu Allāh, wa-lladhīna maʿahu ashiddāʾu 'alā al-kuffāri ruḥamā'u baynahum, tarāhum rukka'an sujjadan yabtaghūna faḍlan mina Allāhi wa-riḍwānan, sīmāhum fī wujūhihim min athari al-sujūd, dhālika mathaluhum fī al-Tawrāh, wa-mathaluhum fī al-Injīli ka-zar'in akhraja shaṭ'ahu fa-āzarahu fa-istaghlaẓa fa-istawā 'alā sūqihi yu'jibu al-zurrā'a li-yaghīẓa bihimu al-kuffār, wa'ada Allāhu alladhīna āmanū wa-'amilū al-ṣāliḥāti minhum maghfiratan wa-ajran 'aẓīmā.

بسم الله الرحمن الرحيم وصلى الله على سيدنا محمد وعلى آله وصحبه وسلم ، ثم أنزل عليكم من بعد الغم أمنة نعاسا يغشى طائفة منكم وطائفة قد أهمتهم أنفسهم يظنون بالله غير الحق ظن الجاهلية يقولون هل لنا من الأمر من شيء قل إن الأمر كله لله يخفون في أنفسهم ما لا يبدون لك يقولون لو كان لنا من الأمر شيء ما قتلنا هاهنا قل لو كنتم في بيوتكم لبرز الذين كتب عليهم القتل إلى مضاجعهم وليبتلي الله ما في صدوركم وليمحص ما في قلوبكم والله عليم بذات الصدور ، محمد رسول الله والذين معه أشداء على الكفار رحماء بينهم تراهم ركعا سجدا يبتغون فضلا من الله ورضوانا سيماهم في وجوههم من أثر السجود ذلك مثلهم في التوراة ومثلهم في الإنجيل كزرع أخرج شطأه فآزره فاستغلظ فاستوى على سوقه يعجب الزراع ليغيظ بهم الكفار وعد الله الذين آمنوا وعملوا الصالحات منهم مغفرة وأجرا عظيما

A Benefit for Rising from Sleep at Whatever Time You Wish (Fā'ida li-l-Qiyām min al-Nawm fī Ayy Waqt Turīduhu)

Before entering into sleep you recite this verse seven times:

Establish the prayer at the declining of the sun until the darkening of the night, and the recitation of dawn; indeed the recitation of dawn is witnessed.

Aqimi al-ṣalāta li-dulūki al-shamsi ilā ghasaqi al-layli wa-qur'āna al-fajr, inna qur'āna al-fajri kāna mashhūdā.

أقم الصلاة لدلوك الشمس إلى غسق الليل وقرآن الفجر إن قرآن الفجر كان مشهودا

and what you desire will come to pass.

A Benefit for Sending the Unseen Caller (Fā'ida li-Irsāl al-Hātif)

You sit at whatever time you wish, in a state of purity, facing the qibla, and you recite this verse a thousand times, which is the saying of God Most High:

And of the satans there were those who dived for him and did work other than that; and We were keepers over them.

Wa-mina al-shayāṭīni man yaghūṣūna lahu wa-yaʿmalūna ʿamalan dūna dhālik, wa-kunnā lahum ḥāfiẓīn.

ومن الشياطين من يغوصون له ويعملون عملا دون ذلك وكنا لهم حافظين

and at the head of every hundred you say:

Answer, O servants of this noble verse, and cross over to so-and-so, son of so-and-so and my likeness; and show him my place, and acquaint him with my desire, and command him to fulfil my need, and frighten him until he comes to me submissive and lowly and fulfils my need, which is such-and-such (here you name your need), quickly, speedily, this very hour. May God bless you and be upon you.

Ajībū yā khuddām hādhihi al-āya al-sharīfa wa-uʿburū ʿalā fulān ibn fulāna fī (...) wa-mithālī wa-(...) lahu wajhī wa-arūhu makānī wa-ʿarrifūhu bi-murādī wa-murūhu bi-qaḍāʾ ḥājatī wa-khawwifūhu ḥattā yaʾtiya ilayya khāḍiʿan dhalīlan wa-yaqḍiya ḥājatī wa-hiya kadhā wa-kadhā wa-tadhkuru ḥājataka al-waḥā al-ʿajal al-sāʿa bāraka Allāhu fīkum wa-ʿalaykum

أجيبوا يا خدام هذه الآية الشريفة واعبروا على فلان ابن فلانة في (...) ومثالي و(...) له وجهي وأروه مكاني وعرفوه بمرادي وأمروه بقضاء حاجتي وخوفوه حتى يأتي إلي خاضعا ذليلا ويقضي حاجتي وهي كذا وكذا وتذكر حاجتك الوحا العجل الساعة بارك الله فيكم وعليكم

A Benefit to Be Recited over Boils and Sores of the Body (Fāʾida Tuqraʾ ʿalā Kull mā Yanbut fī al-Jasad min al-Damāmil wa-l-Qurūḥ)

Recite these verses over everything that grows in the body, of boils and sores:

In the name of God, the Most Gracious, the Most Merciful. Indeed We tried them as We tried the owners of the garden, when they swore that they would surely harvest it in the morning and made no exception. Then a visitation from your Lord passed over it while they slept, and it became as though reaped, and it became as though reaped, and it became as though reaped.

Bismi Allāh al-Raḥmān al-Raḥīm. Innā balawnāhum kamā balawnā aṣḥāba al-janna idh aqsamū la-yaṣrimunnahā muṣbiḥīn wa-lā yastathnūn. Fa-ṭāfa ʿalayhā ṭāʾifun min Rabbika wa-hum nāʾimūn. Fa-aṣbaḥat ka-l-ṣarīm fa-aṣbaḥat ka-l-ṣarīm fa-aṣbaḥat ka-l-ṣarīm.

بسم الله الرحمن الرحيم إنا بلوناهم كما بلونا أصحاب الجنة إذ أقسموا ليصرمنها مصبحين ولا يستثنون فطاف عليها طائف من ربك وهم نائمون فأصبحت كالصريم فأصبحت كالصريم فأصبحت كالصريم

Then take some of your saliva upon your finger and anoint the place of the pain with it, and it will be healed by the permission of God Most High.

A Benefit for Consolation (Fāʾida li-l-Sulwa)

Write what follows in a clean vessel, wash it off with well water or rainwater, and give it to the lover to drink, for he will be consoled of his beloved, the infatuation will pass from him, and he will not remember again. This is what you write:

We had already made a covenant with Adam before, but he forgot, and We found in him no resolve. Likewise let so-and-so son of so-and-so forget so-and-so son of so-and-so, and find in him no resolve.

Wa-la-qad ʿahidnā ilā Ādama min qablu fa-nasiya wa-lam najid lahu ʿazmā. Ka-dhālika yansā fulān ibn fulāna fulān ibn fulāna wa-lam yajid lahu ʿazmā.

ولقد عهدنا إلى آدم من قبل فنسي ولم نجد له عزما كذلك ينسى فلان
ابن فلانة فلان ابن فلانة ولم يجد له عزما

Barbarous names: Kayf Kahyash Aqrīsh Balagh Ghānak Aṣbāʾūt Bahlahūn

كيف كهيش اقريش بلغ غانك أصباؤت بهلهون

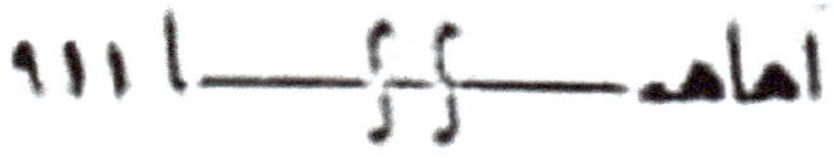

The drawn talismanic line

An Important Benefit for the Success of Affairs and for Healing from All Sicknesses and Ailments (Fāʾida Muhimma li-Najāḥ al-Umūr wa-l-Shifāʾ min Jamīʿ al-Asqām wa-l-ʿIlal)

Write the seal that follows with musk, saffron and rose water in the first hour of Thursday, and pray two rakʿas to God Most High: the first with al-Fātiḥa and al-Inshirāḥ, and the second with al-Fātiḥa and al-Naṣr. Ask forgiveness of God Most High 313 times, invoke blessings upon the Prophet, may God bless him and grant him peace, 313 times, then recite Sūrat al-Ikhlāṣ 1002 times; and at the head of every hundred say:

Answer, O Rūfīl, O Jibrā'īl, O Mīkā'īl, O Isrāfīl, O 'Anyā'īl and O Mamsā'īl, with the attainment of my aim and the utmost of my hope, by the right of the sura of the King, the Truth, the Majestic, and of our master Muḥammad, may God bless him and grant him peace, to whom the revelation and the sending down were given.

Ajib yā Rūfīl wa-yā Jibrā'īl wa-yā Mīkā'īl wa-yā Isrāfīl wa-yā 'Anyā'īl wa-yā Mamsā'īl wa-yā (...) bi-bulūgh maqṣidī wa-muntahā amalī bi-ḥaqq sūrat al-Malik al-Ḥaqq al-Jalīl wa-sayyidinā Muḥammad ṣallā Allāhu 'alayhi wa-sallam alladhī atāhu al-waḥy wa-l-tanzīl.

أجب يا روفيل ويا جبرائيل ويا ميكائيل ويا إسرافيل ويا عنيائيل ويا ممسائيل ويا (...) ببلوغ مقصدي ومنتهى أملي بحق سورة الملك الحق الجليل وسيدنا محمد صلى الله عليه وسلم الذي أتاه الوحي والتنزيل

The form of the seal is as follows:

The form of the seal

Whoever does that will attain the greatest secret, will succeed in all his affairs, and will be cured of all sicknesses and ailments.

A Benefit for General Acceptance (Fā'ida li-l-Qabūl al-ʿĀmm)

Draw the wafq that follows in a fortunate hour and hang it up for seven nights, reciting the whole sura over it 1002 times every night; then carry it. This is its form, as you see:

	٤٤	٧٠	١٦٥	١٦	١٣	٦٦	١١	١٢٠
	يلد	لم	الصمد	الله	أحد	الله	هو	قل
٦	ولم	يلد	لم	الصمد	الله	احد	الله	هو
٥٠	يولد	ولم	يلد	لم	الصمد	الله	أحد	الله
٧٦	ولم	يولد	ولم	يلد	لم	الصمد	الله	أحد
٨٠	يكن	ولم	يولد	ولم	يلد	لم	الصمد	الله
٣٥	له	يكن	ولم	يولد	ولم	يلد	لم	صمد
١٠٧	كفوا	له	يكن	ولم	يولد	ولم	يلد	لم
١٣	أحد	كفوا	له	يكن	ولم	يولد	ولم	ولم

The wafq of Sūrat al-Ikhlāṣ

A Revealing Istikhāra (Istikhāra Kāshifa)

You recite Sūrat Yā-Sīn, and each time you reach the word *mubīn* you repeat it 102 times. When the sura is complete, you invoke blessings upon the Prophet, may God bless him and grant him peace, 35 times, in whatever formula you please. Then say:

O God, by the right of this sura: if this matter is good, show me white or green; and if it is ill, show me black or red.

Allāhumma bi-ḥaqqi hādhihi al-sūra, in kāna hādhā al-amru khayran fa-arinī bayāḍan aw khuḍratan, wa-in kāna sū'an fa-arinī sawādan aw ḥumratan.

اللهم بحق هذه السورة إن كان هذا الأمر خيرا فأرني بياضا أو خضرة وإن كان سوءا فأرني سوادا أو حمرة

Then sleep, and you will see something of that.

A Benefit for Fulfilling Needs and Complete Joy in All Matters (Fāʾida li-Qaḍāʾ al-Ḥawāʾij wa-Tamām al-Surūr fī Jamīʿ al-Umūr)

It is that you recite Yā-Sīn ten times after the two rakʿas of the dawn prayer and before the ṣubḥ prayer, and that you recite after it, seventy times, the Greatest Name, which is:

Barbarous names: Aḥūn Qāf Ādam Ḥā Mīm Hāʾ Amīn

أحون قاف آدم حم هاء أمين

Then say:

I ask You, O God, O You who are Aḥūn Qāf Ādam Ḥā Mīm Hāʾ Āmīn, that You do such-and-such for me.

As'aluka Allāhumma yā man huwa Aḥūn Qāf Ādam Ḥā Mīm Hā' Āmīn an tafʿala lī kadhā wa-kadhā.

أسألك اللهم يا من هو أحون قاف آدم حم هاء آمين أن تفعل لي كذا وكذا

A Benefit for Stirring by Sūrat al-Ikhlāṣ (Fā'ida li-Tahyīj bi-Sūrat al-Ikhlāṣ)

Perform the ablution, pray two rakʿas, and take a palmful of salt free of any ill. Recite the sura 1002 times, and after each time recite the adjuration that follows, breathe into your palm over the salt, and cast some of it into the fire. This is the form of the adjuration. Say:

I adjure you by the servants of this noble sura, and by what I speak over you of the noble names, that you do such-and-such, by the secret of Huyūsh (twice), Shafyūsh, Maṭhūsh, Arḍ, Aryūsh, Aryābūsh. Rather, it shall come upon them suddenly, so that they can neither repel it nor be granted respite. Quickly, swiftly, this very hour.

Aqsamtu ʿalaykum bi-akhdāmi hādhihi al-sūra al-sharīfa wa-mā anā mutakallimun bihi ʿalaykum min al-asmā' al-karīma an tafʿalū kadhā wa-kadhā bi-sirri Huyūsh ٢ Shafyūsh Maṭhūsh Arḍ Aryūsh Aryābūsh, bal ta'tīhim baghtatan fa-lā yastaṭīʿūna raddahā wa-lā hum yunẓarūn. Al-waḥā al-ʿajal al-sāʿa.

أقسمت عليكم بأخدام هذه السورة الشريفة وما أنا متكلم به عليكم من الأسماء الكريمة أن تفعلوا كذا وكذا بسر هيوش ٢ شفيوش مطهوش أرض أريوش أريابوش بل تأتيهم بغتة فلا يستطيعون ردها ولا هم ينظرون الوحا العجل الساعة

A Benefit for Attraction by Sūrat al-Ikhlāṣ (Fā'ida li-l-Jalb bi-Sūrat al-Ikhlāṣ)

You recite the noble sura on the eve of Friday 1002 times, and after each time you say:

Take charge, O 'Abd al-Raḥmān, and O 'Abd al-Wāḥid, and O 'Abd al-Ṣamad: draw and stir so-and-so son of so-and-so with love for so-and-so daughter of so-and-so, by the right of what you hold of this sura.

Tawakkal yā 'Abd al-Raḥmān wa-yā 'Abd al-Wāḥid wa-yā 'Abd al-Ṣamad bi-jalbi wa-tahyīji fulān ibn fulāna bi-maḥabbati fulāna bint fulāna bi-ḥaqqi mā ta'taqidūnahu min hādhihi al-sūra.

توكل يا عبد الرحمن ويا عبد الواحد ويا عبد الصمد بجلب وتهييج فلان ابن فلانة بمحبة فلانة بنت فلانة بحق ما تعتقدونه من هذه السورة

If you want something stronger and swifter than that, take a piece from the trace of the one sought and write upon it these names:

Barbarous names: Baṭmaṭīsh ٢ Aṭīsh ٢ Maṭūsh ٢ 'Alyūsh ٢ Nabṭūsh ٢

بطمطيش ٢ أطيش ٢ مطوش ٢ عليوش ٢ نبطوش ٢

Then make it into a wick, light it in a lamp with good oil, and recite the sura together with the charge as has already passed, and you will see what gladdens you.

A Benefit for Swift Attraction by the Secret of the Letter Jīm and the Noble Sūrat al-Ikhlāṣ (Fāʾida li-l-Jalb al-Sarīʿ bi-Sirr Ḥarf al-Jīm wa-Sūrat al-Ikhlāṣ al-Karīma)

Take a piece from the trace of the one sought and write upon it the letter ج, in this form, 53 times, and between them the letters of the name of the one sought. On its back write his name and his mother's name, with the charge to the servant to draw him to the woman who seeks him. Then make it into a wick, light it in a new lamp with good oil, and adjure it with Sūrat al-Ikhlāṣ together with the adjuration that follows 53 times. The work is done after the night prayer on whatever night you wish. This is the adjuration. Say:

I have drawn by the rank of the beauty of the dominion, and by the might of grandeur and magnificence, and by God, the One, the Unique, the Single, the Eternal Refuge. I have drawn my sought one together with my beloved, and I have no beloved but the Near, the Answering. Answer, O Ṭalqaṭābīl, O servant of the letter ج, by drawing such-and-such to such-and-such, by what is in you of the secret and the churning: Baljīj, and he is Lajīj, and he is Lajīj, Arjīj, Barjīj, like the shimmering of the sun in the blaze, by what you bear, Jawādī, and I have adjured you by the Lord of His servants: answer, O pure spirit Ṭalqaṭabāʾīl, for the drawing of so-and-so to so-and-so, quickly (twice), speedily (twice), this very hour (twice). May God bless you and be upon you.

Jalabtu bi-jāhi jamāli al-jabarūt wa-bi-ʿizzati al-ʿaẓama wa-l-kibriyāʾ wa-bi-Llāhi al-Wāḥid al-Aḥad al-Fard al-Ṣamad, jalabtu maṭlūbī maʿa maḥbūbī wa-laysa lī ḥabībun siwā al-Qarīb al-Mujīb. Ajib yā Ṭalqaṭābīl yā khādima ḥarf al-jīm bi-jalbi kadhā wa-kadhā ilā kadhā wa-kadhā bi-mā fīka min al-sirr wa-l-tajlīj: Baljīj wa-huwa Lajīj wa-huwa Lajīj, Arjīj Barjīj ka-rajīji al-shams fī al-wahīj, bi-ḥamlika Jawādī wa-aqsamtu ʿalayka bi-Rabb al-ʿibād, ajib ayyuhā al-rūḥ al-ṭāhir Ṭalqaṭabāʾīl, jalb kadhā ilā kadhā, al-waḥā ٢ *al-ʿajal* ٢ *al-sāʿa* ٢, *wa-bāraka Allāhu fīkum wa-ʿalaykum.*

جلبت بجاه جمال الجبروت وبعزة العظمة والكبرياء وبالله الواحد الأحد الفرد الصمد جلبت مطلوبي مع محبوبي وليس لي حبيب سوى القريب المجيب أجب يا طلقطابيل يا خادم حرف الجيم بجلب كذا وكذا إلى كذا وكذا بما فيك من السر والتجليج بلجيج وهو لجيج وهو لجيج أرجيج برجيج كرجيج الشمس في الوهيج بحملك جوادي وأقسمت عليك برب العباد أجب أيها الروح الطاهر طلقطبائيل جلب كذا إلى كذا الوحا ٢ العجل ٢ الساعة ٢ وبارك الله فيكم وعليكم

A Noble Benefit for Revealing in a Dream What Has Become Difficult for You (Fāʾida Jalīla li-Kashf mā Ashkala ʿalayka fī al-Manām)

Pray four rakʿas after the night prayer. After al-Fātiḥa recite in the first Sūrat al-Ḍuḥā, in the second Sūrat al-Tīn, in the third Sūrat al-Qadr, and in the fourth Sūrat al-Zalzala, and do not speak after this prayer. Then write Sūrat al-Zalzala on a slip of paper, place it beneath your head, sleep, and say at the moment of sleeping:

O God, show me in my dream the good in such-and-such a matter — and you name what you want — for you will see it plainly.

Allāhumma arinī fī manāmī al-khayra fī kadhā wa-kadhā, wa-tusammī mā turīdu, fa-innaka tarāhu ʿiyānan.

اللهم أرني في منامي الخير في كذا وكذا وتسمي ما تريد فإنك تراه عيانا

A Benefit for Repelling the Harm of a Rabid Dog (Fāʾida li-Dafʿ Adhā al-Kalb al-ʿAqūr)

Whoever recites this verse on meeting a rabid dog, it will not harm him:

O company of jinn and mankind, if you are able to pass beyond the regions of the heavens and the earth, then pass. You will not pass except by an authority.

Yā maʿshara al-jinni wa-l-insi in istaṭaʿtum an tanfudhū min aqṭāri al-samāwāti wa-l-arḍi fa-unfudhū, lā tanfudhūna illā bi-sulṭān.

يا معشر الجن والإنس إن استطعتم أن تنفذوا من أقطار السماوات والأرض فانفذوا لا تنفذون إلا بسلطان

A Benefit for Safety from Drowning When Boarding the Sea (Fāʾida li-l-Amn min al-Gharaq ʿinda Rukūb al-Baḥr)

When boarding the sea, recite these verses seven times, and they are these:

In the name of God, the Most Gracious, the Most Merciful. They did not measure God with His true measure, and the whole earth will be His handful on the Day of Resurrection, and the heavens will be folded up in His right hand. Glory be to Him, and exalted is He above what they associate with Him. In the name of God is its course and its mooring; indeed my Lord is Forgiving, Merciful.

Bismi Allāh al-Raḥmān al-Raḥīm. Wa-mā qadarū Allāha ḥaqqa qadrihi wa-l-arḍu jamīʿan qabḍatuhu yawma al-qiyāmati wa-l-samāwātu maṭwiyyātun bi-yamīnihi, subḥānahu wa-taʿālā ʿammā yushrikūn. Bismi Allāhi majrāhā wa-mursāhā, inna Rabbī la-Ghafūrun Raḥīm.

بسم الله الرحمن الرحيم وما قدروا الله حق قدره والأرض جميعا قبضته يوم القيامة والسماوات مطويات بيمينه سبحانه وتعالى عما يشركون بسم الله مجراها ومرساها إن ربي لغفور رحيم

A Benefit for Fulfilling Needs, with a Wafq (Fāʾida li-Qaḍāʾ al-Ḥawāʾij)

Write the wafq that follows in the hour of Jupiter on Thursday, fumigate it with aloeswood, and recite over it these two verses:

God — there is no god but He, the Living, the Self-Subsisting. Neither drowsiness nor sleep overtakes Him. To Him belongs whatever is in the heavens and whatever is on the earth. Who is there that can intercede with Him except by His permission? He knows what is before them and what is behind them, and they encompass nothing of His knowledge except what He wills. His throne extends over the heavens and the earth, and their preservation does not weary Him, and He is the Most High, the

Magnificent. There is no compulsion in religion; right guidance has become distinct from error. Whoever disbelieves in false gods and believes in God has grasped the firmest handhold, which never breaks; and God is Hearing, Knowing.

Allāhu lā ilāha illā Huwa al-Ḥayyu al-Qayyūm. Lā ta'khudhuhu sinatun wa-lā nawm. Lahu mā fī al-samāwāti wa-mā fī al-arḍ. Man dhā alladhī yashfa'u 'indahu illā bi-idhnih. Ya'lamu mā bayna aydīhim wa-mā khalfahum, wa-lā yuḥīṭūna bi-shay'in min 'ilmihi illā bi-mā shā'. Wasi'a kursiyyuhu al-samāwāti wa-l-arḍ, wa-lā ya'ūduhu ḥifẓuhumā, wa-Huwa al-'Aliyyu al-'Aẓīm. Lā ikrāha fī al-dīn, qad tabayyana al-rushdu mina al-ghayy. Fa-man yakfur bi-l-ṭāghūti wa-yu'min bi-Allāhi fa-qad istamsaka bi-l-'urwati al-wuthqā lā infiṣāma lahā, wa-Allāhu Samī'un 'Alīm.

الله لا إله إلا هو الحي القيوم لا تأخذه سنة ولا نوم له ما في السماوات وما في الأرض من ذا الذي يشفع عنده إلا بإذنه يعلم ما بين أيديهم وما خلفهم ولا يحيطون بشيء من علمه إلا بما شاء وسع كرسيه السماوات والأرض ولا يؤوده حفظهما وهو العلي العظيم لا إكراه في الدين قد تبين الرشد من الغي فمن يكفر بالطاغوت ويؤمن بالله فقد استمسك بالعروة الوثقى لا انفصام لها والله سميع عليم

Recite them seventy-two times and carry it. This is its form, as you see:

٥٦٠٤	٥٦٠٧	٥٦١٠	٥٥٩٧
٥٦٠٩	٥٥٩٨	٥٦٠٣	٥٦٠٨
٥٥٩٩	٥٦١٢	٥٥٠٥	٥٦٠٢
٥٦٠٦	٥٦٠١	٥٦٠٠	٥٦١١

The wafq for fulfilling needs

A Benefit for Awe (Fāʾida li-l-Hayba)

Write the wafq that follows and recite over it the words of God Most High:

As if they were propped-up timbers.

Ka-annahum khushubun musannada.

كأنهم خشب مسندة

Recite it 1177 times, carry it, and enter upon whomever you wish, and you will obtain what you want. This is the form of the wafq, as you see:

٢٦٧	٨٢١	٧٩
٧٣٢	فلان	٤٤٥
١٧٨	٢٥٩	٦٤٣

The wafq for awe

A Benefit for Subjugation and Affection (Fāʾida li-l-Taskhīr wa-l-ʿAṭf)

Pray two rakʿas and recite after al-Fātiḥa in each rakʿa:

Perhaps God will put affection between you and those of them with whom you have been at enmity. God is Powerful, and God is Forgiving, Merciful.

ʿAsā Allāhu an yajʿala baynakum wa-bayna alladhīna ʿādaytum minhum mawaddatan, wa-Allāhu Qadīr, wa-Allāhu Ghafūrun Raḥīm.

عسى الله أن يجعل بينكم وبين الذين عاديتم منهم مودة والله قدير والله غفور رحيم

Recite it seven times. Then recite it seventy-seven times after the closing salutation, and then say:

O God, soften for me the heart of so-and-so, just as You softened iron for David and Solomon, peace be upon them.

Allāhumma layyin lī qalba kadhā wa-kadhā kamā layyanta al-ḥadīda li-Dāwūd wa-Sulaymān ʿalayhimā al-salām.

اللهم لين لي قلب كذا وكذا كما لينت الحديد لداود وسليمان عليهما السلام

A Benefit for Fulfilling Needs, with Seven Dates (Fāʾida li-Qaḍāʾ al-Ḥawāʾij)

Write this verse upon seven dates, each word upon a single date:

To Him ascends good speech, and righteous work raises it.

Ilayhi yaṣʿadu al-kalimu al-ṭayyibu wa-l-ʿamalu al-ṣāliḥu yarfaʿuhu.

إليه يصعد الكلم الطيب والعمل الصالح يرفعه

Then recite it over each date twenty-one times. Then take them all in your closed hand and recite it twenty-one times. Then present them to whomever you wish, and your need will be fulfilled.

A Noble Benefit for Easing Provisions (Fāʾida Jalīla li-Taysīr al-Arzāq)

Recite in the last third of the night, and recite Sūrat al-Ṭalāq eight times, and in each recitation repeat this verse a hundred times:

God will appoint ease after hardship.

Sayajʿalu Allāhu baʿda ʿusrin yusrā.

سيجعل الله بعد عسر يسرا

Then, when that is complete, say:

O God.

Yā Allāh

يا الله

a thousand times, and invoke blessings upon the Prophet, may God bless him and grant him peace, a thousand times; and you will see what gladdens you.

A Benefit for Wealth (Fā'ida li-l-Ghinā)

Whoever keeps to reciting Sūrat al-Wāqiʿa once after the dawn prayer every day, and invokes after it:

O Generous One, O Loving One.

Yā Karīm yā Wadūd

يا كريم يا ودود

a thousand times, no year will pass over him before God has made him independent of all people. In this measure there is sufficiency. God is the granter of success to what is right, and to Him are the return and the final home.

Chapter Three: On Mentioning Some of the Oaths, the Invocations, and the Employments (al-Bāb al-Thālith fī Dhikr Baʿḍ al-Aqsām wa-l-Daʿawāt wa-l-Istikhdāmāt)

The Oath of the Lord Mīṭaṭrūn (Qasam al-Sayyid Mīṭaṭrūn)

You recite it for every matter you desire twenty-one times while you fumigate with male frankincense and coriander. It is that you say:

In the name of God, the Most Gracious, the Most Merciful. In the name of God, who has a name that is never forgotten, a light that is never extinguished, a kingdom that does not pass away, a Throne that does not shift, and a Footstool that does not move. By Him I adjure you, O Lord Mīṭaṭrūn, O king of the spiritual spirits, the righteous ones who dwell beneath the Throne of the Almighty King, who prostrate themselves before God, the One, the Subduer, whose bodies course onward and who dispose of all their acts; and by Him who appointed you over the noble angels, supported you with the hosts and the dominions, gave you this power, chose you for Himself, and created the angels for you: command your servants and your helpers, Daʿyāʾīl and Jahyāʾīl, to come down by the might of their Lord and to come to me with power, by the might of

Bismi Allāh al-Raḥmān al-Raḥīm. Bismi Allāh alladhī lahu ismun lā yunsā wa-nūrun lā yuṭfā wa-mulkun lā yazūlu wa-ʿarshun lā yaḥūlu wa-kursiyyun lā yataḥarraku. Wa-bihi aqsamtu ʿalayka ayyuhā al-Sayyid Mīṭaṭrūn, yā malika al-arwāḥ al-rūḥāniyya al-abrār al-sākinīn taḥta ʿarsh al-Malik al-Jabbār, al-sājidīn li-Llāh al-Wāḥid al-Qahhār, al-jārīn jurmuhum, al-mutaṣarrifīn fī jamīʿ afʿālihim, bi-lladhī wakkalaka ʿalā al-malāʾika al-kirām wa-ayyadaka bi-l-junūd wa-l-amlāk wa-aʿṭāka hādhihi al-quwwa wa-aṣfāka wa-khalaqa laka al-malāʾika, illā mā amarta khuddāmaka wa-aʿwānaka Daʿyāʾīl wa-Jahyāʾīl an yanzilū bi-ʿizzati rabbihim wa-an yajīʾūnī bi-quwwatin min ʿindim bi-ʿizzati

بسم الله الرحمن الرحيم بسم الله الذي له اسم لا ينسى ونور لا يطفى وملك لا يزول وعرش لا يحول وكرسي لا يتحرك وبه أقسمت عليك أيها السيد ميططرون يا ملك الأرواح الروحانية الأبرار الساكنين تحت عرش الملك الجبار الساجدين لله الواحد القهار الجارين جرمهم المتصرفين

في جميع أفعالهم بالذي وكلك على الملائكة الكرام وأيدك بالجنود والأملاك وأعطاك هذه القوة وأصفاك وخلق لك الملائكة إلا ما أمرت خدامك وأعوانك دعيائيل وجهيائيل أن ينزلوا بعزة ربهم وأن يجيئوني بقوة من عندم بعزة

Barbarous names: Shamaʿ ٢ Halaj ٢ Aṭūf ٢ Aḍman ٢ Alṭafā ٢ Aṣbāʾūt ٢

شمع ٢ هلج ٢ أطوف ٢ أضمن ٢ ألطفا ٢ أصباؤت ٢

by the Name with which Gabriel, peace be upon him, came down upon our master Muḥammad, may God bless him and grant him peace: unless you answer, and hasten, and come down with power from you.

bi-l-ism alladhī nazala bihi Jibrīl ʿalayhi al-salām ʿalā sayyidinā Muḥammad ṣallā Allāhu ʿalayhi wa-sallam, illā mā ajabtum wa-asraʿtum wa-nazaltum bi-quwwatin minkum

بالاسم الذي نزل به جبريل عليه السلام على سيدنا محمد صلى الله عليه وسلم إلا ما أجبتم وأسرعتم ونزلتم بقوة منكم

Barbarous names: Hamtha Kahūsh ٢ Aykūsh ٢ Barma ٢ Maqīl ٢ Kabākh ٢

همثة كهوش ٢ أيكوش ٢ برمة ٢ مقيل ٢ كباخ ٢

Where are you, by Aghām, the ifrit of the clouds! Where are you, O Aḥmar! Where are you, by al-Murūdal the Flier! Where are you, O Abā Nūkh! Where are you, O Saydūk! Where are you, O Najāḥ! Where are you, O Falāḥ! Where are you, O Thamlaq! Where are you, O Abānūkh the Black! Where are you, O Barqān!

Where are you, O Dardāʾīl! Where are you, O Rūqiyāʾīl! Where are you, O Jibrāʾīl! Where are you, O ʿAṣmāʾīl! Where are you, O Mīkāʾīl! Where are you, O Ṣarfiyāʾīl! Where are you, O ʿAnyāʾīl! Where are you, O Kasfiyāʾīl! Where are you, O Hashnakal! Where are you, O Kaṭlāyāshīl! Where are you, O Nāṭūs! Where are you, O Zūbiya! Where are you, by Adnāhisha! Where are you, by Aqshāsha! Where are you, O Ghīlān! Where are you, O dwellers of the mountains! Where are you, O dwellers of the wastes! Where are you, O dwellers of the bathhouses! Where are you, O dwellers of the dungheaps! Where are you, O dwellers of the roads! Attend, and may God bless you and be upon you, and do such-and-such; for I have come to you and have laid my command upon you by the covenants and the pacts that Solomon son of David, peace be upon them both, took, and by the Name that was cast to Mary, so that he took on for her the likeness of a well-formed man. And I adjure you by

Aynaka bi-Aghām ʿIfrīt al-Saḥāb, aynaka yā Aḥmar, aynaka bi-l-Murūdal al-Ṭayyār, aynaka yā Abā Nūkh, aynaka yā Saydūk, aynaka yā Najāḥ, aynaka yā Falāḥ, aynaka yā Thamlaq, aynaka yā Abānūkh al-Aswad, aynaka yā Barqān, aynaka yā Dardāʾīl, aynaka yā Rūqiyāʾīl, aynaka yā Jibrāʾīl, aynaka yā ʿAṣmāʾīl, aynaka yā Mīkāʾīl, aynaka yā Ṣarfiyāʾīl, aynaka yā ʿAnyāʾīl, aynaka yā Kasfiyāʾīl, aynaka yā Hashnakal, aynaka yā Kaṭlāyāshīl, aynaka yā Nāṭūs, aynaka yā Zūbiya, aynakum bi-Adnāhisha, aynakum bi-Aqshāsha, aynakum yā Ghīlān, aynakum yā sukkān al-jibāl, aynakum yā sukkān al-qifār, aynakum yā sukkān al-ḥammāmāt, aynakum yā sukkān al-

mazābil, aynakum yā sukkān al-ṭuruqāt. Uḥḍurū, bāraka Allāhu fīkum wa-ʿalaykum, wa-fʿalū kadhā wa-kadhā, fa-innī jiʾtukum wa-ḥakamtu ʿalaykum bi-l-ʿuhūd wa-l-mawāthīq allatī akhadhahā Sulaymān ibn Dāwūd ʿalayhimā al-salām, wa-bi-l-ism alladhī ulqiya ilā Maryam fa-tamaththala lahā basharan sawiyyā. Wa-aqsamtu ʿalaykum

أينك بأغام عفريت السحاب أينك يا أحمر أينك بالمرودل الطيار أينك يا أبا نوخ أينك يا سيدوك أينك يا نجاح أينك يا فلاح أينك يا ثملق أينك يا أبانوخ الأسود أينك يا برقان أينك يا دردائيل أينك يا روقيائيل أينك يا جبرائيل أينك يا عصمائيل أينك يا ميكائيل أينك يا صرفيائيل أينك يا عنيائيل أينك يا كسفيائيل أينك يا هشنكل أينك يا كطلاياشيل أينك يا ناطوس أينك يا زوبية أينكم بادناهشة أينكم باقشاشة أينكم يا غيلان أينكم يا سكان الجبال أينكم يا سكان القفار أينكم يا سكان الحمامات أينكم يا سكان المزابل أينكم يا سكان الطرقات احضروا بارك الله فيكم وعليكم وافعلوا كذا وكذا فإني جيتكم وحكمت عليكم بالعهود والمواثيق التي أخذها سليمان بن داود عليهما السلام وبالاسم الذي ألقي إلى مريم فتمثل لها بشرا سويا وأقسمت عليكم

Barbarous names: Qashhal Fahshūl ʿAlshaqūm ٢

بقشهل وفهشول علشقوم ٢

and by the Name that was sent down upon the solid rock and it split apart, and upon the earth and it spread out, and upon the mountains and they were set firm, and upon the night and it grew dark, and upon the day and it shone; and by the Name with which our Lord called out, so that the mountain came to meet it in dread, the Throne ran with sweat, the earth surged in disquiet, and Moses fell down thunderstruck.

wa-bi-l-ism alladhī unzila ʿalā al-ṣakhra al-ṣammāʾ fa-nshaqqat, wa-ʿalā al-arḍ fa-nbasaṭat, wa-ʿalā al-jibāl fa-rasat, wa-ʿalā al-layl fa-aẓlama, wa-ʿalā al-nahār fa-aḍāʾa, wa-bi-l-ism alladhī nādā bihi Rabbunā fa-qābala al-jabalu faraqan wa-rashaḥa al-ʿarshu ʿaraqan wa-mājat al-arḍu qalaqan wa-kharra Mūsā ṣaʿiqan

وبالاسم الذي أنزل على الصخرة الصماء فانشقت وعلى الأرض فانبسطت وعلى الجبال فرست وعلى الليل فأظلم وعلى النهار فأضاء وبالاسم الذي نادى به ربنا فقابل الجبل فرقا ورشح العرش عرقا وماجت الأرض قلقا وخر موسى صعقا

Barbarous names: Balshāqish ٢ Mahrāqish ٢ Anshāmaqshā ٢ Malqashā ٢ Anshāmaqshā ٢ Shaqmūnhash ٢ Rakthā ٢ Rakshālagh ٢ Hūsh ٢ Nūsh ٢ Mārish ٢ Tūkwā

بلشاقش ٢ مهراقش ٢ أنشامقشا ٢ ملقشا ٢ أنشامقشى ٢ شقمونهش ٢ ركثا ٢ ركشالغ ٢ هوش ٢ نوش ٢ مارش ٢ توكوا

O servants of these names, do such-and-such, by the power of Him from awe of whom the deaf rocks quaked and before whose might the tyrants bowed low. There is no god but He, the Great, the Most High, who brings things forth from nothingness into being. Haste (twice), speed (twice), this very hour (twice)! May God bless you and be upon you. It was but a single cry, and at once they were all arraigned before Us.

Yā khuddāma hādhihi al-asmāʾ, wa-fʿalū kadhā wa-kadhā bi-quwwati alladhī talaqlaqat min haybatihi ṣummu al-ṣukhūr wa-khaḍaʿat al-jabābira li-ʿizzatih. Lā ilāha illā huwa al-Kabīr al-Mutaʿāl, mukhriju al-ashyāʾ min al-ʿadam ilā al-wujūd. Al-waḥā ٢ al-ʿajal ٢ al-sāʿa ٢. Bāraka Allāhu fīkum wa-ʿalaykum. In kānat illā ṣayḥatan wāḥidatan fa-idhā hum jamīʿun ladaynā muḥḍarūn.

يا خدام هذه الأسماء وافعلوا كذا وكذا بقوة الذي تلقلقت من هيبته صم الصخور وخضعت الجبابرة لعزته لا إله إلا هو الكبير المتعال مخرج الأشياء من العدم إلى الوجود الوحا ٢ العجل ٢ الساعة ٢ بارك الله فيكم وعليكم إن كانت إلا صيحة واحدة فإذا هم جميع لدينا محضرون

The Oath for Beginning the Adjurations (Qasam Ibtidāʾ al-ʿAzāʾim)

It is recited for the summoning of the kings, for everything you desire. Its incense is anything of pleasant fragrance. It is that you say:

In the name of God, the Most Gracious, the Most Merciful. I adjure you, O company of the jinn, by the word of God Most High: Say, it has been revealed to me that a company of the jinn listened. And by His word, exalted is He: I adjure you to attend this presence of mine and this station of mine. It was but a single cry, and at once they were all arraigned before Us. Thus are you made to attend, by His word, exalted is He: And when We turned toward you a company of the jinn, listening to the Qurʾān; when they attended it they said, Be silent. Then when it was ended they turned back to their people as warners. They said, O our people, we have heard a book sent down after Moses, confirming what came before it, guiding to the truth and to a straight path. So answer and obey, and do not be like those who said, We have heard, while they do not hear. Had God known any good in them He would have made them hear; and had He made them hear, they would have turned away in refusal. Answer, and hasten on flying wings, with the differing tongues and the wondrous kinds. God has power to gather them whenever He wills. Where are those who fly in the air? Where are those who steal a hearing from heaven? Where are the divers beneath the layers of the earth? Where are the seventy-two tribes of the tribes of the jinn, permitted to obedience beneath the circle of the seal of Solomon son of David, peace be upon them both? Where is King Saydūk, lord of the clamour and of the seal? Welcome to the kings: al-Mudhhab, lord of Sunday; and Murra ibn al-Ḥārith, lord of Monday; and Abū Muḥriz al-Aḥmar, lord of Tuesday; and Barqān al-Yahūdī, lord of Wednesday; and Shamhūrish the judge, son of al-Walīd, lord of Thursday; and Abū al-Nūr al-Abyaḍ Zawbaʿa, lord of Friday; and Maymūn al-Saḥābī, lord of Saturday. Answer in obedience to God, who has called you by the seven oft-repeated verses and the mighty Qurʾān. Welcome, welcome to the kings. If you are obedient, then there is no obedience of one created being to another; rather obedience belongs to the One, the Subduer. Whoever obeys willingly has obeyed God, mighty and majestic, for I have called you only by His names and His words. Whoever disobeys me is burned by a flame of fire, and whoever comes to me obedient is safe from the wrath of the Compeller. So travel forth and attend this assembly of mine with Jibrīl, Mīkā'īl, Isrāfīl, 'Azrā'īl and the angels brought near, who never slacken in the remembrance of their Lord: the Lord of lords, who makes difficult matters easy, the Causer of causes, the Setter-free of necks, the Mighty, the Bestower, before whose greatness the lofty mountains were rent asunder and before whose omnipotence necks were humbled, while everything glorified His lordship, willingly obedient to His command and to His gentle disposing. He is the Light of light, and His light is within light, a light before which every stubborn tyrant and rebellious devil submits, like the light upon the Mount, in a book inscribed. He is God; there is no god but He. To Him belongs praise in the first and in the last, His is the judgement, and to Him you shall be returned. Where are the worshippers of the sun and the worshippers of heaven? Where are the worshippers of idols? Where are the Christians and the Jews? Answer the caller of God. Whoever among you is of the apparitions of the spirits of the Jews, I have adjured you by the covenants, and by what is written in the verses of the sūras, and by the right of Him who made water gush from the hard rock, by the Torah of Moses and the Psalms of David. And whoever is of the apparitions of the spirits of the Christians, I have adjured you by the Gospel of Jesus. And if you are of the apparitions of the spirits of the Muslims, I have adjured you by Muḥammad, the Seal of the Prophets, that you do not exalt yourselves against me, but come to me in submission. I have called you only for the fulfilment of the needs of the Muslims.

Bismi Allāh al-Raḥmān al-Raḥīm. Aʿzimu ʿalaykum yā maʿshar al-jānn bi-qawli Allāh taʿālā: Qul ūḥiya ilayya annahu istamaʿa nafarun mina al-jinn. Wa-bi-qawlihi taʿālā: aʿzimu ʿalaykum an taḥḍurū ilā ḥaḍratī hādhihi wa-maqāmī hādhā. In kānat illā ṣayḥatan wāḥidatan fa-idhā hum jamīʿun ladaynā muḥḍarūn. Ka-dhālika tuḥḍarūna bi-qawlihi taʿālā: Wa-idh ṣarafnā ilayka nafaran mina al-jinni yastamiʿūna al-Qurʾān fa-lammā ḥaḍarūhu qālū anṣitū fa-lammā quḍiya wallaw ilā qawmihim mundhirīn. Qālū yā qawmanā innā samiʿnā kitāban unzila min baʿdi Mūsā muṣaddiqan li-mā bayna yadayhi yahdī ilā al-ḥaqqi wa-ilā ṭarīqin mustaqīm. Fa-ajībū wa-aṭīʿū wa-lā takūnū ka-lladhīna qālū samiʿnā wa-hum lā yasmaʿūn. Wa-law ʿalima Allāhu fīhim khayran la-asmaʿahum wa-law asmaʿahum la-tawallaw wa-hum muʿriḍūn. Ajībū wa-ʿajjilū bi-l-ajniḥa al-ṭayyāra wa-l-lughāt al-mukhtalifa wa-l-aṣnāf al-ʿajība. Inna Allāha ʿalā jamʿihim idhā yashāʾu qadīr. Ayna al-ṭayyārūna fī al-hawāʾ? Ayna al-mustariqūna al-samʿa mina al-samāʾ? Ayna al-ghawwāṣātu taḥta aṭbāqi al-tharā? Ayna al-ithnāni wa-sabʿūna qabīlatan min qabāʾili al-jinni al-maʾdhūnati bi-l-ṭāʿa taḥta dāʾirati khātami Sulaymān ibn Dāwūd ʿalayhimā al-salām? Ayna al-malik Saydūk ṣāḥib al-jalaba wa-l-khātam? Marḥaban bi-l-mulūk, wa-l-Mudhhab ṣāḥib yawm al-aḥad, wa-Murra ibn al-Ḥārith ṣāḥib yawm al-ithnayn, wa-Abū Muḥriz al-Aḥmar ṣāḥib yawm al-thulāthāʾ, wa-Barqān al-Yahūdī ṣāḥib yawm al-arbiʿāʾ, wa-Shamhūrish al-qāḍī ibn al-Walīd ṣāḥib yawm al-khamīs, wa-Abū al-Nūr al-Abyaḍ Zawbaʿa ṣāḥib yawm al-jumʿa, wa-Maymūn al-Saḥābī ṣāḥib yawm al-sabt. Ajībū ṭāʿata Allāh alladhī daʿākum bi-l-sabʿ al-mathānī wa-l-Qurʾān al-ʿaẓīm. Marḥaban marḥaban bi-l-mulūk. An antū ṭāʾiʿīn fa-lā ṭāʿata li-makhlūqin ʿalā makhlūq, bal al-ṭāʿatu li-l-wāḥid al-qahhār. Wa-man aṭāʿa ṭāʾiʿan fa-qad aṭāʿa Allāha ʿazza wa-jall, fa-innī mā daʿawtukum illā bi-asmāʾihi wa-kalāmihi. Wa-man ʿaṣānī fa-qad iḥtaraqa bi-shuwāẓin min nār, wa-man atānī ṭāʾiʿan fa-qad salima min sakhaṭi al-jabbār. Fa-sīḥū wa-aḥḍirū fī majlisī hādhā bi-Jibrīl wa-Mīkāʾīl wa-Isrāfīl wa-ʿAzrāʾīl wa-l-malāʾikati al-muqarrabīn, wa-hum ʿan dhikri rabbihim lā yafturūn: Rabb al-arbāb wa-musahhil al-umūr al-ṣiʿāb wa-musabbib al-asbāb wa-muʿtiq al-riqāb, al-ʿazīz al-wahhāb alladhi taqaṭṭaʿat al-rawāsī al-shāmikhāt li-ʿaẓamatihi wa-dhallat al-riqāb li-jabarūtihi, wa-majjada kullu shayʾin li-rubūbiyyatihi ṭawʿan li-amrihi wa-laṭīfatihi. Fa-huwa nūr al-nūr wa-nūruhu fī nūr, wa-nūrun yakhḍaʿu kullu jabbārin ʿanīd wa-shayṭānin marīd mithl al-nūr ʿalā al-Ṭūr fī kitābin masṭūr. Huwa Allāh alladhī lā ilāha illā huwa, lahu al-ḥamdu fī al-ūlā wa-l-ākhira wa-lahu al-ḥukmu wa-ilayhi turjaʿūn. Ayna ʿubbād al-shams wa-ʿubbād al-samāʾ? Ayna ʿubbād al-awthān? Ayna al-naṣārā wa-l-yahūd? Ajībū dāʿiya Allāh. Man kāna minkum min ashbāḥi arwāḥi al-yahūd fa-innī aqsamtu ʿalaykum bi-l-ʿuhūd wa-bi-mā kutiba fī āyāti al-suwar wa-bi-ḥaqqi man anbaʿa al-māʾa mina al-jalmūd bi-Tawrāti Mūsā wa-Zabūri Dāwūd. Wa-man kāna min ashbāḥi arwāḥi al-naṣārā fa-innī aqsamtu ʿalaykum bi-Injīli ʿĪsā. Wa-in kuntum min ashbāḥi arwāḥi al-muslimīn fa-innī aqsamtu ʿalaykum bi-Muḥammadin khātami al-nabiyyīn an lā taʿlū ʿalayya wa-ʾtūnī muslimīn. Mā daʿawtukum illā fī qaḍāʾi ḥawāʾiji al-muslimīn.

بسم الله الرحمن الرحيم أعزم عليكم يا معشر الجان بقول الله تعالى قل أوحي إلي أنه استمع نفر من الجن وبقوله تعالى أعزم عليكم أن تحضروا إلى حضرتي هذه ومقامي هذا إن كانت إلا صيحة واحدة فإذا هم جميع لدينا محضرون كذلك تحضرون بقوله تعالى وإذ صرفنا إليك نفرا من الجن يستمعون القرآن فلما حضروه قالوا أنصتوا فلما قضي ولوا إلى قومهم منذرين قالوا يا قومنا إنا سمعنا كتابا أنزل من بعد موسى مصدقا لما بين يديه يهدي إلى الحق وإلى طريق مستقيم فأجيبوا وأطيعوا ولا تكونوا كالذين قالوا سمعنا وهم لا يسمعون ولو علم الله فيهم خيرا لأسمعهم ولو أسمعهم لتولوا وهم معرضون أجيبوا وعجلوا بالأجنحة الطيارة واللغات المختلفة والأصناف العجيبة إن الله على جمعهم إذا يشاء قدير أين الطيارون في الهواء أين المسترقون السمع من السماء أين الغواصات تحت أطباق الثرى أين الاثنان وسبعون قبيلة من قبائل الجن المأذونة بالطاعة تحت دائرة خاتم سليمان بن داود عليهما السلام أين الملك سيدوك صاحب الجلبة والخاتم مرحبا بالملوك والمذهب صاحب يوم الأحد ومرة ابن الحارث صاحب يوم الاثنين وأبو محرز الأحمر صاحب يوم الثلاثاء وبرقان اليهودي صاحب يوم الأربعاء وشمهورش القاضي ابن الوليد صاحب يوم الخميس وأبو النور الأبيض زوبعة صاحب يوم الجمعة وميمون السحابي صاحب يوم السبت أجيبوا طاعة الله الذي دعاكم بالسبع المثاني والقرآن العظيم مرحبا مرحبا بالملوك أن أنتوا طائعين فلا

طاعة لمخلوق على مخلوق بل الطاعة للواحد القهار ومن أطاع طائعا فقد أطاع الله عز وجل فإني ما دعوتكم إلا بأسمائه وكلامه ومن عصاني فقد احترق بشواظ من نار ومن أتاني طائعا فقد سلم من سخط الجبار فسيحوا وأحضروا في مجلسي هذا بجبريل وميكائيل وإسرافيل وعزرائيل والملائكة المقربين وهم عن ذكر ربهم لا يفترون رب الأرباب ومسهل الأمور الصعاب ومسبب الأسباب ومعتق الرقاب العزيز الوهاب الذي تقطعت الرواسي الشامخات لعظمته وذلت الرقاب لجبروته ومجد كل شيء لربوبيته طوعا لأمره ولطيفته فهو نور النور ونوره في نور ونور يخضع كل جبار عنيد وشيطان مريد مثل النور على الطور في كتاب مسطور هو الله الذي لا إله إلا هو له الحمد في الأولى والآخرة وله الحكم وإليه ترجعون أين عباد الشمس وعباد السماء أين عباد الأوثان أين النصارى واليهود أجيبوا داعي الله من كان منكم من أشباح أرواح اليهود فإني أقسمت عليكم بالعهود وبما كتب في آيات السور وبحق من أنبع الماء من الجلمود بتوراة موسى وزبور داود ومن كان من أشباح أرواح النصارى فإني أقسمت عليكم بإنجيل عيسى وإن كنتم من أشباح أرواح المسلمين فإني أقسمت عليكم بمحمد خاتم النبيين أن لا تعلوا علي وأتوني مسلمين ما دعوتكم إلا في قضاء حوائج المسلمين

It has very many special properties. Its recitation count is once in the morning and once in the evening, and seven times at every operation. If you recite it and ask for the summoning of an afflicting spirit or of another, it will attend at once and will obey you in everything you command it, whether of good or of evil; so fear God Most High in your works.

The Adjuration of the Oaths by Which One Rebukes in All Operations (ʿAzīmat al-Aqsām allatī Tuzjar bihā fī Jamīʿ al-Aʿmāl)

Its incense is anything of pure fragrance for good and anything of foul odour for evil, and it is recited three times at every operation. It is that you say:

In the name of God, the Most Gracious, the Most Merciful. I adjure you, O seven sanctified kings, by the hands of the Lord of the Worlds:

Bismi Allāh al-Raḥmān al-Raḥīm. Uqsimu ʿalaykum ayyuhā al-mulūk al-sabʿa al-muqaddasūn bi-yaday Rabb al-ʿālamīn

بسم الله الرحمن الرحيم أقسم عليكم أيها الملوك السبعة المقدسون بيدي رب العالمين

Barbarous names: Bilyāhā Sharāhiyā Adonāy Aṣbāʾūt Āl Shaddāy

بلياها شراهيا أدوناي أصباؤت آل شداي

that you descend, O lofty spirits charged with the service of the seven that are above. Descend upon the seven kings of the upper world, and the upper upon the celestial, and the celestial upon the airy, and the airy upon the windy, and the windy upon the misty, and the misty upon the cloudy, and the cloudy upon the fiery, and the fiery upon the rocky, and the rocky upon the dusty, and the dusty upon the earthy, and the earthy upon the watery, and the watery upon those of the deep, and those of the deep upon the divers, and the divers upon whoever disobeys and rebels and transgresses among all the hosts of Iblīs. Seize them by their forelocks and by their mouths, swift and obedient to God, other than whom there is no god, light upon light. This adjuration of mine is laid upon every obstinate tyrant and every rebellious devil among the kings of the jinn, the satans and all the demons: that you do not transgress against me, and that you come to me well-disposed and swift. Whoever turns away from the remembrance of his Lord, He will drive him into a mounting torment; and whoever deviates from Our command, We make him taste of the torment of the Blaze. The jinn already know that they will be brought forward. The heavens are near to bursting apart from it, the earth to splitting open, and the mountains to falling down in ruin. Wherever you may be, God will bring you all together; God has power over everything. Where is Maymūn Abā Nūkh? And you, O Mudhhib al-Salām. And you, O Abyaḍ son of Iblīs; and you, O Aḥmar Abā Muḥriz; and you, O Burqān, lord of the clouds; and you, O Abā al-Walīd Shamhūrish; and you, O Murra Abā al-Ḥārith; and you, O Maymūn, lord of a quarter of the world; and you, O Dahnash, lord of whispering; and you, O Zawbaʿa. Answer, attend, and hasten to obedience to God, the Exalted, the Great: the First, the Last, the Manifest, the Hidden, the King, the Most Holy, Peace, the Granter of Security, the Guardian, the Mighty, the Compeller, the Supreme, the Creator, the Maker, the Restorer, the One, the Eternal Refuge, the Truthful, the Everlasting, the Abiding, the Light, light of the light and light of lights, Inspirer of secrets, who forms the day upon the night and governs the revolving sphere, who knows what is kept secret and what is spoken aloud, to whom belong praise and favour, greatness and grandeur. There is no god but He, the Most Gracious, the Most Merciful. Where is Mīkāʾīl? Where is Isrāfīl? Where is Dardabāʾīl? Where is Rūqāʾīl? Where is ʿAzrāʾīl? Where is Mīṭaṭrūn? Where is the one charged with the spirits of the jinn and the satans? The angels fell down before their Lord in prostration. I adjure you by the right of Him who mounted the Throne and encompassed dominion: answer, and do what you are commanded, you and your helpers and your sons, before We efface faces and turn them back upon their hinder parts, or curse them as We cursed the people of the Sabbath; and the command of God is ever accomplished. O our people, answer the caller of God and believe in him, and He will forgive you your sins and protect you from a painful torment; and whoever does not answer the caller of God cannot escape upon the earth, and he has no protectors besides Him; those are in manifest error.

an tanzilū ayyuhā al-arwāḥ al-ʿulwiyya al-muwakkala bi-khidmat al-sabʿa al-fawqāniyya. Inzilū ʿalā al-sabʿa mulūk al-ʿulwiyya, wa-l-ʿulwiyya ʿalā al-falakiyya, wa-l-falakiyya ʿalā al-hawāʾiyya, wa-l-hawāʾiyya ʿalā al-riyāḥiyya, wa-l-riyāḥiyya ʿalā al-ghayābiyya, wa-l-ghayābiyya ʿalā al-saḥābiyya, wa-l-saḥābiyya ʿalā al-nāriyya, wa-l-nāriyya ʿalā al-ṣakhriyya, wa-l-ṣakhriyya ʿalā al-turābiyya, wa-l-turābiyya ʿalā al-arḍiyya, wa-l-arḍiyya ʿalā al-māʾiyya, wa-l-māʾiyya ʿalā al-qarāriyya, wa-l-qarāriyya ʿalā al-ghawwāṣa, wa-l-ghawwāṣa ʿalā man ʿaṣā wa-tamarrada wa-ṭaghā min junūd Iblīs ajmaʿīn, wa-taʾkhudhū bi-nawāṣīhim wa-bi-afwāhihim musriʿīn ṭāʾiʿīn li-Llāh alladhī lā ilāha illā huwa, nūrun ʿalā nūr. ʿAzīmatī hādhihi ʿalā kull jabbār ʿanīd wa-shayṭān marīd min mulūk al-jinn wa-l-shayāṭīn wa-l-abālisa ajmaʿīn: an lā taʿtadū ʿalayya wa-aʾtūnī muṣliḥīn musriʿīn. Wa-man yuʿriḍ ʿan dhikri rabbihi yasluk-hu ʿadhāban ṣaʿadā, wa-man yazigh minhu amrunā nudhiq-hu min ʿadhāb al-saʿīr, wa-la-qad ʿalimat al-jinnatu innahum la-muḥḍarūn, takādu al-samāwātu yatafaṭṭarna minhu wa-tanshaqqu al-arḍu wa-takhirru al-jibālu haddā, aynamā takūnū yaʾti bikumu Allāhu jamīʿan, inna Allāha ʿalā kull shayʾin qadīr. Ayna Maymūn Abā Nūkh, wa-anta yā Mudhhib al-Salām. Wa-anta yā Abyaḍ ibn Iblīs, wa-anta yā Aḥmar Abā Muḥriz, wa-anta yā Burqān ṣāḥib al-saḥāʾib, wa-anta yā Abā al-Walīd Shamhūrish, wa-anta yā Murra Abā al-Ḥārith, wa-anta yā Maymūn ṣāḥib rubʿ al-dunyā, wa-anta yā Dahnash ṣāḥib al-waswās, wa-anta yā Zawbaʿa. Ajībū wa-uḥḍurū wa-ʿajjilū al-ṭāʿa li-Llāh al-ʿAlī al-Kabīr: al-Awwal al-Ākhir al-Ẓāhir al-Bāṭin al-Malik al-Quddūs al-Salām al-Muʾmin al-Muhaymin al-ʿAzīz al-Jabbār al-Mutakabbir al-Khāliq al-Bāriʾ al-Muʿīd al-Aḥad al-Ṣamad al-Ṣādiq al-Dāʾim al-Bāqī al-Nūr, nūr al-nūr wa-nūr al-anwār, wa-mulhim al-asrār, wa-mukawwin al-nahār ʿalā al-layl, wa-mudabbir al-falak al-dawwār, al-ʿālim bi-l-sirr wa-l-ijhār, alladhī lahu al-ḥamd wa-l-niʿma wa-l-ʿaẓama wa-l-kibriyāʾ, lā ilāha illā huwa al-Raḥmān al-Raḥīm. Ayna Mīkāʾīl, ayna Isrāfīl, ayna Dardabāʾīl, ayna Rūqāʾīl, ayna ʿAzrāʾīl, ayna Mīṭaṭrūn, ayna al-muwakkal bi-arwāḥ al-jinn wa-l-shayāṭīn. Fa-kharrat al-

malāʾikatu li-rabbihim sujjadan. Uqsimu ʿalaykum bi-ḥaqq man ʿalā al-ʿarsh istawā wa-ʿalā al-mulk iḥtawā: ajībū wa-ifʿalū mā tuʾmarūna bihi antum wa-aʿwānukum wa-banīkum min qabli an naṭmisa wujūhan fa-naruddahā ʿalā adbārihā aw nalʿanahum kamā laʿannā aṣḥāb al-sabt wa-kāna amru Allāhi mafʿūlā. Yā qawmanā ajībū dāʿiya Allāh wa-āminū bihi yaghfir lakum min dhunūbikum wa-yujirkum min ʿadhābin alīm, wa-man lā yujib dāʿiya Allāh fa-laysa bi-muʿjizin fī al-arḍ wa-laysa lahu min dūnihi awliyāʾ, ulāʾika fī ḍalālin mubīn.

أن تنزلوا أيها الأرواح العلوية الموكلة بخدمة السبعة الفوقانية انزلوا على السبعة ملوك العلوية والعلوية على الفلكية والفلكية على الهوائية والهوائية على الرياحية والرياحية على الغيابية والغيابية على السحابية والسحابية على النارية والنارية على الصخرية والصخرية على الترابية والترابية على الأرضية والأرضية على المائية والمائية على القرارية والقرارية على الغواصة والغواصة على من عصى وتمرد وطغى من جنود إبليس أجمعين وتأخذوا بنواصيهم وبأفواههم مسرعين طائعين لله الذي لا إله إلا هو نور على نور عزيمتي هذه على كل جبار عنيد وشيطان مريد من ملوك الجن الشياطين والأبالسة أجمعين أن لا تعتدوا علي وأتوني مصلحين مسرعين ومن يعرض عن ذكر ربه يسلكه عذابا صعدا ومن يزغ منه أمرنا نذقه من عذاب السعير ولقد علمت الجنة إنهم لمحضرون تكاد السموات يتفطرن منه وتنشق الأرض وتخر الجبال هدا أينما تكونوا يأت بكم الله جميعا إن الله على كل شيء قدير أين ميمون أبا نوخ وأنت يا مذهب السلام وأنت يا أبيض ابن إبليس وأنت يا أحمر أبا محرز وأنت يا برقان

صاحب السحائب وأنت يا أبا الوليد شمهورش وأنت يا مرة أبا الحارث
وأنت يا ميمون صاحب ربع الدنيا وأنت يا دهنش صاحب الوسواس
وأنت يا زوبعة أجيبوا واحضروا وعجلوا الطاعة لله العلي الكبير الأول
الآخر الظاهر الباطن الملك القدوس السلام المؤمن المهيمن العزيز
الجبار المتكبر الخالق البارئ المعيد الأحد الصمد الصادق الدائم الباقي
النور نور النور ونور الأنوار وملهم الأسرار ومكون النهار على الليل ومدبر
الفلك الدوار العالم بالسر والإجهار الذي له الحمد والنعمة والعظمة
والكبرياء لا إله إلا هو الرحمن الرحيم أين ميكائيل أين إسرافيل أين
دردبائيل أين روقائيل أين عزرائيل أين ميططرون أين الموكل بأرواح الجن
والشياطين فخرت الملائكة لربهم سجدا أقسم عليكم بحق من على
العرش استوى وعلى الملك احتوى أجيبوا وافعلوا ما تؤمرون به أنتم
وأعوانكم وبنيكم من قبل أن نطمس وجوها فنردها على أدبارها أو نلعنهم
كما لعنا أصحاب السبت وكان أمر الله مفعولا يا قومنا أجيبوا داعي الله
وآمنوا به يغفر لكم من ذنوبكم ويجركم من عذاب أليم ومن لا يجب
داعي الله فليس بمعجز في الأرض وليس له من دونه أولياء أولئك في
ضلال مبين

Barbarous names: Dumlākh ٢ Barākhūlā Halā ٢ Shalā Shalā

دملاخ ٢ براخولا هلا ٢ شلا شلا

Hasten, hasten. Answer by the right of Him who neither begets nor is begotten, and to whom none is equal. There is no god but He; He will surely gather you to the Day of Resurrection, in which there is no doubt.

tusri'ūn tusri'ūn. Ajībū bi-ḥaqq man lam yalid wa-lam yūlad wa-lam yakun lahu kufuwan aḥad, lā ilāha illā huwa la-yajma'annakum ilā yawm al-qiyāma lā rayba fīh.

تسرعون تسرعون أجيبوا بحق من لم يلد ولم يولد ولم يكن له كفوا أحد لا إله إلا هو ليجمعنكم إلى يوم القيامة لا ريب فيه

The Solomonic Rebuke (al-Zajr al-Sulaymānī)

This is what our master Solomon son of David — peace be upon them both — would use whenever one of the jinn disobeyed him; he would recite it a single time. It is that you say:

In the name of God, the Most Gracious, the Most Merciful. The Living, the Self-Subsisting, the Most Gracious, the Most Merciful, Lord of Jibrīl and Mīkā'īl.

Bismi Allāh al-Raḥmān al-Raḥīm. Al-Ḥayy al-Qayyūm al-Raḥmān al-Raḥīm, Rabb Jibrīl wa-Mīkā'īl.

بسم الله الرحمن الرحيم الحي القيوم الرحمن الرحيم رب جبريل وميكائيل

Barbarous names: Āh Āh Āh Āh Ahyā Sharāhiyā Ahyā Hāhiyā Tamāhiyā Adonāy Aṣbā'ūt Āl Shaddāy Shalmahmaṣ Shalīqūsh Ṭamṭabkash Ṭaẓkalyūsh Malmūshakh Bahmash 'Amyūsh

Bashhūth Shanāhash Marṭaṭkayūsh Nā Qahlam Ghayūnā Nāfilā Thāwa

آه آه آه أهيا شراهيا أهيا هاهيا تماهيا أدوناي أصباؤت آل شداي
شلمهمص شليقوش طمطبكش طظكليوش ملموشخ بهمش عميوش
بشهوث شناهش مرططكيوش نا قهلم غيونا نافلا ثاوة

How great is this speech! How great is the authority of God! Let whoever disobeys the names of God be burned with the kindled Fire. Strike them down with the quaking, with violent alarm, with mighty dread and with the painful torment.

Mā aʿẓama hādhā al-kalām, mā aʿẓama sulṭān Allāh. Iḥtaraqa man ʿaṣā asmāʾ Allāh bi-l-nār al-mūqada. Aṣʿiqū bihim bi-l-rajīf wa-l-fazaʿ al-shadīd wa-l-rawʿ al-ʿaẓīm wa-l-ʿadhāb al-alīm.

ما أعظم هذا الكلام ما أعظم سلطان الله احترق من عصى أسماء الله
بالنار الموقدة أصعقوا بهم بالرجيف والفزع الشديد والروع العظيم
والعذاب الأليم

The Invocation of the Greatest Name (Daʿwat al-Ism al-Aʿẓam)

It is recited for every matter you desire, whether of good or of evil, and without incense. It is that you say:

Barbarous names: Baghlashalshākh Ān Ibl Bah Wah Wah Mālagh Malmalakh Malmakh Khaym

بغلشلشاخ آن إبل به وه وه مالغ ململخ ملمخ خيم

The mountains are crushed to dust before His awe, and necks bow low before His majesty. He is a God pre-eternal and everlasting, who removes all passing away and has never Himself passed away. Take charge, O servants of the Greatest Name, and accomplish my need, which is such-and-such, by the right of the Greatest Name.

Tadakdakat al-jibāl li-haybatihi wa-khaḍaʿat al-riqāb li-ʿaẓamatihi, ilāh azalī azal, yuzīl al-zawāl wa-lam yazūl. Tawakkalū yā khuddām al-Ism al-Aʿẓam wa-qḍū ḥājatī wa-hiya kadhā wa-kadhā bi-ḥaqq al-Ism al-Aʿẓam.

تدكدكت الجبال لهيبته وخضعت الرقاب لعظمته إله أزلي أزل يزيل الزوال ولم يزول توكلوا يا خدام الاسم الأعظم واقضوا حاجتي وهي كذا وكذا بحق الاسم الأعظم

Forty-five times, at whatever time you wish.

The Beneficial Chain Invocation, for Bringing Buried Hoards to Light, Cleaving the Earth, Making the Cave Speak and Drawing Out Treasures (Daʿwat al-Silsila al-Nāfiʿa li-Iẓhār al-Dafāʾin wa-Shaqq al-Arḍ wa-Istinṭāq al-Ghār wa-Qalʿ al-Kunūz)

It is that you say:

In the name of God, the Most Gracious, the Most Merciful. Answer and present yourselves, O Zawbaʿat al-Riyāḥ, O Ṣalṣalat al-Arḍ, O Ṭāwūs, O Kirākīl, O Bīmūn, O Tamardal the Flier, O Jaljiyāʾīl, and O ʿĀmir of this place. If there is in this place a hidden cache or a buried hoard of gold or silver, bring it forth by the right of the Omnipotent, the All-Encompassing, Lord of the hosts, God, there is no god but He. When the sky is rent asunder, and gives ear to its Lord, as in truth it must, and when the earth is spread out and casts forth what is within it and is emptied —

bring forth the wealth that is in this place, by the right of "Woe to every slanderer and backbiter, who amasses wealth." Gather up the wealth that is in this place, by the right of "Nūn. By the pen and what they inscribe," and by the Day of Gathering and Rising, unless you cleave open this ground, or this wall, or this pillar, or this oven. And bring forth the wealth that is in this place. Answer, O Zawbaʿat al-Riyāḥ, O Ṣalṣalat al-Arḍ, O Ṭārish, O Kirākīl, O Bīmūn, O Thamardal, O Jaljiyāʾīl, and O ʿĀmir of this place, by the right of كهيعص and حم عسق, by the right of Sūrat al-Taghābun, and by the Day of Gathering and Rising, unless you cleave open this ground, or this wall, or this pillar, or this oven, and bring forth what is in it of wealth or buried hoard or hidden cache, whether of silver or of gold or of copper, and do what you are commanded, by the right of these names over you. And whoever of you swerves from Our command, We shall make him taste the torment of the Blaze. Answer, before there is loosed against you both a flame of fire and molten brass, and you shall not be able to defend yourselves, or We curse them as We cursed the people of the Sabbath, and the command of God is ever fulfilled. Quickly! Hurry! This very hour! Do what I have commanded you. May God bless you, and may His blessing be upon you.

Bismi Allāh al-Raḥmān al-Raḥīm. Ajībū wa-ḥḍurū yā Zawbaʿat al-Riyāḥ wa-yā Ṣalṣalat al-Arḍ wa-yā Ṭāwūs wa-yā Kirākīl wa-yā Bīmūn wa-yā Tamardal al-Ṭayyār wa-yā Jaljiyāʾīl wa-yā ʿĀmir hādhā al-makān. In kāna fī hādhā al-makān khabīʾa aw dafīn min dhahab aw fiḍḍa fa-aẓhirūhā bi-ḥaqq al-Qādir al-Muḥīṭ Rabb al-juyūsh Allāh lā ilāha illā huwa. Idhā al-samā'u inshaqqat wa-adhinat li-rabbihā wa-ḥuqqat wa-idhā al-arḍu muddat wa-alqat mā fīhā wa-takhallat, aẓhirū al-māl alladhī fī hādhā al-makān bi-ḥaqq waylun li-kulli humazatin lumaza alladhī jamaʿa mālā, ijmaʿū al-māl alladhī fī hādhā al-makān bi-ḥaqq Nūn wa-l-qalam wa-mā yasṭurūn wa-yawm al-ḥashr wa-l-nushūr, illā mā shaqaqtum hādhihi al-arḍ aw al-ḥā'iṭ aw al-ʿāmūd aw al-tannūr. Wa-aẓhirū al-māl alladhī fī hādhā al-makān. Ajībū yā Zawbaʿat al-Riyāḥ wa-yā Ṣalṣalat al-Arḍ wa-yā Ṭārish wa-yā Kirākīl wa-yā Bīmūn wa-yā Thamardal wa-yā Jaljiyā'īl wa-yā ʿĀmir hādhā al-makān bi-ḥaqq كهيعص حم عسق *wa-bi-ḥaqq Sūrat al-Taghābun wa-yawm al-ḥashr wa-l-nushūr, illā mā shaqaqtum hādhihi al-arḍ aw al-ḥā'iṭ aw al-ʿāmūd aw al-tannūr wa-aẓhartum mā fīhi min al-māl aw al-dafīn aw al-khabī'a min fiḍḍa aw dhahab aw nuḥās wa-fʿalū mā tu'marūna bihi bi-ḥaqq hādhihi al-asmā' ʿalaykum, wa-man yazigh minkum ʿan amrinā nudhiqhu min ʿadhāb al-saʿīr. Ajībū min qabli an yursala ʿalaykumā shuwāẓun min nārin wa-nuḥāsun fa-lā tantaṣirān aw nalʿanahum kamā laʿannā aṣḥāb al-sabt wa-kāna amr Allāh mafʿūlā. Al-waḥā al-ʿajal al-sāʿa, ifʿalū mā amartukum bihi, bāraka Allāhu fīkum wa-ʿalaykum.*

بسم الله الرحمن الرحيم أجيبوا واحضروا يا زوبعة الرياح ويا صلصلة الأرض ويا طاوس ويا كراكيل ويا بيمون ويا تمردل الطيار ويا جلجيائيل ويا عامر هذا المكان إن كان في هذا المكان خبية أو دفين من ذهب أو فضة فأظهروها بحق القادر المحيط رب الجيوش الله لا إله إلا هو إذا

السماء انشقت وأذنت لربها وحقت وإذا الأرض مدت وألقت ما فيها وتخلت أظهروا المال الذي في هذا المكان بحق ويل لكل همزة لمزة الذي جمع مالا اجمعوا المال الذي في هذا المكان بحق ن والقلم وما يسطرون ويوم الحشر والنشور إلا ما شققتم هذه الأرض أو الحائط أو العامود أو التنور وأظهروا المال الذي في هذا المكان أجيبوا يا زوبعة الرياح ويا صلصلة الأرض ويا طارش ويا كراكيل ويا بيمون ويا ثمردل ويا جلجيائيل ويا عامر هذا المكان بحق كهيعص حم عسق وبحق سورة التغابن ويوم الحشر والنشور إلا ما شققتم هذه الأرض أو الحائط أو العامود أو التنور وأظهرتم ما فيه من المال أو الدفين أو الخبية من فضة أو ذهب أو نحاس وافعلوا ما تؤمرون به بحق هذه الأسماء عليكم ومن يزغ منكم عن أمرنا نذقه من عذاب السعير أجيبوا من قبل أن يرسل عليكما شواظ من نار ونحاس فلا تنتصران أو نلعنهم كما لعنا أصحاب السبت وكان أمر الله مفعولا الوحا العجل الساعة افعلوا ما أمرتكم به بارك الله فيكم وعليكم

Its incense is male frankincense, raw wax, hoopoe feathers, pig bristle, sandarac, Indian clove and safflower seed.

The Arjiyya Invocation, for Easing Provision, Subduing Hearts and Winning Acceptance (Daʿwat al-Arjiyya li-Taysīr al-Rizq wa-Taskhīr al-Qulūb wa-l-Qabūl)

It is recited three times every day after the dawn prayer, and it is that you say:

In the name of God, the Most Gracious, the Most Merciful. Arj, Arjaj, Halūj, Halbaj, Hayūj, Jāj, Aj. O company of the spiritual souls, unveil your shining lights, your resplendent rays, your well-pleasing natures and your fragrant selves, and be a help to me in drawing provision and in subduing all creatures, by the right of the holy pre-eternal words, and of the unique and everlasting Essence, and by the right of that by which I have adjured you — truly an oath, and were you to know it, a mighty one, at which the heavens are near to bursting apart, and the earth to splitting open, and the mountains to falling down in ruin. I have rebuked you with a rebuke, and called you with the call of sincerity, from which none of you can flee and from which you have no escape, until you do what you are commanded. Quickly (twice), hurry (twice), this very hour (twice), Hayūm (twice), Harūj (twice), Hayūh (twice), Ah (twice), Aḥā (twice), by Your mercy, O Most Merciful of the merciful.

Bismi Allāh al-Raḥmān al-Raḥīm. Arj Arjaj Halūj Halbaj Hayūj Jāj Aj. Yā maʿshar al-arwāḥ al-rūḥāniyya, ikshifū anwārakum al-muḍīʾa wa-shuʿāʿātikum al-bahiyya wa-akhlāqakum al-raḍiyya wa-anfusakum al-ʿiṭriyya wa-kūnū ʿawnan lī ʿalā jalb al-rizq wa-taskhīr al-khalq bi-ḥaqq al-kalimāt al-muqaddasa al-azaliyya wa-l-Dhāt al-aḥadiyya al-abadiyya wa-bi-ḥaqq mā aqsamtu bihi ʿalaykum la-qasam wa-innahu law taʿlamūna ʿaẓīm, takādu al-samāwātu yatafaṭṭarna minhu wa-tanshaqqu al-arḍu wa-takhirru al-jibālu haddā. Zajartukum zajran wa-daʿawtukum daʿwat al-ikhlāṣ minkum minhā wa-lā mafarra lakum ʿanhā ḥattā tafʿalū mā tuʾmarūna bihi. Al-

waḥā ٢ al-ʿajal ٢ al-sāʿa ٢ Hayūm ٢ Harūj ٢ Hayūh ٢ Ah ٢ Aḥā ٢ bi-raḥmatika yā Arḥam al-rāḥimīn.

بسم الله الرحمن الرحيم أرج أرجج هلوج هلبج هيوج جاج أج يا معشر الأرواح الروحانية اكشفوا أنواركم المضية وشعاعاتكم البهية وأخلاقكم الرضية وأنفسكم العطرية وكونوا عونا لي على جلب الرزق وتسخير الخلق بحق الكلمات المقدسة الأزلية والذات الأحدية الأبدية وبحق ما أقسمت به عليكم لقسم وإنه لو تعلمون عظيم تكاد السموات يتفطرن منه وتنشق الأرض وتخر الجبال هدا زجرتكم زجرا ودعوتكم دعوة الإخلاص منكم منها ولا مفر لكم عنها حتى تفعلوا ما تؤمرون به الوحا ٢ العجل ٢ الساعة ٢ هيوم ٢ هروج ٢ هيوه ٢ أه ٢ أحا ٢ برحمتك يا أرحم الراحمين

Employment of the King Jawāsh al-Wahūma (Istikhdām al-Malik Jawāsh al-Wahūma)

You keep a discipline of seven days, and say every morning and evening:

Kansh (twice), Mash (twice), ʿAksh (twice), Shamlākh (twice). Answer (twice), O Jawāsh, and make me privy to what people keep hidden within them.

Kansh ٢ Mash ٢ ʿAksh ٢ Shamlākh ٢ ajib ٢ yā Jawāsh wa-aẓhirnī ʿalā ḍamāʾir al-nās.

كنش ٢ مش ٢ عكش ٢ شملاخ ٢ أجب ٢ يا جواش وأظهرني على ضمائر الناس

A thousand times, and after every prayer two hundred and ten times, while you fumigate with red sandalwood. Then, after that, if you wish to know the secret of a person, put your head between your knees and speak the name three times, and it will tell you in your ear what that person conceals within. Guard this well-kept secret, and you will be among those who prosper.

Employment of Iblīs (Istikhdām Iblīs)

You write the names that follow with saffron, camphor, rose and musk, and you fumigate with aloeswood, and recite them, and leave them under your head, and sleep. You repeat this operation for seven days while the light is waxing, beginning on a Sunday; then Iblīs and his hosts will appear to you. Take your covenant upon them, and ask for your need, and they will accomplish it for you. These are the names; you say:

Barbarous names: Yāh Yāh Bashhūr yā Hūr yā Harn Anā yā Khabrūm Ḥalūl Ḥāshif Ḥāj Malārdūfī

ياه ياه بشهور يا هور يا هرن أنا يا خبروم حلول حاشف حاج ملاردوفي

Barbarous names: Zaʿzama Ṭaṭmaṭ Kahash Arkatāh Ṭaṭrūsh Nalāwsh Ṣaʿrahā Ṭaysh Qaṭʿāl Qalabshūsh Ashriyūsh Wabras Hayāʾ fī Walūb Hūsh yā Hīn Hayāhīn

زعزمة طططم كهش أركتاه ططروش نلاوش صعرها طيش قطعال
قلبشوش أشريوش وبرس هياء في ولوب هوش يا هين هياهين

Employment of Maymūn Abū Nūkh for the Accomplishment of Every Matter (Istikhdām Maymūn Abī Nūkh li-Qaḍāʾ Kull Amr)

Enter the retreat, fast three days in complete discipline, and recite the names that follow one hundred times after every prayer and one thousand times after the night prayer. On the fourth night a man of handsome face will come to you and say to you, "What do you want of me?" Say to him, "I want obedience from you," and he will obey you in everything you desire; or else let the discipline begin on a Sunday. These are the names; you say:

Anūkh (twice), Shanshanūkh (twice), Nūkh (twice). Answer, O Maymūn Abā Nūkh, and do such-and-such.

Anūkh ٢, Shanshanūkh ٢, Nūkh ٢. Ajib yā Maymūn Abā Nūkh wa-ifʿal kadhā.

أنوخ ٢ شنشنوخ ٢ نوخ ٢ أجب يا ميمون أبا نوخ وافعل كذا

The incense is male frankincense, *jamājim*, and henna blossom; and it is sound to confine oneself to the frankincense alone.

Recite it one thousand times after every prayer, and on the fourth day go out to the open country while you are occupied with the remembrance of the name, and speak to no one at all. A bondsman will meet you, mounted upon a horse, a drawn sword in his hand. Do not fear him. He will say to you, "What is your need?" Return him no answer, but busy yourself with the recitation of the name. Have with you a green palm-frond two cubits long, upon which is written:

Fulfil the covenant of God when you have made a covenant, and do not break your oaths after their confirmation, when you have made God a surety over you.

Wa-awfū bi-ʿahd Allāh idhā ʿāhadtum wa-lā tanquḍū al-aymāna baʿda tawkīdihā wa-qad jaʿaltumu Allāha ʿalaykum kafīlā.

وأوفوا بعهد الله إذا عاهدتم ولا تنقضوا الأيمان بعد توكيدها وقد جعلتم الله عليكم كفيلا

When the bondsman withdraws, the servant comes to you after him. Raise the frond to him, for it is his covenant, and dispose thereafter in whatever you desire. Its incense is everything of a pure fragrance.

Employment of the Helping Aid (Istikhdām al-ʿAwn al-Muʿīn)

Bimāshibākh, Ashmakh (twice), Shāmikh, over every open expanse. I adjure you, O helping aid, by the sanctity of Shanakh (twice), Shamālagh (twice), that you come to me and fulfil my need, by the right of Shaʿshash, Ashmash (twice), Aʿṭūsh. May God bless you and be upon you; and it is indeed a mighty oath, if you but knew.

Bimāshibākh Ashmakh ٢ *Shāmikh ʿalā kull barāḥ. Aqsamtu ʿalayka ayyuhā al-ʿawn al-muʿīn bi-ḥurmat Shanakh* ٢ *Shamālagh* ٢ *an taʾtīnī wa-taqḍiya ḥājatī bi-ḥaqq Shaʿshash*

Ashmash ٢ *Aʿṭūsh. Bāraka Allāhu fīka wa-ʿalayka wa-innahu la-qasamun law taʿlamūna ʿaẓīm.*

بماشباخ أشمخ ٢ شامخ على كل براح أقسمت عليك أيها العون المعين بحرمة شنخ ٢ شمالغ ٢ أن تأتيني وتقضي حاجتي بحق شعشش أشمش ٢ أعطوش بارك الله فيك وعليك وإنه لقسم لو تعلمون عظيم

The manner of employing him is that you enter the retreat on any night before sunset and keep to seclusion there. Then you rise in the morning fasting, and you break your fast upon raisins; and after the night prayer you begin the recitation of the oath two thousand times, without incense. If you perfume the place with incense there is no harm in it. Then sleep, and the servant will come to you and wake you. When you have roused, say to him, "I ask of God, and then of you, such-and-such," and mention your need, and he will accomplish it for you.

Employment of the Obedient Helper (Istikhdām al-ʿAwn al-Muṭīʿ)

Practise the discipline for three days, Tuesday, Wednesday and Thursday, and fast on the Thursday. Recite the name Haylūsh one thousand five hundred times after every prayer while you perfume yourself with a sweet fragrance. The servant will come to you in a comely form and pledge himself to you for whatever you desire; and he disposes in every need, even food and drink.

In this measure there is sufficiency. God is the granter of success to what is right, and to Him are the return and the final home.

Conclusion: On Miscellaneous Benefits from Spiritual Medicine, the Rules of Calculation, and Prized Tested Properties (al-Khātima fī Dhikr Fawā'id Mutafarriqa min al-Ṭibb al-Rūḥānī wa-l-Qawā'id al-Ḥisābiyya wa-l-Khawāṣṣ al-Mujarraba al-'Azīza)

A Benefit: Fortification Before Every Work

The seeker should fortify himself before every one of the works in whose service there stands one of the earthly kings, or their aides, or their servants. Among the impregnable fortifications is that you say:

I have fortified myself with the strong fortress whose foundation is "There is no god but God" and whose gate is "Muḥammad is the Messenger of God"; its walls are "Peace — a word from a Merciful Lord"; and its circuit is "For him are successive angels before him and behind him, who guard him by the command of

God." Its seal is: I am the lion, she is put to flight, my arrow has struck home, by the grace of: In the name of God, the Most Gracious, the Most Merciful. Say: He is God, One; God, the Eternal Refuge; He neither begets nor is begotten, and there is none comparable to Him. In the name of God, the Most Gracious, the Most Merciful. Say: I seek refuge in the Lord of the daybreak, from the evil of what He created, from the evil of darkness when it settles, from the evil of those who blow upon knots, and from the evil of an envier when he envies. In the name of God, the Most Gracious, the Most Merciful. Say: I seek refuge in the Lord of mankind, the King of mankind, the God of mankind, from the evil of the retreating whisperer, who whispers in the breasts of mankind, from among jinn and mankind. I have fortified myself by the Living, the Self-Subsisting, who never dies, and I have repelled from myself all evil and harm. By a thousand thousand: there is no power and no strength except through God, the Most High, the Magnificent. And may God bless our master Muḥammad and his family and companions and grant them peace.

Ḥaṣṣantu nafsī bi-l-ḥiṣn al-qawī asāsuhu lā ilāha illā Allāh wa-bābuhu Muḥammad rasūl Allāh wa-ḥīṭānuhu Salāmun qawlan min Rabbin Raḥīm, wa-dā'iratuhu Lahu mu'aqqibātun min bayni yadayhi wa-min khalfihi yaḥfaẓūnahu min amr Allāh. Khitāmuhā Anā al-asad, hiya sharad, sahmī nafadh, bi-faḍl Bismi Allāh al-Raḥmān al-Raḥīm. Qul huwa Allāhu aḥad, Allāhu al-ṣamad, lam yalid wa-lam yūlad, wa-lam yakun lahu kufuwan aḥad. Bismi Allāh al-Raḥmān al-Raḥīm. Qul a'ūdhu bi-Rabb al-falaq, min sharri mā khalaq, wa-min sharri ghāsiqin idhā waqab, wa-min sharri al-naffāthāti fī al-ʿuqad, wa-min sharri ḥāsidin idhā ḥasad. Bismi Allāh al-Raḥmān al-Raḥīm. Qul aʿūdhu bi-Rabb al-nās, Malik al-nās, Ilāh al-nās, min sharri al-waswās al-khannās, alladhī yuwaswisu fī ṣudūr al-nās, min al-jinnati wa-l-nās. Ḥaṣṣantu nafsī bi-l-Ḥayy al-Qayyūm alladhī lā yamūtu abadan wa-dafaʿtu ʿannī al-sūʾ wa-l-adhā, bi-alf alf lā ḥawla wa-lā quwwata illā bi-Allāh al-ʿAlī al-ʿAẓīm wa-ṣallā Allāhu ʿalā sayyidinā Muḥammad wa-ʿalā ālihi wa-ṣaḥbihi wa-sallam

حصنت نفسي بالحصن القوي أساسه لا إله إلا الله وبابه محمد رسول الله وحيطانه سلام قولا من رب رحيم ودائرته له معقبات من بين يديه ومن خلفه يحفظونه من أمر الله ختامها أنا الأسد هي شرد سهمي نفذ بفضل بسم الله الرحمن الرحيم قل هو الله أحد الله الصمد لم يلد ولم يولد ولم يكن له كفوا أحد بسم الله الرحمن الرحيم قل أعوذ برب الفلق من شر ما خلق ومن شر غاسق إذا وقب ومن شر النفاثات في العقد ومن شر حاسد إذا حسد بسم الله الرحمن الرحيم قل أعوذ برب الناس ملك الناس إله الناس من شر الوسواس الخناس الذي يوسوس في صدور الناس من الجنة والناس حصنت نفسي بالحي القيوم الذي لا يموت أبدا ودفعت عني السوء والأذى بألف ألف لا حول ولا قوة إلا بالله العلي العظيم وصلى الله على سيدنا محمد وعلى آله وصحبه وسلم

A Benefit: Hastening a Slow Servant

If you perform an operation and its servant is slow in carrying it out for you, then say, following the recitation of its oath:

Hasten, O servant, to do what I have commanded you; otherwise I shall rebuke you with Zakhnīf Thūrā.

ʿajjil ayyuhā al-khādim bi-fiʿl mā amartuka bihi wa-illā zajartuka bi-Zakhnīf Thūrā

عجل أيها الخادم بفعل ما أمرتك به وإلا زجرتك بزخنيف ثورا

A Benefit for Dismissing the Dwellers of the Place (Fāʾida li-Ṣarf ʿUmmār al-Makān)

Since no work among the operations is brought to completion for anyone except after dismissing the dwellers of the place in which he performs his work, and since without dismissing them the works fail and the benefit is lost, the scholars of this art have laid down methods for it. The most eminent of these is that you write what follows on a sheet of paper and set it in the wall of the place, or in its roof if it is a building; and if it is in the open desert, it is set upon a palm-frond. This is what is written:

This is a letter from Muḥammad the Messenger of God, may God bless him and grant him peace, to whoever leaves this place, of the dwellers and the visitors. To proceed: for us and for you there is room enough in what is right. If you, O dweller, are an infatuated lover, or a debauched intruder, or one who lays claim to a right while in the wrong, this is the Book of God, which speaks against you with the truth: Indeed We were having transcribed whatever you used to do; and Our messengers write down what you plot. Leave the bearer of this letter of mine and go off to the worshippers of idols. And whoever calls upon another god together with God: there is no god but He;

everything is perishing except His Face; His is the judgement, and to Him you shall be returned. They shall not be helped. حم عسق, the enemies of God are scattered and the proof of God has reached its mark. There is no power and no strength except through God, the Most High, the Magnificent. God will suffice you against them, and He is the Hearing, the Knowing. And may God bless our master Muḥammad and his family and companions and grant them peace.

hādhā al-kitāb min ʿind Muḥammad Rasūl Allāh ṣallā Allāhu ʿalayhi wa-sallam ilā man taraka hādhā al-makān min al-ʿummār wa-l-zuwwār. Ammā baʿd fa-inna lanā wa-lakum fī al-ḥaqq saʿa fa-in kunta ayyuhā al-ʿāmir ʿāshiqan mūlaʿan aw fājiran muqtaḥiman aw zāʿiman ḥaqqan mubṭilan hādhā kitāb Allāh yanṭiqu ʿalaykum bi-l-ḥaqq innā kunnā nastansikhu mā kuntum taʿmalūn wa-rusulunā yaktubūna mā tamkurūn utrukū ṣāḥib kitābī hādhā wa-nṭaliqū ilā ʿabadat al-awthān wa-man yadʿu maʿa Allāh ilāhan ākhar lā ilāha illā huwa kullu shayʾin hālikun illā wajhahu lahu al-ḥukm wa-ilayhi turjaʿūn lā yunṣarūn حم عسق *tafarraqa aʿdāʾ Allāh wa-balaghat ḥujjat Allāh wa-lā ḥawla wa-lā quwwata illā bi-Allāh al-ʿAlī al-ʿAẓīm fa-sa-yakfīkahum Allāh wa-huwa al-Samīʿ al-ʿAlīm wa-ṣallā Allāhu ʿalā sayyidinā Muḥammad wa-ʿalā ālihi wa-ṣaḥbihi wa-sallam*

هذا الكتاب من عند محمد رسول الله صلى الله عليه وسلم إلى من ترك هذا المكان من العمار والزوار. أما بعد فإن لنا ولكم في الحق سعة فإن

كنت أيها العامر عاشقا مولعا أو فاجرا مقتحما أو زاعما حقا مبطلا هذا كتاب الله ينطق عليكم بالحق إنا كنا نستنسخ ما كنتم تعملون ورسلنا يكتبون ما تمكرون اتركوا صاحب كتابي هذا وانطلقوا إلى عبدة الأوثان ومن يدع مع الله إلها آخر لا إله إلا هو كل شيء هالك إلا وجهه له الحكم وإليه ترجعون لا ينصرون حم عسق تفرق أعداء الله وبلغت حجة الله ولا حول ولا قوة إلا بالله العلي العظيم فسيكفيكهم الله وهو السميع العليم وصلى الله على سيدنا محمد وعلى آله وصحبه وسلم

An Important Benefit for Dispelling Whisperings While Engaged in the Operations (Fā'ida Muhimma li-Ṣarf al-Wasāwis Ḥāl al-Ishtighāl bi-l-Aʿmāl)

Drink a draught of sugar, gather your resolve, and set about your work. If no whispering comes upon you in it, well and good; otherwise say, with the intention of dispelling the whispering:

I have sought protection through the Messenger of God, may God bless him and grant him peace.

istajartu bi-Rasūl Allāh ṣallā Allāhu ʿalayhi wa-sallam

استجرت برسول الله صلى الله عليه وسلم

Say it seven times, and increase the prayer and the peace upon the Messenger of God, may God bless him and grant him peace, until it departs from you. If it does not depart, place your right palm upon your heart and say seven times:

Glory be to the King, the Holy, the Great Creator, the Doer. If He wills, He will take you away and bring forth a new creation, and that is no great matter for God.

subḥān al-Malik al-Quddūs al-Khallāq al-Faʿʿāl in yashaʾ yudhhibkum wa-yaʾti bi-khalqin jadīd wa-mā dhālika ʿalā Allāh bi-ʿazīz

سبحان الملك القدوس الخلاق الفعال إن يشأ يذهبكم ويأت بخلق جديد وما ذلك على الله بعزيز

Then recite Sūrat al-Nās seven times, and it will depart from you without fail.

A Benefit for Gathering Resolve (Fāʾida li-Jamʿ al-Himma)

Persevere in the recollection of His name, Most High, al-Faʿʿāl, 181 times after sunset every day.

An Important Benefit for Knowing the Direction of the Men of the Unseen and Seeking Their Aid in the Accomplishment of Desires (Fāʾida Muhimma li-Maʿrifat Jihat Rijāl al-Ghayb wa-l-Istiʿāna bihim ʿalā Tanfīdh al-Raghāʾib)

The shaykh, the knower of God Most High, the Pole of Existence, Muḥyī al-Milla wa-l-Dīn Ibn al-ʿArabī al-Ḥātimī al-Ṭāʾī al-Andalusī, may his precious secret be sanctified, said: The Pole is the Ghawth; he dwells at Mecca the Honoured. The Substitutes and the Men of the Unseen exercise disposal in all the directions, for the welfare of the world and the ordering of affairs. The Substitutes are seven men upon the creed of Abraham, upon him and upon our Prophet be the most excellent prayer and peace. So whoever is perplexed in any matter should turn toward their direction and seek support through them.

The world is divided into eight directions: the East, al-Aysān, the North, al-Bāyid, the West, al-Yart, the South and al-Bakā. On the seventh, the fourteenth, the twenty-second and the twenty-ninth days of the month they are in the East. On the sixth, the twenty-first and the twenty-eighth days of the month they are in al-Aysān. On the third, the fifteenth, the twenty-third and the thirtieth days of the month they are in the North. On the fifth, the thirteenth and the twentieth days of the month they are in al-Bāyid. On the fourth, the twelfth, the nineteenth and the twenty-seventh days of the month they are in the West. On the second, the tenth, the seventeenth and the twenty-fifth days of the month they are in al-Yart. And on the eighth, the eleventh, the eighteenth and the twenty-sixth of the month, they are in the South; and on the first, the ninth, the sixteenth and the twenty-fourth they are in al-Bakā. So when the one who turns toward them faces the direction in which they are, let him say these words:

Peace be upon you, O men of the unseen, O holy spirits. Aid me with succour and look upon me with a glance, O Ruqabāʾ, O Nuqabāʾ, O Nujabāʾ, O Abdāl, O Awtād, O Ghawth, O Quṭb. Aid me by the right of Muḥammad, may God bless him and grant him peace.

al-Salāmu ʿalaykum yā rijāl al-ghayb, yā ayyuhā al-arwāḥ al-muqaddasa. Aghīthūnī bi-ghawtha wa-unẓurūnī bi-naẓra, yā

Ruqabā', yā Nuqabā', yā Nujabā', yā Abdāl, yā Awtād, yā Ghawth, yā Quṭb. Aghīthūnī bi-ḥaqq Muḥammad ṣallā Allāhu ʿalayhi wa-sallam.

السلام عليكم يا رجال الغيب يا أيها الأرواح المقدسة أغيثوني بغوثة وانظروني بنظرة يا رقباء يا نقباء يا نجباء يا أبدال يا أوتاد يا غوث يا قطب أغيثوني بحق محمد صلى الله عليه وسلم

Then let him incline toward their side as one seeking support from them. It is best that his garment and his body be pure, with tenderness of heart, humble entreaty and submissiveness. This is a circle by which the directions are known, as you see:

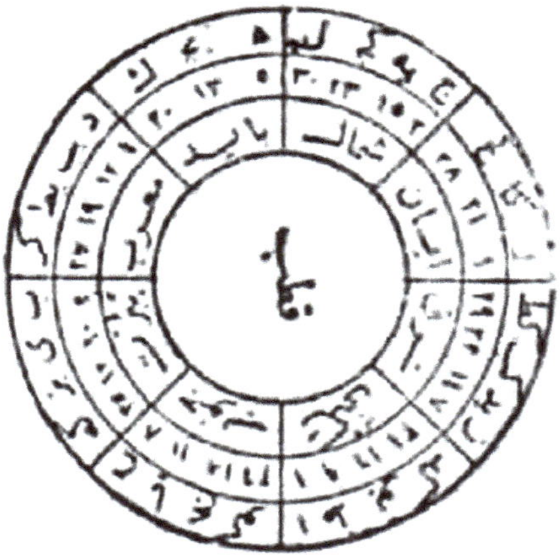

The circle by which the directions are known

An Important Benefit for Uncovering the Spiritual Worlds and Subjugating Them (Fā'ida Muhimma li-Kashf al-ʿAwālim al-Rūḥāniyya wa-Taskhīrihim)

When you speak these names, the spiritual beings will obey you and their worlds will be uncovered to you. They are these:

Barbarous names: Būh Bāhū Hayūh Shīd Khaj Bāshbākhūt ʿAzbālagh Hūh Shaymūnāhīj

بوه باهو هيوه شيد خج باشباخوت عزبالغ هوه شيموناهيج

You are You; there is no god but You. You are the First, and there is nothing before You. You are the Last, and there is nothing after You. You are the Manifest, and there is nothing that resembles You. You are the Hidden, and there is nothing that sees You. You are the One without repetition, and You are the Pearl that none can point out. Glory be to You, glory be to You.

Anta Anta, lā ilāha illā Anta. Anta al-Awwal fa-lā shay'a qablak. Wa-Anta al-Ākhir fa-lā shay'a baʿdak. Wa-Anta al-Ẓāhir fa-lā shay'a yushbihuk. Wa-Anta al-Bāṭin fa-lā shay'a yarāk. Wa-Anta al-Wāḥid bilā takrīr. Wa-Anta al-Durr bilā mushīr. Subḥānaka subḥānaka.

أنت أنت لا إله إلا أنت أنت الأول فلا شيء قبلك وأنت الآخر فلا شيء بعدك وأنت الظاهر فلا شيء يشبهك وأنت الباطن فلا شيء يراك وأنت الواحد بلا تكرير وأنت الدر بلا مشير سبحانك سبحانك

A Benefit for Love (Fā'ida li-l-Maḥabba)

It is written on Friday at sunrise, with saffron, in a clean vessel or upon paper and the like, and you give it to drink to whomever you wish, male or female. This is the wafq:

حب	بكلام	انطق	عليه	هاج	هواه	حبيب	زاد	ود	حب
ود	حب	بكلام	انطق	عليه	هاج	هواه	حبيب	زاد	ود
زاد	ود	حب	بكلام	انطق	عليه	هاج	هواه	حبيب	زاد
حبيب	زاد	ود	حب	بكلام	انطق	عليه	هاج	هواه	حبيب
هواه	حبيب	زاد	ود	حب	بكلام	انطق	عليه	هاج	هوه
هاج	هواه	حبيب	زاد	ود	حب	بكلام	انطق	عليه	هاج
عليه	هاج	هواه	حبيب	زاد	ود	حب	بكلام	انطق	علية
انطق	عليه	هاج	هواه	حبيب	زاد	ود	حب	بكلام	انطق
بكلام	انطق	عليه	هاج	هواه	حبيب	زاد	ود	حب	بكلام
حب	بكلام	انطق	عليه	هاج	هواه	حبيب	زاد	ود	حب

The ten-by-ten wafq for love

And around it, on the four sides, is written:

I have cast love upon you from myself, O so-and-so son of so-and-so, that you may be fashioned before my eye.

Wa-alqaytu 'alayka maḥabbatan minnī yā fulān ibn fulāna, wa-li-tuṣna'a 'alā 'aynī.

وألقيت عليك محبة مني يا فلان ابن فلانة ولتصنع على عيني

That is if the working is for yourself. If it is for someone other than yourself, then write thus:

I have cast love upon you, O so-and-so son of so-and-so, from so-and-so son of so-and-so.

Wa-alqaytu 'alayka maḥabbatan yā fulān ibn fulāna min fulān ibn fulāna.

وألقيت عليك محبة يا فلان ابن فلانة من فلان ابن فلانة

A Benefit for Bewildering a Man until He Returns to His Wife Submissive and Obedient (Fā'ida li-Taḥyīr al-Rajul Ḥattā Yarjiʿa ilā Zawjatihi Khāḍiʿan Ṭā'iʿan)

It is written and suspended in the air, and it is that you write these words:

In the name of God, the Most Gracious, the Most Merciful. The hand of God is before my hand, in accordance with the command, from before and from after. O God, the heaven is Your heaven, the earth is Your earth, the plain is Your plain, the dry land is Your dry land, the sea is Your sea, and the servants are Your servants; and You, there is no god but You. I ask You, O God, by the light of Your majesty and the greatness of Your sovereignty, to make the lands and the cities and the villages press narrow upon so-and-so son of so-and-so until he returns to his wife, so-and-so daughter of so-and-so. O God, make the world narrower upon him than the ring of a signet upon the finger; and the Trumpet is blown, and We gather them all together. O God, bewilder so-and-so son of so-and-so until he returns to so-and-so daughter of so-and-so, just as the camel is bewildered in its tether, and the bird to its nest, and the child to the love of its mother, until he returns to her house and to her place from which he went out. And the trumpet will be blown, and at once they will rush from the graves to their Lord. They will say: Woe to us! Who has raised us from our resting place? This is what the Merciful promised, and the messengers spoke the truth. It will be but a single cry, and at once they will all be brought before Us. No land shall contain him, no house shall contain him, and no place, until he returns to his wife so-and-so daughter of so-and-so and to her place. O God, as You returned Joseph to Jacob, and as You returned Moses to his mother, O God, O Gatherer of what is scattered, O Gatherer of mankind for a day about which there is no doubt, return so-and-so son of so-and-so to so-and-so daughter of so-and-so and to her place from which he went out, and gather her into union with him. Truly You have power over all things.

Bismi Allāh al-Raḥmān al-Raḥīm. Yad Allāh qabla yadī, wafqa al-amr min qabl wa-min baʿd. Allāhumma inna al-samāʾa samāʾuk, wa-l-arḍa arḍuk, wa-l-sahla sahluk, wa-l-barra barruk, wa-l-baḥra baḥruk, wa-l-ʿibāda ʿibāduk, wa-Anta lā ilāha illā Anta. Asʾaluka Allāhumma bi-nūri jalālika wa-ʿaẓīmi sulṭānika an tajʿala al-buldāna wa-l-muduna wa-l-qurā ḍayyiqatan ʿalā fulān ibn fulāna ḥattā yarjiʿa ilā zawjatihi fulāna bint fulāna. Allāhumma ijʿal ʿalayhi al-dunyā aḍyaqa min ḥalqati al-khātim ʿalā al-iṣbaʿ, wa-nufikha fī al-ṣūr fa-jamaʿnāhum jamʿan. Allāhumma ḥayyir fulān ibn fulāna ḥattā yarjiʿa ilā fulāna bint fulāna kamā ḥuyyira al-jamal fī ʿaqlihi, wa-l-ṭayru fī wakrihi wa-l-waladu ʿalā maḥabbati ummihi ḥattā yarjiʿa ilā baytihā wa-makānihā alladhī kharaja minhu. Wa-nufikha fī al-ṣūri fa-idhā hum mina al-ajdāthi ilā rabbihim yansilūn. Qālū yā waylanā man baʿathanā min marqadinā. Hādhā mā waʿada al-Raḥmānu wa-ṣadaqa al-mursalūn. In kānat illā ṣayḥatan wāḥidatan fa-idhā hum jamīʿun ladaynā muḥḍarūn. Wa-lā taḥwīhi arḍun wa-lā taḥwīhi dārun wa-lā makānun ḥattā yarjiʿa ilā zawjatihi fulāna bint fulāna wa-ilā makānihā.

Allāhumma kamā radadta Yūsufa ʿalā Yaʿqūba wa-kamā radadta Mūsā ilā ummihi. Allāhumma yā jāmiʿa al-shatāti yā jāmiʿa al-nāsi li-yawmin lā rayba fīhi, rudda fulān ibn fulāna ʿalā fulāna bint fulāna wa-ilā makānihā alladhī kharaja minhu, wa-jmaʿ shamlahā bi-shamlihi, innaka ʿalā kulli shay'in qadīr.

بسم الله الرحمن الرحيم يد الله قبل يدي وفق الأمر من قبل ومن بعد اللهم إن السماء سماؤك والأرض أرضك والسهل سهلك والبر برك والبحر بحرك والعباد عبادك وأنت لا إله إلا أنت أسألك اللهم بنور جلالك وعظيم سلطانك أن تجعل البلدان والمدن والقرى ضيقة على فلان ابن فلانة حتى يرجع إلى زوجته فلانة بنت فلانة اللهم اجعل عليه الدنيا أضيق من حلقة الخاتم على الأصبع ونفخ في الصور فجمعناهم جمعا اللهم حير فلان ابن فلانة حتى يرجع إلى فلانة بنت فلانة كما حير الجمل في عقله والطير في وكره والولد على محبة أمه حتى يرجع إلى بيتها ومكانها الذي خرج منه ونفخ في الصور فإذا هم من الأجداث إلى ربهم ينسلون قالوا يا ويلنا من بعثنا من مرقدنا هذا ما وعد الرحمن وصدق المرسلون إن كانت إلا صيحة واحدة فإذا هم جميع لدينا محضرون ولا تحويه أرض ولا تحويه دار ولا مكان حتى يرجع إلى زوجته فلانة بنت فلانة وإلى مكانها اللهم كما رددت يوسف على يعقوب وكما رددت موسى إلى أمه اللهم يا جامع الشتات يا جامع الناس ليوم لا ريب فيه رد فلان ابن فلانة على فلانة بنت فلانة وإلى مكانها الذي خرج منه واجمع شملها بشمله إنك على كل شيء قدير

A Benefit for Releasing the Bound Man and Nullifying Sorcery from Him (Fāʾida li-Ḥall al-Marbūṭ wa-Ibṭāl al-Siḥr ʿanhu)

Write this wafq as you see it:

٢٧	٤٣	٣٥
ول	حل	٢
١٣	٣٤	٣٩

The wafq for releasing the bound man and nullifying sorcery

Then write these verses around it:

In the name of God, the Merciful, the Compassionate. Did We not expand your breast for you, and remove from you your burden which weighed down your back, and raise high your remembrance? Truly with hardship comes ease; truly with hardship comes ease. So when you have finished, stand up (three times). Likewise let the member of so-and-so son of so-and-so stand erect upon the vulva of so-and-so daughter of so-and-so. Or one who was dead, and He gave him life: likewise let the member of so-and-so son of so-and-so come to life upon the vulva of so-and-so daughter of so-and-so. And the trumpet is blown, and We gather them together in one gathering: likewise let the member of so-and-so son of so-and-so be joined upon the vulva of so-and-so daughter of so-and-so. So the two set out, until, when they had embarked in the ship, he made a hole in it: likewise let the member of so-and-so son of so-and-so pierce the vulva of so-and-so daughter of so-and-so. God has truly fulfilled His Messenger's vision in truth: you shall surely enter the Sacred Mosque, if God wills, in security, with heads shaved and hair shortened, fearing none; and He knew what you did not know, and He granted, besides that, a near victory. Likewise let the member of so-and-so son of so-and-so open the vulva of so-and-so daughter of so-and-so. He it is who sent His Messenger with guidance and the religion of truth, that He might make it prevail over every religion; and God suffices as witness. Muḥammad is the Messenger of God, and those with him are severe against the unbelievers, merciful among themselves. You see them bowing and prostrating, seeking bounty from God and good pleasure. Their mark is upon their faces from the trace of prostration. That is their likeness in the Torah, and their likeness in the Gospel is as a seed that puts forth its shoot, then strengthens it, so that it grows stout and stands upright. Likewise let the member of so-and-so son of so-and-so stand upright against the vulva of so-and-so daughter of so-and-so. He let the two seas flow forth, and they meet: likewise let the member of so-and-so son of so-and-so meet the vulva of so-and-so daughter of so-and-so. And may God bless our master Muḥammad and his family and his companions, and grant them peace.

Bismi Allāh al-Raḥmān al-Raḥīm. A-lam nashraḥ laka ṣadraka, wa-waḍaʿnā ʿanka wizraka, alladhī anqaḍa ẓahraka, wa-rafaʿnā laka dhikraka. Fa-inna maʿa al-ʿusri yusrā, inna maʿa al-ʿusri yusrā. Fa-idhā faraghta fa-nṣab ٣*. Ka-dhālika yantaṣibu dhakaru fulān ibn fulāna ʿalā farji fulāna bint fulāna. Aw man kāna maytan fa-aḥyāhu, ka-dhālika yaḥyā dhakaru fulān ibn fulāna ʿalā farji fulāna bint fulāna. Wa-nufikha fī al-ṣūri fa-jamaʿnāhum jamʿan, ka-dhālika yajtamiʿu dhakaru fulān ibn fulāna ʿalā farji fulāna bint fulāna. Fa-nṭalaqā ḥattā idhā rakibā fī al-safīnati kharaqahā, ka-dhālika yakhriqu dhakaru fulān ibn fulāna farja fulāna bint fulāna. La-qad ṣadaqa Allāhu rasūlahu al-ruʾyā bi-l-ḥaqqi la-tadkhulunna al-masjida al-ḥarāma in shāʾa Allāhu āminīna muḥalliqīna ruʾūsakum wa-muqaṣṣirīna lā takhāfūna fa-ʿalima mā lam taʿlamū fa-jaʿala min dūni dhālika fatḥan qarīban. Ka-dhālika yaftaḥu dhakaru yaftaḥu fulān ibn fulāna farja fulāna bint fulāna. Huwa alladhī arsala rasūlahu bi-l-hudā wa-dīni al-ḥaqqi li-yuẓhirahu ʿalā al-dīni kullihi wa-kafā bi-Allāhi shahīdan. Muḥammadun rasūlu Allāh, wa-alladhīna maʿahu ashiddāʾu ʿalā al-kuffāri ruḥamāʾu baynahum, tarāhum rukkaʿan sujjadan yabtaghūna faḍlan mina Allāhi wa-riḍwānan, sīmāhum fī wujūhihim min athari al-sujūdi, dhālika mathaluhum fī al-Tawrāti wa-mathaluhum fī al-Injīli ka-zarʿin akhraja shaṭʾahu fa-āzarahu fa-staghlaẓa fa-stawā. Ka-dhālika yastawī dhakaru fulān ibn fulāna bi-farji fulāna bint fulāna. Maraja al-baḥrayni yaltaqiyān, ka-dhālika yaltaqī dhakaru fulān ibn fulāna bi-farji fulāna bint fulāna. Wa-ṣallā Allāhu ʿalā sayyidinā Muḥammadin wa-ʿalā ālihi wa-ṣaḥbihi wa-sallam.*

بسم الله الرحمن الرحيم ألم نشرح لك صدرك ووضعنا عنك وزرك الذي أنقض ظهرك ورفعنا لك ذكرك فإن مع العسر يسرا إن مع العسر يسرا فإذا فرغت فانصب ٣ كذلك ينتصب ذكر فلان ابن فلانة على فرج فلانة بنت فلانة أو من كان ميتا فأحياه كذلك يحيا ذكر فلان ابن فلانة على فرج فلانة بنت فلانة ونفخ في الصور فجمعناهم جمعا كذلك يجتمع ذكر فلان ابن فلانة على فرج فلانة بنت فلانة فانطلقا حتى إذا ركبا في السفينة خرقها كذلك يخرق ذكر فلان ابن فلانة فرج فلانة بنت فلانة لقد صدق الله رسوله الرؤيا بالحق لتدخلن المسجد الحرام إن شاء الله آمنين محلقين رؤوسكم ومقصرين لا تخافون فعلم ما لم تعلموا فجعل من دون ذلك فتحا قريبا كذلك يفتح ذكر يفتح فلان ابن فلانة فرج فلانة بنت فلانة هو الذي أرسل رسوله بالهدى ودين الحق ليظهره على الدين كله وكفى بالله شهيدا محمد رسول الله والذين معه أشداء على الكفار رحماء بينهم تراهم ركعا سجدا يبتغون فضلا من الله ورضوانا سيماهم في وجوههم من أثر السجود ذلك مثلهم في التوراة ومثلهم في الإنجيل كزرع أخرج شطأه فآزره فاستغلظ فاستوى كذلك يستوي ذكر فلان ابن فلانة بفرج فلانة بنت فلانة مرج البحرين يلتقيان كذلك يلتقي ذكر فلان ابن فلانة بفرج فلانة بنت فلانة وصلى الله على سيدنا محمد وعلى آله وصحبه وسلم

The man carries it upon his back, and the sorcery is loosed from him and he attains his desire.

A Benefit for the Woman Who Has Not Conceived (Fāʾida li-l-Marʾa allatī lam Taḥbal)

Write this talisman as you see it:

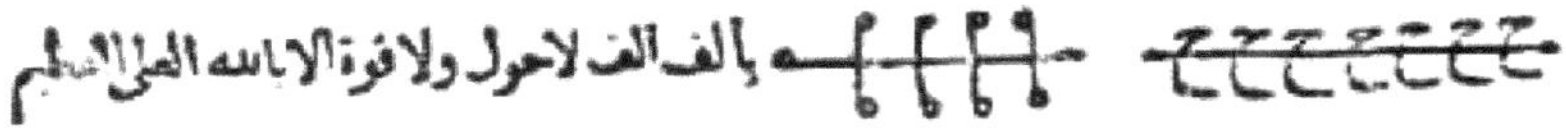

The talisman for the woman who has not conceived

Hang it upon the barren woman and she will conceive; and if you hang it upon a hen that does not lay, she will lay.

A Benefit by Which You May Know Whether a Woman Is Fertile or Barren (Fāʾida Taʿrifu bihā al-Marʾa hal hiya Walūd am ʿĀqir)

Write this talisman as you see it:

The talisman for knowing whether a woman is fertile or barren

Command her to lick it with her tongue; if she urinates she is fertile, and if she does not urinate she is barren.

A Benefit for Cough, Fever, and Easing Childbirth (Fāʾida li-l-Suʿāl wa-l-Ḥummā wa-Tashīl al-Wilāda)

If you wish to remove a cough, take a green palm-leaf strip and write upon it what follows, in separate letters, and hang it upon the patient's neck, and he will be healed.

And if you wish to remove a fever, write it upon three leaves and fumigate the patient with them; whenever the fever comes upon him it departs and does not return. And if you wish to ease childbirth, take four morsels, write upon each morsel one word of the four words, and feed them to the woman whose delivery is difficult, for she will give birth swiftly.

And this is what you write:

In the name of God, the Merciful, the Compassionate. There is no god but God: it shone, and so was illumined. There is no god but God: about the Throne it circled. There is no god but God: as though it had never been and had never been created. There is no god but God: it visited and then it sank away. And may God bless our master Muḥammad and his family and his companions, and grant them peace.

Bismi Allāh al-Raḥmān al-Raḥīm. Lā ilāha illā Allāh, nārat fa-stanārat. Lā ilāha illā Allāh, ḥawla al-ʿarshi dārat. Lā ilāha illā Allāh, ka-annahā mā kānat wa-lā khuliqat. Lā ilāha illā Allāh, zārat thumma ghārat. Wa-ṣallā Allāhu ʿalā sayyidinā Muḥammadin wa-ʿalā ālihi wa-ṣaḥbihi wa-sallam.

بسم الله الرحمن الرحيم لا إله إلا الله نارت فاستنارت لا إله إلا الله حول العرش دارت لا إله إلا الله كأنها ما كانت ولا خلقت لا إله إلا الله زارت ثم غارت وصلى الله على سيدنا محمد وعلى آله وصحبه وسلم

A Benefit for Headache and the Striking Pain (Fā'ida li-l-Ṣudāʿ wa-l-Ḍārib)

Take a green palm-rib and write upon it the letters of this verse:

Should every hateful thing alight upon you, a wide-eyed one has effaced the glance of the star.

In ḥallat ilayka kullu karīha, ḥawrā'u ʿan laḥẓi al-najmi māḥat.

إن حلت إليك كل كريهة حوراء عن لحظ النجم ماحت

And these are the letters: ا ح ا ك ك ح ع ل ا م. Then order the patient to place his finger upon the seat of the pain. Take a nail and set it upon the first letter, recite the adjuration mentioned below three times, and at each recitation strike the head of the nail a single blow. If the pain subsides, fix the nail in that letter; if it does not, move it to the second letter and repeat the recitation in the same way, and so on until the pain subsides. This is the form of the adjuration. You say:

In the name of God, the Merciful, the Compassionate. I adjure you, O striker, and whatever it is you strike, unto red blood in a green vein. If you are in the bone, come out into the flesh; and from the flesh into the skin; and from the skin into the hair; and from the hair into the earth.

Bismi Allāh al-Raḥmān al-Raḥīm. Innī uʿazzimu ʿalayka ayyuhā al-ḍāribu wa-mā anta ḍāribun ilā damin aḥmara fī ʿirqin akhḍara. In kunta fī al-ʿaẓmi fa-khruj ilā al-laḥmi, wa-min al-laḥmi ilā al-jildi, wa-min al-jildi ilā al-shaʿri, wa-min al-shaʿri ilā al-arḍi.

بسم الله الرحمن الرحيم إني أعزم عليك أيها الضارب وما أنت ضارب إلى دم أحمر في عرق أخضر إن كنت في العظم فاخرج إلى اللحم ومن اللحم إلى الجلد ومن الجلد إلى الشعر ومن الشعر إلى الأرض

Barbarous names: wa-l-Sā

بحق (...) (...) والسا

By al-Ṭāriq, and what shall make you know what al-Ṭāriq is? The piercing star. There is no soul but has a guardian over it. So let man consider from what he was created: he was created from a gushing fluid that issues from between the loins and the ribs. Just as the Throne of the Merciful rests beneath the Merciful, and to Him belongs whatever dwells in the night and the day, and He is the All-Hearing, the All-Knowing: come out, O striker, from the head of so-and-so son of so-and-so, by the right of: Glorify the name of your Lord the Most High, who created and fashioned, and who ordained and guided, and guided, and guided.

Wa-l-ṭāriqi wa-mā adrāka mā al-ṭāriqu, al-najmu al-thāqibu, in kullu nafsin lammā ʿalayhā ḥāfiẓun. Fa-l-yanẓuri al-insānu mimma khuliqa, khuliqa min māʾin dāfiqin yakhruju min bayni al-ṣulbi wa-l-tarāʾibi. Kamā sakana ʿarshu al-Raḥmāni taḥta al-Raḥmāni wa-lahu mā sakana fī al-layli wa-l-nahāri wa-huwa al-Samīʿu al-ʿAlīmu. Ukhruj ayyuhā al-ḍāribu min raʾsi fulān ibn fulāna bi-ḥaqqi sabbiḥi isma rabbika al-aʿlā alladhī khalaqa fa-sawwā wa-alladhī qaddara fa-hadā fa-hadā fa-hadā.

والطارق وما أدراك ما الطارق النجم الثاقب إن كل نفس لما عليها حافظ فلينظر الإنسان مم خلق خلق من ماء دافق يخرج من بين الصلب

والترائب كما سكن عرش الرحمن تحت الرحمن وله ما سكن في الليل
والنهار وهو السميع العليم اخرج أيها الضارب من رأس فلان ابن فلانة
بحق سبح اسم ربك الأعلى الذي خلق فسوى والذي قدر فهدى فهدى
فهدى

A Benefit for Fever (Fāʾida li-l-Ḥummā)

It is written upon three leaves, which are then effaced with water; and the fevered man is given it to drink for three days on an empty stomach. This is what you write. Upon the first:

In the name of God, the Merciful, the Compassionate. Indeed We have given you al-Kawthar. God desires to lighten your burden.

Bismi Allāh al-Raḥmān al-Raḥīm. Innā aʿṭaynāka al-kawthar. Yurīdu Allāh an yukhaffifa ʿankum.

بسم الله الرحمن الرحيم إنا أعطيناك الكوثر يريد الله أن يخفف عنكم

Upon the second:

So pray to your Lord and sacrifice. That is a lightening from your Lord, and a mercy.

Fa-ṣalli li-rabbika wa-nḥar. Dhālika takhfīfun min rabbikum wa-raḥma.

فصل لربك وانحر ذلك تخفيف من ربكم ورحمة

Upon the third:

Indeed it is he who hates you who is cut off. Now God has lightened it for you.

Inna shāni'aka huwa al-abtar. Al-āna khaffafa Allāh 'ankum.

إن شانئك هو الأبتر الآن خفف الله عنكم

A Benefit for Pain of the Spleen (Fā'ida li-Waja' al-Ṭiḥāl)

The talisman that follows is written upon a leaf and laid upon the spleen, over the shirt. Then take a new spoon, put in it a little ash, and set a live coal above the ash; then place the spoon above the talisman and adjure over it with the verse written in the circle as many times as the number of the patient's name, and he will be healed. This is the form of the talisman, as you see:

The talisman for pain of the spleen

A Benefit for Boils and Whatever Arises in the Body

It is written for whatever arises in the body, such as a boil or the like; it is effaced with water and drunk, and he will be healed. And this is what you write:

In the name of God, the Merciful, the Compassionate. A disavowal from God and His Messenger to every ailment: it shall never prosper, if God Most High wills. A seed has sprung from a solid rock: it has no root that holds fast and no branch that holds fast. In the name of God, I charm you, and God heals you and grants you well-being. They ask you about the mountains. Say: My Lord will scatter them utterly, and leave them a level plain in which you will see no crookedness and no unevenness. O pain, fixed in the skin that dies, die by the power of the Living One who does not die. And may God bless our master Muḥammad and his family and his companions, and grant them peace.

Bismi Allāh al-Raḥmān al-Raḥīm. Barā'atun min Allāh wa-rasūlihi ilā kulli ʿillatin lā tufliḥu wa-lā (...) abadan in shā'a Allāh taʿālā. Ḥabbatun ṭalaʿat min ṣakhratin ṣammā', lā aṣla lahā thābitun wa-lā farʿa lahā thābitun. Bismi Allāh arqīka, wa-Allāhu yashfīka wa-yuʿāfīka wa-yas'alūnaka ʿani al-jibāli qul yansifuhā rabbī nasfan fa-yadharuhā qāʿan ṣafṣafan lā tarā fīhā ʿiwajan wa-lā amtan. Ayyuhā al-alamu al-thābitu fī al-jildi alladhī yamūtu, mut bi-qudrati al-Ḥayyi alladhī lā yamūtu. Wa-ṣallā Allāhu ʿalā sayyidinā Muḥammadin wa-ʿalā ālihi wa-ṣaḥbihi wa-sallam.

بسم الله الرحمن الرحيم براءة من الله ورسوله إلى كل علة لا تفلح ولا (...) أبدا إن شاء الله تعالى حبة طلعت من صخرة صماء لا أصل لها ثابت ولا فرع لها ثابت بسم الله أرقيك والله يشفيك ويعافيك ويسألونك عن الجبال قل ينسفها ربي نسفا فيذرها قاعا صفصفا لا ترى فيها عوجا

ولا أمتا أيها الألم الثابت في الجلد الذي يموت مت بقدرة الحي الذي
لا يموت وصلى الله على سيدنا محمد وعلى آله وصحبه وسلم

A Benefit for Every Swelling

It is written upon every swelling, even if it be dropsy, and the swelling passes away. The letters are these: د ح ا د و ه ي ط ح, and it is better that you write them thus:

ا	ح	د
ه	و	د
ح	ط	ى

The letter grid for every swelling

A Benefit for Ringworm (Fā'ida li-l-Qūb)

Draw around the ringworm with a needle moistened from your saliva seven times, and each time you say:

A bare tree upon a solid rock, having no root that holds fast and no branch that puts forth. Jonah came out of the belly of the fish; strike it with his staff, and it burned, and it burned.

Shajaratun jammā fī ṣakhratin ṣammā, lā aṣla lahā thābitun wa-lā farʿa lahā nābitun. Yūnus kharaja min baṭni al-ḥūti, iḍribhā bi-ʿaṣāhu fa-ḥtaraqat fa-ḥtaraqat.

شجرة جما في صخرة صما لا أصل لها ثابت ولا فرع لها نابت يونس خرج من بطن الحوت اضربها بعصاه فاحترقت فاحترقت

A Benefit for Fever Written on Willow Leaves (Fāʾida li-l-Ḥummā)

It is written upon three willow leaves, and the fevered person is fumigated with them, and the fever passes away from him. This is what you write upon the first, upon the second, and upon the third, each in its own written form.

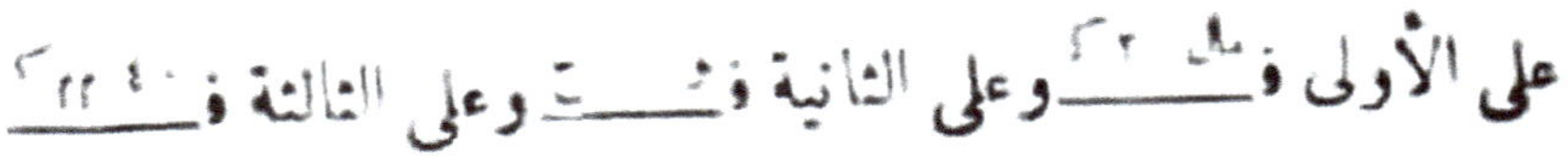

The three written forms for the willow leaves

An Amulet for Fever (Tamīma li-l-Ḥummā)

In the name of God, the Merciful, the Compassionate. There is no god but God; Moses is the one who spoke with God. There is no god but God; Jesus is the Spirit of God. There is no god but God; Abraham is the intimate friend of God. The blessings of God and His peace be upon them all. By God, and by the right of every Book He has sent down, let the fire of the fever be lifted from the bearer of this writing of mine. We said: O fire, be coolness and peace upon Abraham. And We send down of the Qur'an that which is a healing and a mercy for the believers.

Bismi Allāhi al-Raḥmāni al-Raḥīm. Lā ilāha illā Allāh, Mūsā kalīmu Allāh. Lā ilāha illā Allāh, ʿĪsā rūḥu Allāh. Lā ilāha illā Allāh, Ibrāhīmu khalīlu Allāh. Ṣalawātu Allāhi wa-salāmuhu ʿalayhim ajmaʿīn. Bi-Allāhi bi-ḥaqqi kulli kitābin anzalahu an tartafiʿa nāru al-ḥummā ʿan ḥāmili kitābī hādhā. Qulnā yā nāru kūnī bardan wa-salāman ʿalā Ibrāhīm. Wa-nunazzilu mina al-Qur'āni mā huwa shifā'un wa-raḥmatun li-l-mu'minīn.

بسم الله الرحمن الرحيم لا إله إلا الله موسى كليم الله لا إله إلا الله عيسى روح الله لا إله إلا الله إبراهيم خليل الله صلوات الله وسلامه عليهم أجمعين بالله بحق كل كتاب أنزله أن ترتفع نار الحمى عن حامل كتابي هذا قلنا يا نار كوني بردا وسلاما على إبراهيم وننزل من القرآن ما هو شفاء ورحمة للمؤمنين

A Benefit for Fever Written with Three Names (Fā'ida li-l-Ḥummā)

It is written upon three leaves: upon the first, Pharaoh (*Firʿawn* / فرعون); upon the second, Hāmān (هامان); and upon the third, Qārūn (قارون). Reckon each one of the three names by its numerical weight as far as you are able, and fumigate the fevered person with them, one leaf at each coming of the fever, and the fever goes and does not return.

Another Benefit for Fever (Fā'ida Ukhrā li-l-Ḥummā)

It is written and hung upon the upper arm of the fevered person, and he recovers swiftly by the permission of God the Exalted.

This is what you write:

In the name of God, the Merciful, the Compassionate. A declaration of immunity from God, the Mighty, the Wise, to Umm Mildam, who eats flesh, drinks blood, and shatters bone. To proceed: O Umm Mildam, if you are a believing woman, then by the right of Muḥammad, may God bless him and grant him peace; and if you are a Jewish woman, then by the right of Moses who spoke with God, peace be upon him; and if you are a Christian woman, then by the right of Jesus the Messiah, peace be upon him; and if you are a Magian woman, then by the right of the fire and the light and the revolving sphere: that you eat no flesh of so-and-so son of so-and-so, and drink no blood of his, and shatter no bone of his, and that you turn away from him to whoever has taken another god alongside God. Otherwise you are quit of God and His Messenger, and God and His Messenger are quit of you. God suffices us, and excellent is the Guardian. There is no power and no strength save in God, the Exalted, the Mighty. And may God bless our master Muḥammad and his family and his companions, and grant them peace.

Bismi Allāhi al-Raḥmāni al-Raḥīm. Barāʾatun mina Allāhi al-ʿAzīzi al-Ḥakīmi ilā Umm Mildam allatī taʾkulu al-laḥma wa-tashrabu al-dama wa-tuhashshimu al-ʿaẓma. Ammā baʿdu, yā Umm Mildam, fa-in kunti muʾminatan fa-bi-ḥaqqi Muḥammadin ṣallā Allāhu ʿalayhi wa-sallam, wa-in kunti yahūdiyyatan fa-bi-ḥaqqi Mūsā al-Kalīmi ʿalayhi al-salām, wa-in kunti naṣrāniyyatan fa-bi-ḥaqqi ʿĪsā al-Masīḥi ʿalayhi al-

salām, wa-in kunti majūsiyyatan fa-bi-ḥaqqi al-nāri wa-l-nūri wa-l-falaki alladhī yadūru, an lā ta'kulī li-fulān ibn fulāna laḥman wa-lā tashrabī lahu daman wa-lā tuhashshimī lahu 'aẓman, wa-taḥawwalī 'anhu ilā man ittakhadha ma'a Allāhi ilāhan ākhar. Wa-illā fa-anti barī'atun mina Allāhi wa-rasūlihi, wa-Allāhu wa-rasūluhu barī'āni minki. Wa-ḥasbunā Allāhu wa-ni'ma al-wakīl, wa-lā ḥawla wa-lā quwwata illā bi-Allāhi al-'Alī al-'Aẓīm. Wa-ṣallā Allāhu 'alā sayyidinā Muḥammadin wa-'alā ālihi wa-ṣaḥbihi wa-sallam.

بسم الله الرحمن الرحيم براءة من الله العزيز الحكيم إلى أم ملدم التي تأكل اللحم وتشرب الدم وتهشم العظم أما بعد يا أم ملدم فإن كنت مؤمنة فبحق محمد صلى الله عليه وسلم وإن كنت يهودية فبحق موسى الكليم عليه السلام وإن كنت نصرانية فبحق عيسى المسيح عليه السلام وإن كنت مجوسية فبحق النار والنور والفلك الذي يدور أن لا تأكلي لفلان ابن فلانة لحما ولا تشربي له دما ولا تهشمي له عظما وتحولي عنه إلى من اتخذ مع الله إلها آخر وإلا فأنت بريئة من الله ورسوله والله ورسوله بريئان منك وحسبنا الله ونعم الوكيل ولا حول ولا قوة إلا بالله العلي العظيم وصلى الله على سيدنا محمد وعلى آله وصحبه وسلم

Another Remedy That Benefits Fever (Mimmā Yanfa'u li-l-Ḥummā Ayḍan)

Take three palm-leaf strips and write upon the first, "the fever is from Hellfire" (*al-ḥummā mina al-jaḥīm* / الحمى من الجحيم); upon the second, "and its heat is from Hellfire" (*wa-ḥarruhā mina al-jaḥīm* / وحرها من الجحيم); and upon the third, "and its origin is from the accursed Satan" (*wa-aṣluhā mina al-shayṭāni al-rajīm* / وأصلها من الشيطان الرجيم). Then take three leaves and write upon the first:

There is no god but God; Muḥammad is the Messenger of God. Around the Throne it turned.

Lā ilāha illā Allāh, Muḥammadun Rasūlu Allāh. Ḥawla al-ʿarshi dārat.

لا إله إلا الله محمد رسول الله حول العرش دارت

And upon the second:

There is no god but God; Muḥammad is the Messenger of God. It blazed, and then it shone.

Lā ilāha illā Allāh, Muḥammadun Rasūlu Allāh. Nārat fa-stanārat.

لا إله إلا الله محمد رسول الله نارت فاستنارت

And upon the third:

There is no god but God; Muḥammad is the Messenger of God. The fever grew faint and sank away. Does He who created not know? And He is the Subtle, the Aware.

Lā ilāha illā Allāh, Muḥammadun Rasūlu Allāh. Khaffati al-ḥummā wa-ghārat. A-lā yaʿlamu man khalaqa wa-huwa al-Laṭīfu al-Khabīr.

لا إله إلا الله محمد رسول الله خفت الحمى وغارت ألا يعلم من خلق وهو اللطيف الخبير

Then he is fumigated with them for three days, each day with one palm-leaf strip and one leaf, and the fever goes and never returns.

A Benefit for Chill and Burning Heat (Fāʾida li-l-Burūda wa-l-Sukhūna)

It is written upon a yellow leaf and hung upon the head of the sick person, and the sickness goes and will not return. This is what you write, as you see it, and you write around it:

That is an alleviation from your Lord, and a mercy. God desires to lighten your burden, for man was created weak. Now God has lightened your burden, and He knows that there is weakness in you. O fire, be coolness and peace upon Abraham. Our Lord, lift the torment from us; we are believers. If God touches you with harm, none can remove it but He; and if He touches you with good, He is powerful over all things. And may God bless our master Muḥammad and his family and his Companions, and grant them peace.

Dhālika takhfīfun min rabbikum wa-raḥma, yurīdu Allāhu an yukhaffifa ʿankum wa-khuliqa al-insānu ḍaʿīfan, al-āna khaffafa Allāhu ʿankum wa-ʿalima anna fīkum ḍaʿfan, yā nāru kūnī bardan wa-salāman ʿalā Ibrāhīm, rabbanā ikshif ʿannā al-ʿadhāba innā muʾminūn, wa-in yamsaska Allāhu bi-ḍurrin fa-lā kāshifa lahu illā huwa wa-in yamsaska bi-khayrin fa-huwa ʿalā kulli shayʾin qadīr, wa-ṣallā Allāhu ʿalā sayyidinā Muḥammadin wa-ʿalā ālihi wa-ṣaḥbihi wa-sallam.

ذلك تخفيف من ربكم ورحمة يريد الله أن يخفف عنكم وخلق الإنسان
ضعيفا الآن خفف الله عنكم وعلم أن فيكم ضعفا يا نار كوني بردا
وسلاما على إبراهيم ربنا اكشف عنا العذاب إنا مؤمنون وإن يمسسك الله
بضر فلا كاشف له إلا هو وإن يمسسك بخير فهو على كل شيء قدير
وصلى الله على سيدنا محمد وعلى آله وصحبه وسلم

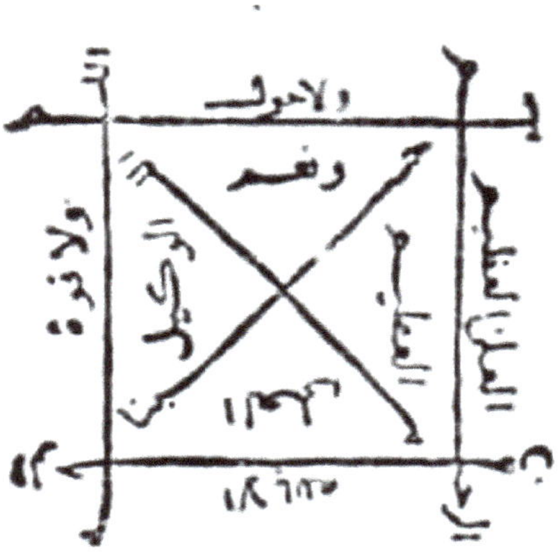

The talisman for chill and burning heat

A Benefit for Burning Heat (Fāʾidat al-Sukhūna)

Write upon an egg, wrap it in a rag or a thread, and roast it in the ashes. Then peel it, hang its shell together with the rag in which it was roasted upon the sick person, and feed the egg to him, and he will recover. This is what you write:

Barbarous names: Laṭīf Ṭaf Kaṭīf Kaf Laṭīf Laf Khafīf Haf

لطيف طف كطيف كف لطيف لف خفيف هف

A Benefit for Sexual Potency (Fāʾida li-Quwwat al-Bāh)

Write upon gazelle parchment and place it upon the left upper arm. This is the talisman:

Barbarous names: Alaysūmalṭahā Kaskaskalṭ

أليسوملطها كسكسكلط

A Benefit for Retaining Semen (Fāʾida li-Imsāk al-Manī)

Write upon gazelle parchment and bind it upon the left thigh, and the fluid will not descend until it is removed. This is the talisman:

١١١ ٦ م ١١١١٨٥١ ٦٦٦٦٦ ٨ ط

A Benefit for Removing Palpitation (Fāʾida li-Izālat al-Khafaqān)

Write it upon the palm of the hand and lick it off. This is the name:

Barbarous names: Baṭamṭamṭamshā

بطمطمطمشا

A Benefit for Fulfilling Needs (Fāʾida li-Qaḍāʾ al-Ḥawāʾij)

Rise in the last third of the night, pray two cycles, and sit facing the qibla; then recite this formula a thousand times. It is to say:

O God, bless our master and patron Muḥammad, grant him peace, and bestow Your favour upon him with a prayer by which You loosen my knot, relieve my distress, deliver me from my mire, and fulfil my need.

Allāhumma ṣalli wa-sallim wa-bārik ʿalā sayyidinā wa-mawlānā Muḥammadin ṣalātan taḥullu bihā ʿuqdatī wa-tufarriju bihā karbī wa-tunqidhu bihā waḥlatī wa-taqḍī bihā ḥājatī.

اللهم صل وسلم وبارك على سيدنا ومولانا محمد صلاة تحل بها عقدتي وتفرج بها كربي وتنقذ بها وحلتي وتقضي بها حاجتي

A Benefit for Removing Inflammation of the Eye (Fā'ida li-Izālat Ramad al-'Ayn)

Write what follows upon a sheet of paper and hang it between the eyes of the sick person, and he will be healed. This is what you write:

O inflammation, O thing inflamed, I have charmed you by the Torah of Moses, the Gospel of Jesus, the Psalter of David, and the Arabic Qur'ān. Do not fester, do not persist, and do not become a burden upon him. Come out from the eye of this son of Adam as Jonah came out from the belly of the fish, and as Joseph came out from the pit and the prison, by a thousand thousand. There is no power and no strength save in God, the Most High, the Magnificent.

Yā ayyuhā al-ramadu al-marmūdu raqaytuka bi-Tawrāti Mūsā wa-Injīli 'Īsā wa-Zābūri Dāwūda wa-l-Qur'āni al-'Arabī, lā taqbuḥ wa-lā tabraḥ wa-lā takūnu lahu rahaqan. Ukhruj min 'ayni hādhā al-ādamī kamā kharaja Yūnusu min baṭni al-ḥūti wa-kamā kharaja Yūsufu min al-jubbi wa-l-sijni bi-alfi alfin, lā ḥawla wa-lā quwwata illā bi-Allāhi al-'Alī al-'Aẓīm.

يا أيها الرمد المرمود رقيتك بتوراة موسى وإنجيل عيسى وزابور داود والقرآن العربي لا تقبح ولا تبرح ولا تكون له رهقا أخرج من عين هذا الآدمي كما خرج يونس من بطن الحوت وكما خرج يوسف من الجب والسجن بألف ألف لا حول ولا قوة إلا بالله العلي العظيم

A Benefit for Keeping Off Bedbugs (Fā'ida li-Man' al-Baqq)

Write the following talisman upon three sheets of paper and paste each sheet upon a wall, save the wall in which the door stands, and the bedbugs will depart from that place. This is the form of the talisman, as you see:

The talisman for keeping off bedbugs

A Benefit for the Qarīna (Fā'ida li-l-Qarīna)

Write the following wafq:

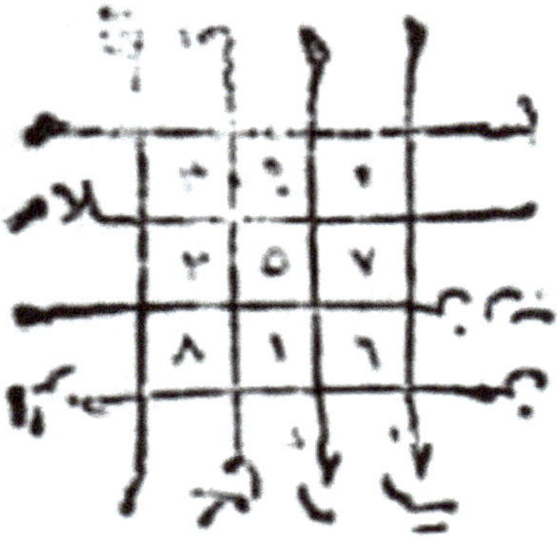

The wafq for the qarīna

And write around it: ا ب ت ث ج ح ع د ذ ر ز س ش ص ض ط. Then write a hundred mīms, thus: م م م. Then write:

Barbarous names: Kahū Lahū

كهو لهو

Then write the following names twenty-four times:

Barbarous names: Ahyā Sharāhiyā Adūnāy Aṣbā'ūt wa-Āl Shaddāy

أهيا شراهيا أدوناي أصباؤت وآل شداي

Then write the Verse of the Throne fourteen times. Then hang it upon the one afflicted by the qarīna, and he will be healed.

A Benefit for Headache (Fā'ida li-l-Ṣudāʿ)

Take a green palm rib and write these letters upon it: ل م ق ف ن ج ل. Then, with your finger and with saliva, write an inverted nūn upon the eye of the afflicted person. Then order him to place his hand upon the seat of the pain, set a small nail upon the first letter, and tap upon it while you recite the Fātiḥa silently one time. Then order him to lift his hand, and question him. If it has subsided, order him to walk a little and return to you; and if it remains quiet, fix the nail.

Strike it, and place the palm-leaf strip in a dark spot. If the pain returns, move the nail to the second letter, repeat the recitation and the operation as already described, and continue in this way until the pain is stilled and does not come back.

A Benefit for Protection from Ophthalmia (Fā'ida li-l-Ḥifẓ min al-Ramad)

Write these letters on a small sheet on the Saturday of Light. Whoever swallows it is safe from ophthalmia for that year. These are the letters: الم المص المر الر كهيعص طه طسم يس ص حم عسق ق ن. And likewise, whoever writes these letters obtains what we have mentioned:

ا ل م ر ك (...) ع ط س ح ق ه ن

A Benefit for Piercing Pain, Throbbing Pain, and Headache (Fāʾida li-l-Zarq wa-l-Ḍārib wa-l-Ṣudāʿ)

Bid the sick person set his finger upon the site of the pain, and recite these verses:

By the heaven and the night-comer! And what will make you know what the night-comer is? The piercing star. There is no soul but that over it is a keeper. So let man look at that from which he was created. He was created from a gushing fluid, issuing from between the backbone and the ribs. Glorify the name of your Lord, the Most High, who created and proportioned, and who measured and guided, and guided, and guided (three times).

Wa-l-samāʾi wa-l-ṭāriq. Wa-mā adrāka mā al-ṭāriq. Al-najmu al-thāqib. In kullu nafsin lammā ʿalayhā ḥāfiẓ. Fa-l-yanẓuri al-insānu mimma khuliq. Khuliqa min māʾin dāfiq. Yakhruju min bayni al-ṣulbi wa-l-tarāʾib. Sabbiḥi isma rabbika al-aʿlā alladhī khalaqa fa-sawwā, wa-lladhī qaddara fa-hadā fa-hadā fa-hadā thalātha marrāt.

والسماء والطارق وما أدراك ما الطارق النجم الثاقب إن كل نفس لما عليها حافظ فلينظر الإنسان مم خلق خلق من ماء دافق يخرج من بين الصلب والترائب سبح اسم ربك الأعلى الذي خلق فسوى والذي قدر فهدى فهدى فهدى ثلاث مرات

The pain will then vanish by the leave of God Most High.

A Benefit for Conception (Fāʾida li-l-Ḥabal)

Write Sūrat al-Jumuʿa in a clean vessel, wash it off with water, and let her bathe with it at mid-month. Then take seven dates or raisins and write upon each one of them one of the seven names given below, and give them to the woman: she breaks her fast upon one of them each day before sunrise, beginning on Friday. Then write Sūrat al-Mulk together with the words of God Most High:

Then the truth came to pass, and what they had been doing was made void.

Fa-waqaʿa al-ḥaqqu wa-baṭala mā kānū yaʿmalūn

فوقع الحق وبطل ما كانوا يعملون

Write this on paper, fold it, and hang it over her belly. Forty days will not pass over her before she conceives, by the will of God Most High. And these are the names:

God, the Bestower, the Provider, the Opener, the Creator, the Fashioner, the Originator.

Allāh, al-Wahhāb, al-Razzāq, al-Fattāḥ, al-Khāliq, al-Muṣawwir, al-Badīʿ

الله، الوهاب، الرزاق، الفتاح، الخالق، المصور، البديع

A Benefit for Consolation (Fāʾidat al-Salwa)

Write this in a glazed vessel, wash it off with water, and give it to the lover to drink. These are the letters:

Barbarous names: Ah Ah Ah Ah Ah Ah Ah Ah Hū Hū Hū Hū Hū Hū Hū Hū Hī Hī Hī Hī Hī Ḥayy Ḥayy Ḥayy Ḥayy Ḥayy

Ḥayy Ḥayy Farāhiyā Sharāhiyā Farāhiyā Sharāhiyā Farāhiyā Sharāhiyā Farāhiyā Sharāhiyā Farāhiyā Sharāhiyā Hayyā Hayyā

اه اه اه اه اه اه اه هو هو هو هو هو هو هو هي هي هي هي هي هي
حي حي حي حي حي حي حي فراهيا شراهيا فراهيا شراهيا فراهيا شراهيا
فراهيا شراهيا فراهيا شراهيا هيا هيا ص ص ص ص ص ل ل ل ل ل ل ل ع
ع ع ع ع ع ع ع ف ف ف ف ف ف ف ط ط ط ط ط ط ط م م م
م م م م

And with them:

And We had already made a covenant with Adam before, but he forgot, and We found in him no resolve.

Wa-laqad ʿahidnā ilā Ādama min qablu fa-nasiya wa-lam najid lahu ʿazmā

ولقد عهدنا إلى آدم من قبل فنسي ولم نجد له عزما

A Benefit for Stabbing Pain (Fāʾidat al-Nakhza)

Write it and hang it up. These are the words:

Kathr (three times), ʿUmq (three times). Be still, O pain and throbbing, by the right of the Lord of the easts and the wests. Indeed, He is able to return it, by the right of these names and verses.

Kathr ٣ ʿUmq ٣ uskun ayyuhā al-wajaʿu wa-l-ḍārib, bi-ḥaqqi rabbi al-mashāriqi wa-l-maghārib, innahu ʿalā rajʿihi la-qādir, bi-ḥaqqi hādhihi al-asmāʾi wa-l-āyāt.

كثر ٣ عمق ٣ اسكن أيها الوجع والضارب بحق رب المشارق والمغارب
إنه على رجعه لقادر بحق هذه الأسماء والآيات

Another Benefit for Stabbing Pain (Fāʾida Ukhrā li-l-Nakhza)

It is likewise:

Barbarous names: Kūḥ Kalūḥ Ṣūḥ Ṭī Ṭī Ṭī Ṭī Ṭī Ṭī Ṭī Ṭī Ṭī

كوح كلوح صوح طي طي طي طي طي طي طي طي طي

A Benefit for Back Pain (Fāʾida li-Wajaʿ al-Ẓahr)

Write it and hang it upon him. It is:

In the name of God, the Merciful, the Compassionate. Have We not expanded for you your breast, and removed from you your burden which weighed down your back, and raised high for you your remembrance? For indeed, with hardship comes ease. O God, drive away the pain and the throbbing from the bearer of this writing of mine, and make health enter his body as You made it enter Adam, the father of humankind, and bring the pain and the throbbing out from the bone to the flesh, from the flesh to the blood, from the blood to the skin, and from the skin to the earth, by the right of Him who says to a thing "Be," and it is. Hayyā Hayyā Ashrāhiyā Ashrāhiyā Ashrāhiyā, and by a thousand thousand. There is no power and no strength except through God, the Most High, the Magnificent. If You deliver us from this, we shall surely be among the thankful.

Bismi Allāhi al-Raḥmāni al-Raḥīm. Alam nashraḥ laka ṣadrak, wa-waḍaʿnā ʿanka wizrak, alladhī anqaḍa ẓahrak, wa-rafaʿnā laka dhikrak, fa-inna maʿa al-ʿusri yusrā. Allāhumma idfaʿi al-wajaʿa wa-l-ḍarabān ʿan ḥāmili kitābī hādhā, wa-adkhili al-ṣiḥḥata fī jasadihi kamā adkhalta fī Ādama abū al-bashar, wa-akhriji al-wajaʿa wa-l-ḍarabān mina al-ʿaẓmi ilā al-laḥm, wa-

mina al-laḥmi ilā al-dam, wa-mina al-dami ilā al-jild, wa-mina al-jildi ilā al-arḍ, bi-ḥaqqi man yaqūlu li-l-shay'i kun fa-yakūn. Hayyā Hayyā Ashrāhiyā Ashrāhiyā Ashrāhiyā wa-bi-alf alf. Lā ḥawla wa-lā quwwata illā bi-Allāhi al-ʿAlī al-ʿAẓīm. La-in anjaytanā min hādhihi la-nakūnanna mina al-shākirīn.

بسم الله الرحمن الرحيم ألم نشرح لك صدرك ووضعنا عنك وزرك الذي أنقض ظهرك ورفعنا لك ذكرك فإن مع العسر يسرا اللهم ادفع الوجع والضربان عن حامل كتابي هذا وأدخل الصحة في جسده كما أدخلت في آدم أبو البشر وأخرج الوجع والضربان من العظم إلى اللحم ومن اللحم إلى الدم ومن الدم إلى الجلد ومن الجلد إلى الأرض بحق من يقول للشيء كن فيكون هيا هيا اشراهيا اشراهيا اشراهيا وبألف ألف لا حول ولا قوة إلا بالله العلي العظيم لئن أنجيتنا من هذه لنكونن من الشاكرين

A Benefit for Pain in the Side (Fā'ida li-Wajaʿ al-Janb)

Write it and hang it upon him. It is:

In the name of God, the Merciful, the Compassionate. She cried out and was granted a child; Mary went into labour with Jesus and gave birth; at the spring of Sulwān she washed. Be still, O pain of the side, as the Throne of the All-Merciful came to rest beneath the All-Merciful, by a thousand thousand recitations of: There is no power and no strength save in God, the Most High, the Magnificent.

Bismi Allāhi al-Raḥmāni al-Raḥīm Zaʿaqat ruziqat Maryam ṭalaqat bi-ʿĪsā waladat ʿalā ʿayn Sulwān ightasalat. Uskun

ayyuhā al-janb kamā sakana ʿarsh al-Raḥmān taḥta al-Raḥmān bi-alf alf lā ḥawla wa-lā quwwata illā bi-Allāh al-ʿAlī al-ʿAẓīm.

بسم الله الرحمن الرحيم زعقت رزقت مريم طلقت بعيسى ولدت على عين سلوان اغتسلت اسكن أيها الجنب كما سكن عرش الرحمن تحت الرحمن بألف ألف لا حول ولا قوة إلا بالله العلي العظيم

A Benefit for Pain, with a Chewed Morsel

It is written upon a morsel; the sick person chews it and throws it to a dog, and the dog eats it. As soon as the dog has eaten it, the sick person is healed. This is what you write: و ل ط ع

A Benefit for Arresting the Scorpion's Venom and Wiping Away Its Hurt (Fāʾida li-Tawqīf Samm al-ʿAqrab wa-Masḥ Adhāh)

You say:

Barbarous names: Darkhīsh Ranīsh ʿAlfīsh Fayrūq Marʿūq

درخيش رنيش علفيش فيروق مرعوق

O Khāriq, ward off the evil of the scorpion's venom, by the right of the prophets, the first of whom is Adam and the last of whom is Muḥammad — the blessings of God and His salutations be upon them all.

Yā Khāriq ikfi sharra samm al-'aqrab bi-ḥaqq al-anbiyā' alladhīna awwaluhum Ādam ākhiruhum Muḥammad ṣalawāt Allāh wa-taslīmātuhu 'alayhim ajma'īn.

يا خارق اكفي شر سم العقرب بحق الأنبياء الذين أولهم آدم آخرهم محمد صلوات الله وتسليماته عليهم أجمعين

It is then placed upon the place of the sting, until you kill it.

A Benefit for Arresting the Scorpion (Fā'ida li-Tawqīf al-'Aqrab)

You say:

Barbarous names: Akraka Akalka

أكركه أكلكه

It will not stir, but will remain standing where it is until you kill it.

A Benefit for Expelling the Jinn from a Place (Fāʾida li-Ṭard al-Jānn min al-Makān)

It is written and set down in the place, and they will go out from it and will not return to it so long as it remains there. This is the talisman:

The talisman for expelling the jinn from a place

A Benefit for All Diseases and Ailments (Fāʾida li-Jamīʿ al-Amrāḍ wa-l-ʿIlal)

It is carried or drunk. From the Master al-Munīr, may God have mercy on him, who said:

Five ه, and a line above a line, and a cross with four dots about it; and hamzas which, if you count them, are seven, and you will find no error in them. Then و, then ه with its extension; then ص, then م in the middle. It cleanses away sicknesses, and that malady before which the physicians of the Nabaṭ stood powerless.

This is how it is written:

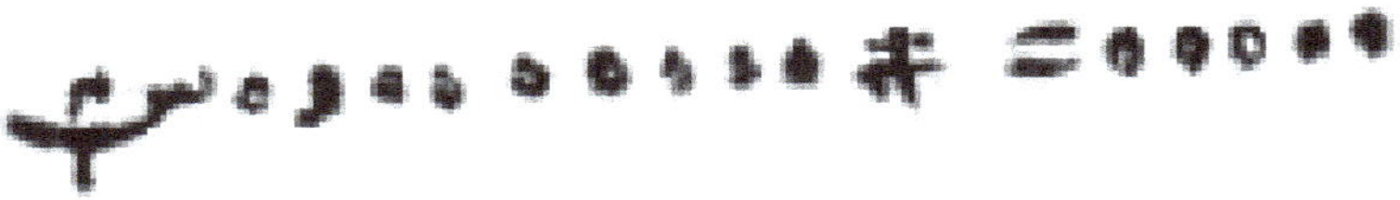

The written form for all diseases and ailments

A Benefit to Be Said in Time of Plague to Ward Off Its Harm (Fāʾida Tuqāl fī Zaman al-Ṭāʿūn li-Manʿ Adhāh)

You say:

Hold back the far one from us, that he may not come to us, and the near one, that he may not harm us. God is Living, Eternal, Everlasting, and He has a shelter. I have entered into the shelter of God and sought protection with the Messenger of God, may God bless him and grant him peace.

Iḥbisū al-baʿīd ʿannā lā yaʾtīnā wa-l-qarīb lā yuʾdhīnā. Allāh ḥayy ṣamad bāqin wa-lahu kanaf. Wa-innī dakhaltu fī kanaf Allāh wa-istajartu bi-Rasūl Allāh ṣallā Allāh ʿalayhi wa-sallam.

احبسوا البعيد عنا لا يأتينا والقريب لا يؤذينا الله حي صمد باق وله كنف وإني دخلت في كنف الله واستجرت برسول الله صلى الله عليه وسلم

A Benefit for Releasing the Man Who Is Bound (Fāʾida li-Ḥall al-Marbūṭ)

The bound man goes out from his house, away from his wife, into the open country, on condition that he speak to no one. He searches out a stone from among the ant-mounds, then returns to his house under the condition already named, and he is released at once.

A Benefit for One Whose Water Outstrips Him Before Union (Fāʾida li-Man Yasbiquhu al-Māʾ Qabl al-Iltiḥāq)

He takes an olive leaf and writes upon it:

Issuing from between the backbone and the ribs. Indeed He is able to bring him back.

Yakhruju min bayn al-ṣulb wa-l-tarāʾib innahu ʿalā rajʿihi la-qādir.

يخرج من بين الصلب والترائب إنه على رجعه لقادر

Then he binds it upon his waist, and it will not descend save by his own will.

A Benefit for Knowing Whether the Water That Outstrips a Man Before Union Comes from Sorcery, from the Jinn, or from Moisture (Fāʾida li-Maʿrifat Ḥāl Man Yasbiquhu al-Māʾ Qabl al-Iltiḥāq Hal Huwa min al-Siḥr aw min al-Jinn aw min al-Ruṭūba)

If the water outstrips him before he penetrates, it is from the afflicting jinn. If it outstrips him together with the shrinking of his member and its drawing back into his belly, it is from human sorcery. And if it outstrips him after some part of it has entered the vulva, then it is from moisture.

A Benefit for Measuring the Trace of the Sick Person (Fāʾida li-Qiyās Athar al-Marīḍ)

You take the sick person's handkerchief or his shirt and tie a knot at its edge. Then you measure off from it, level with the knot, a portion by your three fingers — the ring finger, the forefinger and the middle finger. Then you say over it:

Barbarous names: Aqnash ٢ Maqash ٢ Shaqmūsh ٢ ʿAjlīkh ٢

أقنش ٢ مقش ٢ شقموش ٢ عجليخ ٢

Descend, O Nūkh, and you, O Maymūn, and you, O servants of these names, upon this trace, and tell me what ails its owner. If it is from human beings, lengthen it; if it is from the jinn, shorten it; and if it is from another cause, show it forth as it is — by the right of these noble names, which are upon you and whose obedience is with you: quickly (twice), in haste (twice), this very hour (twice). May God bless you and be upon you.

Inzil yā Nūkh wa-anta yā Maymūn wa-antum yā khuddām hādhihi al-asmā' 'alā hādhā al-athar wa-yunbi'ū lī mā bi-ṣāḥibih. Fa-in kāna min al-ins fa-ṭawwilūh wa-in kāna min al-jinn fa-qaṣṣirūh wa-in kāna min (...) fa-aẓhirūhu 'alā ḥālih bi-ḥaqq hādhihi al-asmā' al-sharīfa 'alaykum wa-ṭā'atuhā ladaykum al-waḥā ٢ al-'ajal ٢ al-sā'a ٢ bāraka Allāh fīkum wa-'alaykum.

انزل يا نوخ وأنت يا ميمون وأنتم يا خدام هذه الأسماء على هذا الأثر وينبوا لي ما بصاحبه فإن كان من الإنس فطولوه وإن كان من الجن فقصروه وإن كان من (...) فأظهروه على حاله بحق هذه الأسماء الشريفة عليكم وطاعتها لديكم الوحا ٢ العجل ٢ الساعة ٢ بارك الله فيكم وعليكم

Say it three times, then measure it a second time.

If the measured portion lengthens, the sickness is from human beings; if it shortens, it is from the jinn; and if it neither increases nor decreases, it is from God. If it becomes clear that it is from human beings, repeat the operation a second time and seek the disclosure of his condition: whether it is from envy or from sorcery. And if it becomes clear that it is from the jinn, repeat it likewise, to determine whether it is a passing affliction or one of the kinds of domination brought about by adjurations and the like. Whenever the matter sought becomes clear, treat him with what suits it.

A Benefit for Knowing the State of the Sick Person (Fā'ida li-Maʿrifat Ḥāl al-Marīḍ)

Write the names given below upon your right palm and lay it upon the sick person's head. If he weeps, the affliction is from the jinn; if he laughs, it is from human beings; and if he neither weeps nor laughs, it is from God. This is the form of the names:

Barbarous names: Makahīl Makahīl Saʿlīṭ Saʿlīṭ

مكهيل مكهيل سعليط سعليط (...) (...)

A Benefit for Knowing the Sick Person's Outcome (Fā'ida li-Maʿrifat ʿĀqibat al-Marīḍ)

Take a hen's egg and write upon it:

And thus We revealed to you a spirit from Our command. You did not know what the Book was, nor faith, but We made it a light by which We guide whom We will of Our servants, and indeed you guide to a straight path. O Lord, make clear to me and inform me of the outcome of this sick person in this egg, by the right of the light of Your noble face and by the right of Your Prophet, our master Muḥammad, may God bless him and grant him peace.

Wa-kadhālika awḥaynā ilayka rūḥan min amrinā mā kunta tadrī mā al-kitābu wa-lā al-īmānu wa-lākin jaʿalnāhu nūran nahdī bihi man nashā'u min ʿibādinā wa-innaka la-tahdī ilā ṣirāṭin mustaqīm. Yā Rabb bayyin lī wa-aʿlimnī bi-ʿāqibat hādhā al-marīḍ fī hādhihi al-bayḍa bi-ḥaqq nūr wajhika al-karīm wa-bi-ḥaqq nabiyyika sayyidinā Muḥammad ṣallā Allāh ʿalayhi wa-sallam.

وكذلك أوحينا إليك روحا من أمرنا ما كنت تدري ما الكتاب ولا الإيمان ولكن جعلناه نورا نهدي به من نشاء من عبادنا وإنك لتهدي إلى صراط مستقيم يا رب بين لي وأعلمني بعاقبة هذا المريض في هذه البيضة بحق نور وجهك الكريم وبحق نبيك سيدنا محمد صلى الله عليه وسلم

Then break it over the sick person's head. If blood is found in it, his sickness will be long and its outcome will be recovery. If something black is found in it, that indicates his death. And if it does not change, that is a sign of his swift recovery.

A Benefit for Removing Epilepsy (Fā'ida li-Izālat al-Ṣar')

Take a piece of red angora wool and write upon it these four names:

Muḥyī, Khāliq (twice).

Muḥyī Khāliq ٢

محيي خالق ٢

Then take a sheet of paper and write upon it the Verse of the Throne in separated letters, wrap it around the aforementioned piece of wool, and hang it upon the epileptic; his epilepsy will depart.

A Benefit for All the Natural Winds, the Released among Them and the Night-Visitor (Fā'ida li-Kāffat al-Aryāḥ al-Ṭabī'iyya al-Ṭāliq minhā wa-l-Ṭāriq)

Write the adjuration given below, gathered together, in a glazed vessel, and efface it with good oil. Put upon the oil a powder compounded of harmal, cumin, and garden-cress seed, and anoint the sick person's body with it, save for the tips of the fingers of his hands and his feet. Then write the adjuration a second time in another vessel, efface it with water from a well upon which neither sun nor moon looks, and give it to the sick person to drink for seven consecutive days, morning and evening; he will be healed, by the permission of God Most High. This is the form of the adjuration; you say:

Barbarous names: Aj Aj Rūh Rūh Sitr Sattār

أج أج روه روه ستر ستار

Exalted be the majesty of God, the One, the Subduer.

Jalla jalāl Allāh al-Wāḥid al-Qahhār

جل جلال الله الواحد القهار

Barbarous names: Hayūl wa-Hudhud Fahdā

هيول وهدهد فهدى

Āh yāh, O God, O Muḥammad. Āh yāh, O God, O Jibrāʾīl. Āh yāh, O God, O Mīkāʾīl. Āh yāh, O God, O Isrāfīl. Āh yāh, O God, O ʿAzrāʾīl. Āh yāh, O God, O Ḥayzūm. Āh yāh, O God. God is subtle with His servants; He provides for whom He wills, and He is the Strong, the Mighty. O servants of these noble names, descend upon the wind that has come over this body; shake it, make it thunder, and drive it out of this body, the body of so-and-so son of so-and-so, or so-and-so daughter of so-and-so, by the right of Him who says to a thing "Be," and it is, and by the right of

Āh yāh yā Allāh yā Muḥammad. Āh yāh yā Allāh yā Jibrā'īl. Āh yāh yā Allāh yā Mīkā'īl. Āh yāh yā Allāh yā Isrāfīl. Āh yāh yā Allāh yā 'Azrā'īl. Āh yāh yā Allāh yā Ḥayzūm. Āh yāh yā Allāh. Allāh laṭīf bi-'ibādihi yarzuqu man yashā'u wa-huwa al-Qawī al-'Azīz. Yā khuddām hādhihi al-asmā' al-karīma inzilū 'alā al-rīḥ al-'āriḍ li-hādhihi al-juththa wa-huzzūhu wa-ar'idūhu wa-akhrijūhu min hādhihi al-juththa juththat fulān ibn fulāna aw fulāna bint fulāna bi-ḥaqq man yaqūlu li-l-shay' kun fa-yakūn wa-bi-ḥaqq

أه ياه يا الله يا محمد أه ياه يا الله يا جبرائيل أه ياه يا الله يا ميكائيل أه ياه يا الله يا إسرافيل أه ياه يا الله يا عزرائيل أه ياه يا الله يا حيزوم أه ياه يا الله الله لطيف بعباده يرزق من يشاء وهو القوي العزيز يا خدام هذه الأسماء الكريمة انزلوا على الريح العارض لهذه الجثة وهزوه وأرعدوه وأخرجوه من هذه الجثة جثة فلان ابن فلانة أو فلانة بنت فلانة بحق من يقول للشيء كن فيكون وبحق

Barbarous names: 'Alshāqash Mihrāqash Aqshāmanash Aqnash Marūsh Shalshala fī Shalshala Ṣamṣama Ṣamṣama Dāyis Lāyis anta Hadūsh

علشاقش مهراقش أقشامنش أقنش مروش شلشلة في شلشلة صمصمة صمصمة دايس لايس أنت هدوش

O God, O Lord: healing, healing, healing, healing, healing that leaves behind neither ailment nor sickness. And I adjure you, O servants of these names, by God and then by God, by the right of the truth of God, by the might of the might of God, by the light of the face of God, and by what the Pen has caused to flow from

God to the best of God's creation, our master Muḥammad, may God bless him and grant him peace, son of ʿAbd Allāh and Messenger of God: if this wind be in bone, or in marrow, or in sinew, or in veins, or in blood, or in flesh, or in skin, or in hair, then you shall surely shake it, make it thunder, and drive it out of this body, the body of such-and-such, by the right of Him who gives life to the bones when they are decayed, and by the right of

Allāhumma yā Rabb shifāʾ shifāʾ shifāʾ shifāʾ shifāʾ lā yughādiru suqman wa-lā maraḍan. Wa-aʿzimu ʿalaykum yā khuddām hādhihi al-asmāʾ bi-Allāh thumma bi-Allāh wa-bi-ḥaqq ḥaqq Allāh wa-bi-ʿizz ʿizz Allāh wa-bi-nūr wajh Allāh wa-bi-mā jarā bihi al-qalam min ʿinda Allāh ilā khayr khalq Allāh sayyidinā Muḥammad ṣallā Allāh ʿalayhi wa-sallam ibn ʿAbd Allāh wa-Rasūl Allāh. In kāna hādhā al-rīḥ fī ʿaẓm aw fī mukhkh aw fī ʿaṣab aw fī ʿurūq aw fī dam aw fī laḥm aw fī jild aw fī shaʿr illā mā hazzaytumūhu wa-arʿadtumūhu wa-akhrajtumūhu min hādhā al-jasad jasad (kadhā kadhā) bi-ḥaqq man yuḥyī al-ʿiẓām wa-hiya ramīm wa-bi-ḥaqq

اللهم يا رب شفاء شفاء شفاء شفاء شفاء لا يغادر سقما ولا مرضا وأعزم عليكم يا خدام هذه الأسماء بالله ثم بالله وبحق حق الله وبعز عز الله وبنور وجه الله وبما جرى به القلم من عند الله إلى خير خلق الله سيدنا محمد صلى الله عليه وسلم ابن عبد الله ورسول الله إن كان هذا الريح في عظم أو في مخ أو في عصب أو في عروق أو في دم أو في لحم أو في جلد أو في شعر إلا ما هزيتموه وأرعدتموه وأخرجتموه من هذا الجسد جسد (كذا كذا) بحق من يحيي العظام وهي رميم وبحق

Barbarous names: Dāʿūj Māʿūj Taljalaj

داعوج ماعوج تلجلج

And indeed it is a mighty oath, if only you knew. And you see the mountains, supposing them fixed, while they pass by like the passing of the clouds: the handiwork of God, who has perfected all things. Indeed, He is well aware of what you do. And when you killed a soul and fell to disputing over it, and God brings out what you were concealing.

Wa-innahu la-qasamun law taʿlamūna ʿaẓīm. Wa-tarā al-jibāla taḥsabuhā jāmidatan wa-hiya tamurru marra al-saḥāb ṣunʿa Allāh alladhī atqana kulla shayʾ innahu khabīrun bi-mā tafʿalūn. Wa-idhā qataltum nafsan fa-iddāraʾtum fīhā wa-Allāh wa-Allāhu mukhrijun mā kuntum taktumūn, wa-Allāhu mukhrijun mā kuntum taktumūn

وإنه لقسم لو تعلمون عظيم وترى الجبال تحسبها جامدة وهي تمر مر السحاب صنع الله الذي أتقن كل شيء إنه خبير بما تفعلون وإذا قتلتم نفسا فادارأتم فيها والله والله مخرج ما كنتم تكتمون والله مخرج ما كنتم تكتمون

The adjuration is complete. After it has been written in a vessel, you recite it over him seven times.

A Benefit for Removing the Afflicting Spirit, the Evil Eye, the Glance and Sorcery (Fāʾida li-Izālat al-ʿĀriḍ wa-l-ʿAyn wa-l-Naẓra wa-l-Siḥr)

Write what follows on three sheets of paper. In each sheet place a portion of this compound: fetid alum, frankincense, coriander,

Maghrebi fāsūkh, harmal seed and black seed, in equal parts by weight. Fumigate the sick person with one sheet before sunset each day, and he will be healed. This is what is written:

Barbarous names: Tanbashlūk Tanbashlūk Ṭalmāsaʿ Ṭalmāsaʿ Aṭlaṭī Aṭlaṭī Malwiya Salwiya Ẓahīr Ẓahīr Ḥakwā Ḥakū Tanbīh Tanbīh

تنبشلوك تنبشلوك طلماسع طلماسع أطلطى أطلطى ملويه سلويه ظهير ظهير حكوا حكو تنبيه تنبيه

By the right of these names, veil, O master Maṭṭārūn, and nullify from so-and-so and so-and-so the wind, every affliction, sickness, sorcery and evil eye, by ل م ق ن ج ل. There is no power and no strength except in God, the Most High, the Magnificent. May God bless our master Muḥammad, his family and his Companions.

Bi-ḥaqqi hādhihi al-asmāʾ uḥjub yā sayyid Maṭṭārūn wa-abṭil ʿan kadhā wa-kadhā al-rīḥa wa-kulla ʿāriḍin wa-maraḍin wa-siḥrin wa-ʿaynin wa-ʿanī ل م ق ن ج ل *wa-lā ḥawla wa-lā quwwata illā bi-Allāhi al-ʿAlīyi al-ʿAẓīm, wa-ṣallā Allāhu ʿalā sayyidinā Muḥammadin wa-ʿalā ālihi wa-ṣaḥbih*

بحق هذه الأسماء أحجب يا سيد مططارون وأبطل عن كذا وكذا الريح وكل عارض ومرض وسحر وعين وعنى ل م ق ن ج ل ولا حول ولا قوة إلا بالله العلى العظيم وصلى الله على سيدنا محمد وعلى آله وصحبه

A Benefit for Burning the Afflicting Spirit (Fā'ida li-Ḥarq al-'Āriḍ)

Write these letters, ا ر د ه ى ل ر, upon the forehead of the afflicted person and in a vessel, together with Sūrat al-Burūj. Recite it over him three times, then erase it with water and give it to the afflicted person to drink, and his afflicting spirit will be burned.

A Benefit for Reviving One Who Has Fallen in a Fit (Fā'ida li-Ifāqat al-Maṣrū')

Recite over him Sūrat al-Fātiḥah, the Verse of the Throne and the first five verses of Sūrat al-Jinn over pure water, and sprinkle the face of the afflicted person with it, and he will revive.

A Benefit for One Whose Children Die from the Qarīn (Fā'ida li-man Tamut Awlāduhā min al-Qarīn)

Write Sūrat al-Mujādalah, on condition that you first write the word *bism* of the noble basmalah on a line by itself, and then set the Name of Majesty at the head of every line after that, provided that it belongs to the sura and is not added to it. Then fold what has been written, and place with it a small piece of tortoise bone, and hang it upon the pregnant woman, or upon the child if his birth has already taken place. The condition is that the writing be done in an odd-numbered month.

A Benefit Written with Forty Mīms

Write forty Arabic mīms, thus م, in a circle around the name of the person concerned, on a piece of white cloth, and hang it upon his left shoulder, and he will recover.

A Benefit for Removing the Qarīnah (Fā'ida li-Izālat al-Qarīna)

It is written and carried. This is what is written, as you see:

الله	٩٦	٢٩٦	٩٢	٦٦	٣٢	٦٧
الله	٩٧	٩٢	٢٩٦	٩٢	٦٦	٣٦
الله	٣٢	٦٧	٩٦	٢٩٦	٩٢	٦٦
الله	٦٦	٣٠	٦٧	٩٦	٢٩٦	٩٢
الله	٩٢	٦٦	٣٢	٦٧	٩٢	٢٩٦
الله	٢٩٦	٩٢	٦٦	٣٢	٦٧	٩٢
	الله	الله	الله	الله	الله	الله

The wafq for removing the qarīna

A Benefit for Removing Hemorrhage (Fā'ida li-Izālat al-Nazīf)

Write these letters, ح ل ظ, on three pieces of bread and feed them to the sick woman, one each day, and she will be healed.

A Benefit for Preventing a Pregnant Woman from Miscarrying the Fetus (Fā'ida li-Manʿ Isqāṭ al-Ḥāmil al-Janīn)

If this word, هشية, is written on forty-five lemon leaves, and the woman who is accustomed to miscarrying her fetuses is fumigated with them, she will miscarry no more.

A Benefit for Preventing Sleep (Fā'ida li-Manʿ al-Nawm)

Write on a sheet of paper and carry it beneath the pillow. These are the words:

Barbarous names: Baṭāmāsh Shāsh Kābūsh Marāsh

بطاماش شاش كابوش مراش

Section on the Arithmetical Rules (Faṣl fī al-Qawāʿid al-Ḥisābiyya)

A rule. The Imam Abū al-ʿAbbās al-Būnī said in his book *Shams al-Maʿārif*: Know, may God grant success to me and to you, that if you wish to know the condition of a sick man or of one who is absent, learn the day on which the sick man fell ill or the traveller set out. Reckon his name and his mother's name by the greater jummal, add to it what has passed of the Arabic month, and add to that the basis, twenty. Take the whole of the number that results and cast it away twenty by twenty until twenty or less remains with you. Then look at the number that is left over and set it against what I have described to you of the two tablets, which I have named the Tablet of Life and the Tablet of Death. Wherever the reckoning falls, judge by it, whether death or life, and you will see that.

So likewise for the condition of a married couple, whether they will agree or separate, and whether one of them will die before the other. Reckon the name of each of them by the greater jummal, add to it what remains of the Arabic month, add to them the basis, twenty, cast it away, and compare it against the Tablet of Life and the Tablet of Death. If they both fall in the Tablet of Life, they will come together and will not separate. If one of them falls in the Tablet of Life and the other in the Tablet of Death, then either that one will part from the other, or will die. Measure other cases by this. So too when a man enters a city: learn the day on which he entered it, reckon it with the name of the ruler, add to it what has passed of the Arabic month and the basis as we have set out above, take what is left over, set it against the two tablets, and judge by what appears to you, whether death or life.

So likewise for the condition of a pregnant woman, and what she will bear, and whether it will live or die in this birth. That is, you reckon her name, her mother's name, and the name of the day you are in of that month, and you add to it the basis and what has passed of the month, as has been mentioned. Cast it away and compare it. If it falls in the Tablet of Life, judge that it will live; and if it falls in the Tablet of Death, judge that it will not live. Reckon in the same way for the seeker and the sought, and for every difficult matter. God, glorified and exalted, knows best what is right.

And this is the form of the two tablets, as you see. Understand it.

٦	٥	٤
١٠	٩	٨
١٨	١٥	١٢
٥٧	٢٤	٢١
٣٠	٢٩	٢٧

٣	٢	١
١٣	١١	٧
١٨	١٦	١٤
٢٣	٢	١٩
٢٢	٢٦	١٣

The Tablet of Life (right) and the Tablet of Death (left)

Some of the scholars have laid down a fine mnemonic for these two tablets, and it is these words:

The physician, I fell in love with him the day he began to love a young girl, whoever desired.

al-Ṭabīb ʿashiqtuhu yawma badaʾa yuḥibbu ṣabiyya man raghiba

الطبيب عشقته يوم بدأ يحب صبية من رغب

The undotted letters belong to the Tablet of Life, and the dotted letters to the Tablet of Death.

A Rule for Knowing Whether a Woman Is Pregnant or Not, and Whether the Pregnancy Is Female or Male (Qāʿida li-Maʿrifat al-Marʾa Hal bihā Ḥaml am Lā wa-Hal al-Ḥaml bi-Unthā am bi-Dhakar)

You reckon the woman's name, her mother's name, and the name of the day of the question, then cast the total away two by two and look at what remains. If one remains, there is no pregnancy in her; and if two remain, she is pregnant. Then, if it has appeared that she is pregnant and she wishes to know whether it is female or male, add to the total already mentioned the number of her husband's name and cast the sum away in the same manner. If one remains, it is male; and if two remain, it is female.

A Rule for Knowing the Condition of an Absent Person (Qāʿida li-Maʿrifat Ḥāl al-Ghāʾib)

You reckon his name, his mother's name, and the name of the day of the question, then cast the total away four by four. If one remains, he is imprisoned. If two remain, he is glad and will come quickly. If two remain, he is dead. If four remain, it is a journey that will not be long, and perhaps he will return.

Another Rule for the Same, Cast by Four (Qāʿida Ukhrā li-Dhālika)

You reckon the name of the seeker and the name of the day of the question only, and you subtract the total four by four. If one remains, his heart is preoccupied with the matter of his livelihood; and if two remain, he is imprisoned or sick; and if three remain, he is in company; and if four remain, he is in joy and gladness.

A Rule for Knowing the Pregnant Woman (Qāʿida li-Maʿrifat al-Ḥāmil)

You reckon her name and her mother's name on the day of the question, then cast the total away four by four. If one remains, she is pregnant with a male; if two remain, she is pregnant with a female; if three remain, she will miscarry; and if four remain, she will bear twins.

A Rule for Knowing the Condition of the Two Spouses and Which of Them Will Die Before the Other (Qāʿida li-Maʿrifat Ḥāl al-Zawjayn wa-Man Yamūtu minhumā Qabla al-Ākhar)

You reckon the names of them both and subtract the total three by three. If one remains, the man will die before the woman; if two remain, the woman will die before the man; and if three remain, they will die together.

A Rule for Knowing the Thief (Qāʿida li-Maʿrifat al-Sāriq)

You reckon the name of the stolen thing and its day, then cast the total away three by three. If one remains, the thief is one of the neighbours; if two remain, he is of the people of the house in which the theft took place; and if three remain, he is a stranger.

A Rule for Knowing the Condition of the Sick Person (Qāʿida li-Maʿrifat Ḥāl al-Marīḍ)

You reckon the name of the sick person and the name of the day of the question, add three to the total, then cast the sum away seven by seven. If one remains, it is from the jinn; if two remain, from air; if three remain, from sorcery; if four remain, from the eye; if five remain, from blood; if six remain, from yellow bile; and if seven remain, from black bile.

Another Rule for the Same, Cast by Twelve (Qāʿida Ukhrā li-Dhālika)

You reckon the name of the sick person, his mother's name and the name of the day of the question, then subtract the total twelve by twelve. If one remains, it is from the sorcery of the jinn; if two remain, from the eye of a female; if three remain, his sickness is incurable and will not leave him until he dies; if four remain, from the eye of a man; if five remain, from a male qarīn; if six remain, from a natural wind; if seven remain, from an earthly ʿāriḍ; if eight remain, from a change in the blood; if nine remain, from yellow bile; if ten remain, from the sorcery of a human being; if eleven remain, from a female qarīna; and if twelve remain, from grief and distress.

A Benefit for Knowing the Condition of the Two Partners and the Two Spouses, Whether They Will Agree or Separate (Fāʾida li-Maʿrifat Ḥāl al-Sharīkayn wa-l-Zawjayn Hal Yattafiqān aw Yaftariqān)

You reckon the names of the two spouses or the two partners, add seven to them, cast the total away nine by nine, and look at what remains. If one remains, there is love followed by separation. If two remain, there is kindness and blessing. If three remain, there is evil and quarrelling. If four remain, there is a coming together followed by separation. If five remain, there is gain and ease, or wealth and support. If six remain, its beginning is good and its end is worry and grief. If eight remain, there is agreement and contentment. If nine remain, there is strife and quarrelling, evil and separation.

Section on the Rīm Reckoning, for Knowing the Victor and the Vanquished and the Outcome of Every Seeker and Sought (Faṣl fī Ḥisāb al-Rīm li-Maʿrifat al-Ghālib wa-l-Maghlūb wa-ʿĀqibat Kull Ṭālib wa-Maṭlūb)

One of the men of refinement, among the most eminent of the sages, said:

Keep the Rīm in memory, and you will win what you long for
and attain what you love and what you seek.

ʿAlayka bi-ḥifẓi al-Rīm taẓfar bi-l-munā wa-tablughu mā tahwā wa-mā anta ṭālibu

عليك بحفظ الريم تظفر بالمنى وتبلغ ما تهوى وما أنت طالب

A reckoning whose secret is made plain by the casting away of nines, and upon it there are proven trials by the names of kings.

Ḥisābun bi-ṭarḥi al-tisʿi yaẓharu sirruhu bi-asmāʾi amlākin ʿalayhi tajāribu

حساب بطرح التسع يظهر سره بأسماء أملاك عليه تجارب

In the even and in the odd the lesser of them rises, and the greater of them prevails when they differ.

Fa-fī al-zawji wa-l-ifrādi yasmū aqalluhā wa-aktharuhā ʿinda al-takhālufi ghālibu

ففي الزوج والإفراد يسمو أقلها وأكثرها عند التخالف غالب

And that is the one sought when the even is equal; and when the odd is equal, the seeker prevails.

Wa-dhāka maṭlūbun idhā al-zawju yastawī wa-ʿinda istiwāʾi al-fardi yaghlibu ṭālibu

وذاك مطلوب إذا الزوج يستوي وعند استواء الفرد يغلب طالب

His words, "Keep the Rīm in memory," are meant to urge the student to commit to memory this rule, which is well known among the scholars under that name. It is an arithmetical rule that resembles the well-known abjad reckoning but differs from it in the ordering of the letters. Here is its exposition in this table, as you see:

ك	ن	س	ب	ا	ر	ى	حروف
٧	٦	٥	٤	٣	٢	١	جملها
و		م	ص	ن	ز	ج	حروف
٥٠	٤٠	٣٠	٢٠	١٠	٩	٨	جملها
ف	ه	ق	د	ح	ت	ص	حروف
٣٠٠	٢٠٠	١٠٠	٩٠	٨٠	٧٠	٦٠	جملها
ظ	ط	ث	ع	خ	ش	ع	حروف
١٠٠٠	٩٠٠	٨٠٠	٧٠٠	٦٠٠	٥٠٠	٤٠٠	جملها

The letter-value table

Letter	Value	Letter	Value
ي	1	ص	60
ر	2	ت	70
ا	3	ح	80
ب	4	د	90
س	5	ق	100
ن	6	ه	200
ك	7	ف	300
ج	8	ع	400
ز	9	ش	500
ن	10	خ	600
ص	20	ع	700

Letter	Value	Letter	Value
م	30	ت	800
(...)	40	ط	900
و	50	ظ	1000

And some of the learned have mentioned three verses by which it may be memorized, and said:

O Rīm, awaken a soul upon an enchanting night; how many a blossom has been generous and enduring.

Yā Rīmu ayqiẓ bi-laylin sāḥirin nafsā kam jāda zahrun laḥā ḍurr mādūm

يا ريم أيقظ بليل ساحر نفسا كم جاد زهر لحى ضر مادوم

And he was ashamed, troubled and dazed with love; so have mercy upon a man who is sick, staring, and ruined.

Wa-staḥā (...) ḥaznādhī wayy qaliqā haymāna fa-rḥam ʿalīlan shākhiṣan kharibā

واستحى (...) حزناذى وى قلقا هيمان فارحم عليلا شاخصا خربا

His passion is fixed and his bird athirst; my portion has come to its end for me, and perhaps it has understood.

Gharāmuhu thābitun ẓamʾānu ṭāʾiruh qad intahā lī naṣībī rubbamā waʿā

غرامه ثابت ظمآن طائره قد انتهى لي نصيبي ربما وعى

His words, "a reckoning by casting out nines," and so forth, point to the way of working with this rule and to its benefit. The explanation of that is this: when you wish to know the strong from the weak, and the dominant from the dominated, between any two partners, two spouses, two adversaries set against one another, or the like, take the name of the seeker and the name of the sought, reckon the number of each of them according to the table already given, cast the total of each out nine by nine, and look at the two remainders. If they agree in evenness or in oddness but differ in quantity, then the owner of the lesser prevails over the owner of the greater. If they differ in evenness and oddness, then the owner of the greater prevails over the owner of the lesser. If they are equal in evenness, then the sought prevails over the seeker; and if they are equal in oddness, then the seeker prevails over the sought.

This rule carries a splendid benefit that most people do not know, namely that every operation bound up with a seeker and a sought does not come to success unless the seeker in it is dominant; so that when it appears that he is the one dominated, there must be joined to him — even from the names of God Most High — that which will be a cause of his preponderance and his ascendancy over the one he seeks. This is a hidden secret that none perceives save the one who has the longer hand in this art. Here is a table setting out the result of every pair of remainders, which I have laid down in approximate fashion, for the benefit, as you see:

باقين	نتيجة	باقين	نتيجة	باقين	نتيجة	باقين	نتيجة
١و١	الطالب يغلب	٢و٥	الاكثر يغلب	٤و٤	المطلوب يغلب	٦و٦	المطلوب يغلب
١و٢	الاكثر »	٢و٦	الأقل »	٤و٥	الاكثر »	٦و٧	الأكثر »
١و٣	الاقل »	٢و٧	الأكثر »	٤و٦	الاقل »	٦و٨	الأقل »
١و٤	الاكثر »	٢و٨	الأقل »	٤و٧	الأكثر »	٦و٩	الأكثر »
١و٥	الاقل »	٢و٩	الأكثر »	٤و٨	الاقل »	٧و٧	الطالب »
١و٦	الاكثر »	٣و٣	الطالب »	٤و٩	الاكثر »	٧و٨	الأكثر »
١و٧	الاقل »	٣و٤	الأكثر »	٥و٥	الطالب »	٧و٩	الأقل »
١و٨	الاكثر »	٣و٥	الاقل »	٥و٦	الاكثر »	٨و٨	المطلوب »
١و٩	الاقل »	٣و٦	الأكثر »	٥و٧	الاقل »	٨و٩	الأكثر »
٢و٢	المطلوب »	٣و٧	الاقل »	٥و٨	الاكثر »	٩و٩	الطالب »
٢و٣	الاكثر »	٣و٨	الأكثر »	٥و٩	الأقل »		
٢و٤	الاقل »	٣و٩	الاقل »				

The table of remainder outcomes

Remainders	Result	Remainders	Result	Remainders	Result	Remainders	Result
1 and 1	the seeker prevails	2 and 5	the greater prevails	4 and 4	the sought prevails	6 and 6	the sought prevails
1 and 2	the greater prevails	2 and 6	the lesser prevails	4 and 5	the greater prevails	6 and 7	the greater prevails
1 and 3	the lesser prevails	2 and 7	the greater prevails	4 and 6	the lesser prevails	6 and 8	the lesser prevails
1 and 4	the greater prevails	2 and 8	the lesser prevails	4 and 7	the greater prevails	6 and 9	the greater prevails

Remainders	Result	Remainders	Result	Remainders	Result	Remainders	Result
1 and 5	the lesser prevails	2 and 9	the greater prevails	4 and 8	the lesser prevails	7 and 7	the seeker prevails
1 and 6	the greater prevails	3 and 3	the seeker prevails	4 and 9	the greater prevails	7 and 8	the greater prevails
1 and 7	the lesser prevails	3 and 4	the greater prevails	5 and 5	the seeker prevails	7 and 9	the lesser prevails
1 and 8	the greater prevails	3 and 5	the lesser prevails	5 and 6	the greater prevails	8 and 8	the sought prevails
1 and 9	the lesser prevails	3 and 6	the greater prevails	5 and 7	the lesser prevails	8 and 9	the greater prevails
2 and 2	the sought prevails	3 and 7	the lesser prevails	5 and 8	the greater prevails	9 and 9	the seeker prevails
2 and 3	the greater prevails	3 and 8	the greater prevails	5 and 9	the lesser prevails		
2 and 4	the lesser prevails	3 and 9	the lesser prevails				

Section on Important Benefits that Dispense with the Physician when No Physician Is to Be Found (Faṣl fī Fawāʾid Muhimma Tughnī ʿan al-Ṭabīb ʿinda ʿAdam Wujūd al-Ṭabīb)

A Benefit: Some of the sages have said that in Egypt there are nine peels thrown upon the face of the earth, and all of them hold benefits. They are: 1. onion peel; 2. yellow melon rind; 3. green watermelon rind; 4. hazelnut shell; 5. bitter-orange peel;

6. pomegranate peel; 7. walnut shell; 8. poppy husk; 9. banana peel.

As for onion peel, among its benefits is that if it is burned, pounded, and sprinkled upon the head of a bald man after he has shaved his head in the bathhouse, his hair will grow. And if it is burned, kneaded in bee's honey, worked into a wad of camel wool, and carried by a woman who suffers from bleeding, the blood will stop.

As for yellow melon rind, among its benefits is that if it is dried, pounded, and sifted, and a mithqāl of it is taken, wrapped in a clean rag, and thrown into the pot holding meat that has not cooked through because of its age, that meat will cook through, become pleasant to eat, and take on a sweet fragrance.

As for green watermelon rind, among its benefits is that if it is dried in the shade and pounded fine, and one who suffers from retention of urine is given a draught of it in two ūqiyyas of jullāb syrup while he is in the bathhouse beside the hot basin, he will be cured at once.

As for hazelnut shell, among its benefits is that one takes a portion of it filling both palms, puts it in a vessel, and covers it with clear water for a whole night; then he sets it over a gentle fire until the water turns red like the jujube. Then he strains it, washes his armpits with cold water and wipes them with a rag, then washes them a second time with the hazelnut water and dries them in the air without a rag, and repeats this three times. After that no odour will appear from his armpits for the rest of his life, and their scent will be sweet. And if weak hair is anointed with it, it will grow long and fine.

As for bitter-orange peel, whoever eats half a dirham by weight of it is guarded from griping, colic, wind, flatulence, and rumbling of the belly; it digests the food and prevents corruption of the stomach.

As for pomegranate peel, among its benefits is that if it is boiled and a patient suffering from dysentery drinks of it, he will be cured. And if it is pounded fine, and the ringworm is worked until the yellow water runs from it, and it is then dressed with the pomegranate peel and left upon it until it falls away of itself, the ringworm will heal and will not return after that.

As for walnut shell, among its benefits is that if it is boiled in water and one who has a cough drinks of it, he will be cured.

As for poppy husk, among its benefits is that if it is pounded fine and sifted, and a mithqāl of it is taken, and there are added to it a mithqāl of Aswān clay and a mithqāl of white cumin as well, and the whole is mixed together and sifted and made into a powder, and he takes a dose of it over three days, a mithqāl each day, it will cut off from him blood, tenesmus, and diarrhoea.

As for banana peel, among its benefits is that if some of it is taken while it is still green, pounded, and its water extracted, and that water is dripped upon a deep wound, the wound will close and heal.

A Benefit for Retention of Urine (Fāʾida li-ʿUsr al-Bawl)

You take a portion of onion to the measure of three dirhams and add to it an ūqiyya of white sugar, and give it to the patient to drink over three days; he will be cured.

A Benefit for Expelling Worms from the Belly (Fāʾida li-Ikhrāj al-Dūd min al-Baṭn)

Some of the sages said: whoever has worms in his belly and wishes to cast them out without a purgative should take to wheat and mint. Let him take two grains of wheat and chew them, drawing his saliva over them, on condition that he not swallow the residue. Then let him sleep for an hour, rise, and drink of mint water; he will cast out the strong worms in his belly.

Likewise, whoever takes a portion of peach leaves, pounds them, extracts their water, anoints with it the navel of one who has worms in his belly, and gives him a draught of it to drink on an empty stomach, the worms in his belly will die.

Likewise, whoever takes the roots of the sour pomegranate and of the sweet, crushes them in a mortar, steeps them in fresh water for a week, then boils them until a third of the water remains, and drinks a draught of that water on an empty stomach, it will cast out whatever worms are in his belly at once.

Likewise, whoever grinds bitter lupine, kneads it with cane honey and vinegar, and eats of it, it will kill whatever worms are in his belly.

A Benefit for Killing Bedbugs (Fā'ida li-Qatl al-Baqq)

If the water in which lupine has been steeped is sprinkled in the places where bedbugs are, it kills them and spoils their eggs.

A Benefit: The Uses of Garlic

Some physicians said: if a man roasts garlic, takes of it the measure of two dirhams with half an ūqiya of bee honey, and licks it on an empty stomach, it brings out the phlegm and kills the worms of the belly. If you take garlic and pound it until it becomes like an ointment, and you place it upon the bite of vermin or the sting of a scorpion, it takes the pain away. Whoever travels and finds the water changed upon him on his journey should eat a clove of garlic, and he will be safe from the change, and nothing will harm him.

Whoever complains of a chronic cough should take a portion of garlic cloves after peeling them, put them in a disk of dough, and bake it in the oven until the dough is done. Then he should take it out, strip the dough away from the garlic, put the garlic in bee honey, and eat it, and he will be cured.

Whoever has a leech enter his mouth or his throat should take a head of garlic and put it in the fire; when its smoke rises, let him receive it with his mouth, and the leech will fall at once.

Whoever complains of pain in the molars and the teeth should take garlic, pound it, put it in vinegar with salt and honey, and steep it until it becomes like an ointment. Then let him place the weight of one dirham of it upon the decayed molar, and it will fall out; and if he places it upon the aching molar, its pain will be stilled.

Whoever is afflicted with ringworm should take garlic and burn it until it becomes ash, then place it upon powdered pomegranate peel, steep it in vinegar, and rub the ringworm until its yellow fluid comes out. Afterward let him smear the place with the garlic already mentioned, and he will be cured.

Whoever complains of pain in his back should take three dirhams of garlic, as much again of black seed, and as much again of caraway. Let him mix the three, put them in a clay pan, pour over them three dirhams of sesame oil and an ūqiya of good oil, and set it over the fire until the garlic is charred. Then let him take the garlic out, work it, and put three eggs into the oil; and when the eggs have set, let him take the oil down from the fire, take three dirhams of pounded elecampane root, and scatter it over the eggs. Let him eat all of that with an ūqiya of bread, on condition that he take nothing cold along with it and that he hold back from drinking water for one astronomical hour. By this he will be safe from pain in the back for a full year.

A Benefit Concerning the Uses of Onion (Fāʾida fī Manāfiʿ al-Baṣal)

Some physicians said: it is hot, and there is moisture in it. It wards off the change of water and repels the harm of the simoom wind. If a man is travelling in the heat, let him smell an onion and eat nothing of it, and the harm of the simoom wind will be repelled from him. It whets the appetite, strengthens the stomach, excites sexual vigor, increases the seed, improves the complexion, cuts phlegm, and dries the stomach.

Whoever is afflicted with vitiligo on his body should take onion seed, pound it, and let it drip; then let him take some of the onion water and smear the vitiligo with it, and he will be cured. Whoever is afflicted with alopecia in his chin or in his hair should take onion seed, grind it with black cumin, steep the two in good oil, and anoint the place of the alopecia with it, and he will be cured. Whoever is afflicted with warts upon his fingers, which are called al-sanṭ, should take onion seed, grind it with salt, steep it in vinegar, and anoint the warts with it, and they will go away.

Whoever drinks a purgative medicine and is seized with vomiting and nausea should smell an onion, and that will leave him. If onion is dripped into an ear whose hearing is dull, the harm that is in it will depart. Every riding beast upon whose eye a whiteness has settled should have its eye treated with onion water and bee honey, and the whiteness will go from the beast's eye.

Cooked onion benefits jaundice, cough, and roughness of the chest; it makes the urine flow, softens the temperament, and benefits the bite of a dog when it is smeared upon the bite with water, salt, and rue. If onion is roasted and stuck upon boils and hemorrhoids, it ripens them, softens them, opens them, and cleanses them of blood and matter. Whoever is afflicted with a nosebleed should grind frankincense pebbles, steep them in onion water, and drink it.

Or he may put some of it into a cloth and lay it upon the nose, and the nosebleed will stop.

Benefits for Removing Nosebleed (Fawāʾid li-Idhhāb al-Ruʿāf)

Whoever fumigates beneath the nose of one suffering a nosebleed with pigeon dung, the nosebleed will stop. If rue is pulverized and put into the nose of the one who is bleeding, it will go away. Whoever is afflicted with a nosebleed should write his name with his own blood upon his palm and set the writing before his eyes, and his nosebleed will stop. To stop it there is also this: he binds the little finger and the ring finger of both hands and opens his palm, and it will cease from him.

A Benefit Concerning the Uses of Rue (Fāʾida fī Manāfiʿ al-Sadhāb)

If it is boiled in good oil and the body is anointed with it, it kills lice. If it is stuffed into the ear while it is still green, it stops the throbbing pain. Whoever is much troubled by nocturnal emission should take a stalk of rue and a stone from the pits of the green olive, wrap the two in a good cloth, and bind them upon his right forearm; he will not fall into ritual impurity even if he remains a hundred years.

A Benefit Concerning Excess in Eating

Some of the sages said: eating too much corrupts the stomach and the belly. The physicians have warned against taking food before the earlier food has been digested. And He who is mighty in speech said:

O children of Adam, take your adornment at every place of prayer, and eat and drink, but do not be excessive; indeed He does not love the excessive.

Yā banī Ādama khudhū zīnatakum ʿinda kulli masjidin wa-kulū wa-shrabū wa-lā tusrifū innahu lā yuḥibbu al-musrifīn.

يا بني آدم خذوا زينتكم عند كل مسجد وكلوا واشربوا ولا تسرفوا إنه لا يحب المسرفين

And he, may God bless him and grant him peace, said:

The son of Adam fills no vessel worse than his belly. A few morsels that keep his back upright are enough for the son of Adam. If there must be more, then a third for his food, a third for his drink, and a third for his breath.

Mā malaʾa ibn Ādama wiʿāʾan sharran min baṭnihi, ḥasbu ibn Ādama luqaymātun yuqimna ṣulbahu, fa-in kāna wa-lā budda fa-thuluthun li-ṭaʿāmihi wa-thuluthun li-sharābihi wa-thuluthun li-nafasihi.

ما ملأ ابن آدم وعاء شر من بطنه حسب ابن آدم لقيمات يقمن صلبه فإن كان ولا بد فثلث لطعامه وثلث لشرابه وثلث لنفسه

A Benefit Concerning the Powder Called al-Nattāsh (Fāʾida fī Bayān al-Safūf al-Musammā bi-l-Nattāsh)

Some of the physicians said:

O you who pass the night and do not sleep, for the troubled pains that meet you; if you complain of poor digestion from too much food and too much feeding, or if you complain of wind in the ribs, then listen, and heed truly what is said. Our powder, the one known as al-Nattāsh, has come to run through the limbs with benefit. Or if you pass the night complaining of wind or of rumbling, or of a belching whose pain has grown stupefying, then your cure is pure and clear myrrh, and frankincense pebbles, white and translucent, and anise, and likewise cinnamon, and Egyptian acacia pods, and likewise cumin. Add to it the root known as janāḥ, and licorice, for in it there is good. Be diligent for purslane seed, and above all if you add chicory seed. Add to it two more of the simples, wherever their benefit is to be found. And reinforce it with rose, young man; do not omit celery seed, and add fennel to it. And likewise a sweet one you must never forget: mastic, for in purity there is nothing like it. All that I have set in order is for a gathered benefit, and seven more follow it. It is an excellent medicine for one who complains of harm within his belly; it restores the digestion of food. This medicine quenches the blaze in the entrails, and truly the heat of the rumbling stomach. By itself it clears the yellowness from the eye and changes the ugly complexion to a fair one.

The Counsel of the Sage Buqrāṭ to His Son (Waṣiyyat al-Ḥakīm Buqrāṭ li-Waladih)

Buqrāṭ said to his son: My son, whoever makes a habit of breaking his fast upon water weakens his powers. Whoever sleeps while thirsty is treated without knowing it, and whoever places jasmine beneath his head is not safe from black water descending in his eye, even if only after a time. My son, whoever walks much in the heat while barefoot and then puts cold water upon his feet is not safe from scabies in his eye and from a hair sprouting in his eye. My son, whoever travels in the heat barefoot, takes shade beneath a tree or beneath a wall, and uncovers his head is not safe from migraine, headache, and throbbing. My son, whoever travels while sated and leaps onto the back of his beast is not safe from rupture. My son, whoever travels while hungry and breaks his fast upon water is not safe from dropsy. My son, do not combine milk and fish in a single state, for when the two come together they beget colic, wind, hemorrhoids, and aching of the molars. My son, beware of eating garlic and onion at one time, for the two of them darken the sight. My son, beware of eating fish and eggs at one time, for that bequeaths pain of the spleen and winds at the head of the stomach. My son, long tarrying in the privy bequeaths the deep-seated disease. Whoever eats his fill, enters the bathhouse, and is struck with palsy should blame none but himself. Whoever goes in to his wife while she is menstruating, and his child is afflicted with leprosy, should blame none but himself. Whoever eats citron by night and becomes cross-eyed should blame none but himself.

Know, my son, that many people read this book of mine and say within themselves, "For a long time this food and this drink have gathered in my belly, and I have seen nothing but good." If only such a man knew that the thief, had he known he would be seized at the very first time he stole, would never have dared; instead he returns time after time until his affair is exposed, and the end of it is that he wrecks the house and leaves nothing useful in it, so that the owner of the house comes to regret how little he guarded it.

Know, my son, that the body of the son of Adam is like the earth: whenever its owner attends to it with labour it profits him, its condition is praised, its yield grows plentiful, and its crop thrives; and if he neglects it, it spoils and grass springs up in it. So too is the body in this same station, in the ordering of its condition by foods and drinks.

Know, my son, that the body has need of sustenance. A man should look to what agrees with his stomach among food and drink, for if he accepts what does not agree with the body, there befalls him weakness in the heart, aching of the head, wind in the breast, ophthalmia in the eyes, and the like of that.

My son, do not hold back urine or stool, even if you are upon the back of your horse, for it bequeaths the deep-seated disease into the belly.

My son, do not have intercourse upon your right side, nor upon your left side, nor upon your back, nor while standing, nor beneath a fruit-bearing tree, nor in the bathhouse, nor while you are enraged, nor while you are sated or hungry, nor at the beginning of the night nor at its end; and do not do it early, at the time of the morning meal.

My son, intercourse is blood that descends from all the organs, and when one of you performs the motion of intercourse, a drop of blood is drawn out from beneath every hair.

My son, intercourse is the light of your eyes and the marrow of your shins; yet the sages say that intercourse is the strength of bodies, and whoever abandons intercourse for a long period, the powers of his organs weaken, their channels flatten, and his member shrinks.

My son, a man should hold himself to three things: that he not abandon walking, for if he has need of it one day he will be equal to it; that he not abandon eating, for his bowels grow narrow; and that he not abandon intercourse, for a well, if it is not drawn from, its water goes.

My son, the sages likened the man who has intercourse to a jar filled with water: when it is upturned onto its side, part of the water comes down and part of it remains, and if it is not turned over upon its mouth, what is in it does not clear out. So too the man: when he has intercourse upon his side, part of the water descends and part of it remains, and that bequeaths ailments in his body, hidden from people and indeed from himself, and everyone who sees him by his outward condition supposes him to be in the utmost health.

But inwardly he is on the brink of a pit of sickness, so that his bed, for all its flourishing, is a ruin. He passes the night in his bed with the woman and supposes that by doing so no order of his is disturbed, whereas the truth is that, even if the fire of his appetite has cooled for the moment, in the end the woman must inevitably demand of him what he used to do with her of the sweetness of union. He will not be able to do it, for his own condition preoccupies him and holds him back from her, and concealing his state will not avail him. It may be that the woman will then shoot him with the arrows of reproach — and I take refuge in God from the pain that women inflict upon men, for to the man of sense that is harder to bear than the striking of arrows. What a disappointment it is, and what a disappointment! There is no cause for this stubborn malady but coming to her upon the side at the time of union.

My son, among people there is the man who complains of arriving swiftly before the arrival, so that the need is discharged and yet is not discharged. Among them is the man who cannot sleep for the abundance of his emission, as though his emission welled up from a spring whose supply is never cut off, and the times he rises to it cannot be numbered. Among them is the man who finds, after the emission, something congealed and of the colour of milk. The sages say: the most frequent causes of death are coupling upon the side, and disorder, because a vessel is not cleared of what is in it unless it is tipped upon its head; and the residue of the dead seed within the body has consequences that are not to be praised. The nearest thing to be generated from it is difficulty of urine, and the splitting of the emission into two parts as it comes out.

A Benefit Concerning the Properties of al-Ḥazanbal (Fāʾida fī Khawāṣṣ al-Ḥazanbal)

O you who seek the secret of al-Ḥazanbal among mankind, you have been singled out by the Lord with every excellence. Whoever complains of an old chill as his affliction, and of its pains at every time and hour: take two mithqāls of it after it has been pounded, with the honey of a bee added to it, young man. For three days let it be his morning draught; and if it be a week, you will praise my prescription. So too for one who has been stung: it is chewed fine and smeared upon the place of the pain, and he is healed within the hour. You will see a wonder of its secret and of its healing in the sting of the stung and the burning away of the sting. Whoever complains that the member is limp, it restores it, and at coupling, when he emits too quickly, it is pounded and boiled in the milk of a she-ass, and with it the urethra is anointed every night. You will see a wonder of its secret and of its benefit, in the sweetness of coupling and the savoring of desire. Let the man afflicted with thick winds pound it with sugar, its measure being three mithqāls; he takes of it the weight of one mithqāl and no more, and follows it with ginger, gently. It dispels winds and colic without delay, and brings relief and a mending of appetite. Whoever has weakness of the eyes, and sees only half a sight, or little of seeing, let cinnamon be added to it in equal measure, and a portion of sugar, so that it becomes a fine powder. It will clear his two eyes after a film upon them, and they will be made pure of whiteness and of burning. It profits a man in his state of weakness, a healing for him from every disease and catarrh. Whoever has a comely face marred by sallowness, it gives him redness after that pallor. It is pounded and boiled in an infusion left to steep, and he is given it to drink: it preserves for him beauty and strength. Whoever is of the people of dullness, whose heart is slow to retain what it learns.

Glossary

Abjad أبجد — The Arabic letter-number system (gematria) where each letter has a numerical value. Used extensively in composing magic squares from divine names.

al-Aḥad الأحد — Sunday; the day governed by the Sun. First day in the Islamic week for planetary hour calculations.

al-Aḥmar الأحمر — The Red One; one of the seven kings of jinn. Rules over Tuesday and the northern direction.

al-Arbi'ā' الأربعاء — Wednesday; the day governed by Mercury.

Asās أساس — Basis or foundation number; the constant sum to which all rows, columns, and diagonals of a magic square must equal.

'Azā'im عزائم — Adjurations (plural of 'azima); binding oaths and conjurations used in spirit summoning. The central ritual technology of this text.

'Azīma عزيمة — Adjuration; a binding conjuration used to compel spirits to obey the practitioner. Central to the Solomonic magical tradition.

Bāb باب — Chapter; literally 'door' or 'gate.' Used to mark major sections of the text.

Barqān برقان — One of the seven kings of jinn. Rules over Wednesday and the western direction. Associated with Mercury.

Basmala بسملة — The formula "In the name of God, the Most Gracious, the Most Merciful," recited or written by count in several of the book's rites.

Bukhūr بخور — Incense or fumigation. Specific aromatic substances burned during talismanic and spiritual operations, each corresponding to a particular planet or spirit.

Daʿwa دعوة — Invocation; a formal calling upon God, angels, or spirits. Used alongside talismans and divine names to initiate spiritual operations.

Fā'ida فائدة — "Benefit." The book's own rubric for a self-contained remedy, rite or property; most of the Conclusion is a sequence of such benefits.

Faṣl فصل — Section; a subdivision within a chapter. Used to mark topical divisions throughout the text.

Hātif هاتف — An unseen caller; a voice sent to a person to convey a command or a summons.

Ḥijāb حجاب — Amulet or protective covering; a written talisman folded and worn on the body for protection or to achieve a specific goal.

Ḥirz حرز — Protective amulet; a written talisman carried for defense against harm, illness, or evil spirits.

Ḥisāb al-Jummal حساب الجمل — The numerical reckoning of the letters. The lesser reckoning assigns each letter its abjad value; the greater reckoning counts the letters of the letter's spelled-out name.

Ism Allāh اسم الله — Divine Name; one of the names of God used in invocations and talismanic inscriptions. Each divine name has specific properties and planetary correspondences.

Istiḥḍār استحضار — Summoning; the act of making a spiritual being appear before the practitioner. The central operation described in this grimoire.

Istikhāra استخارة — Seeking a decision from God, here a dream-oracle produced by a prescribed recitation before sleep and read from the colours seen.

al-Ithnayn الاثنين — Monday; the day governed by the Moon.

Jalb جلب — "Attraction": an operation that draws a person, or a benefit, to the practitioner.

Jinn جن — Spiritual beings created from smokeless fire, according to Islamic cosmology. They inhabit a parallel world and can interact with humans. The seven kings of jinn are a central topic of this text.

al-Jumʿa الجمعة — Friday; the day governed by Venus and the Islamic day of congregational prayer.

Kawkab كوكب — Planet or star. The seven classical planets (Sun, Moon, Mars, Mercury, Jupiter, Venus, Saturn) govern spiritual operations by day, hour, and zodiac sign.

Khādim خادم — Servant spirit; a spiritual being assigned to serve the practitioner, bound through covenants and adjurations.

Khalwa خلوة — Spiritual retreat; a period of seclusion for focused prayer, fasting, and spiritual purification prior to performing major operations.

al-Khamīs الخميس — Thursday; the day governed by Jupiter.

Khātam خاتم — Seal or ring; a talismanic seal inscribed with divine names and symbols, used to bind or invoke spiritual entities.

Kundur كندر — Frankincense, the fumigant most often prescribed in the book, usually as "male" (lubān dhakar) frankincense.

Malak ملك — Angel; celestial beings associated with specific heavens, days, and divine names. Angels serve as intermediaries in spiritual operations.

Manāzil al-Qamar منازل القمر — Stations of the Moon; the 28 lunar mansions used in astrological timing of operations. Each station has specific properties and governing spirits.

Mandal مندل — A ritual circle or diagram drawn on the ground, within which the practitioner sits during spirit summoning operations.

al-Mirrīkh المريخ — Mars; the fifth classical planet, governing Tuesday. Associated with war, overpowering, discord, and hostile operations.

Mīthāq ميثاق — Covenant or pact; a binding agreement between the practitioner and a spiritual entity, establishing the terms of service.

Murra مرة — One of the seven kings of jinn. Rules over Monday and the southern direction.

al-Mushtarī المشتري — Jupiter; the sixth classical planet, governing Thursday. Associated with justice, wisdom, nobility, health, and the dispensing of affairs.

Naqsh نقش — Inscription; the act of writing or engraving talismanic content onto a surface as part of a ritual operation.

Qāʿida قاعدة — "Rule." A rubric of the Conclusion for an arithmetical procedure (casting a name-sum by fours, sevens, nines or twelves) that yields a prognosis.

al-Qamar القمر — The Moon; the first classical planet, governing Monday. Associated with travel, fulfilling needs, opening locks, and dispatching deputies.

Qarīn قرين — The spirit-companion attached to a person from birth; a qarīna (feminine) is the companion held responsible for the loss of infants and for a woman's afflictions.

Rijāl al-Ghayb رجال الغيب — The Men of the Unseen: the hidden hierarchy of saints (the Pole, the Pegs, the Substitutes, the Nobles, the Chiefs, the Watchers) whose station moves around the compass through the month and who are greeted facing it.

Rūḥānī روحاني — Spiritual being; a celestial spirit. Also used as an adjective meaning 'spiritual' or 'of the spirit realm.'

Sāʿa ساعة — Planetary hour; the system by which each hour of day and night is governed by one of the seven classical planets, determining which operations are auspicious.

al-Sabt السبت — Saturday; the day governed by Saturn.

al-Shams الشمس — The Sun; the fourth classical planet, governing Sunday. Associated with love, affection, beauty, authority, and the dispelling of darkness and sorcery.

Sulaymān سليمان — Solomon (Prophet); the archetypal master of jinn and spiritual beings in Islamic tradition. His seal and authority underpin most conjuration practices.

Tahyīj تهييج — "Stirring": an operation that agitates a person with love or longing for another.

Taskhīr تسخير — Subjugation; compelling a spirit (jinn, angel, or ruhani) to serve the practitioner's will through divine authority and ritual means.

al-Thulāthā' الثلاثاء — Tuesday; the day governed by Mars.

Ṭilasm طلسم — Talisman; a physical object inscribed with symbols, names, or numbers to produce specific spiritual effects.

ʿUṭārid عطارد — Mercury; the second classical planet, governing Wednesday. Associated with trickery, concealment, transformation, messages, and intellectual operations.

Voces Magicae — Barbarous names; non-Arabic mystical syllables and divine names used in invocations. Transliterated exactly, without interpretation. Called ʿajamiyyah in Arabic.

Wafq وفق — Magic square; a grid of numbers or letters arranged so that rows, columns, and diagonals produce equal sums. Used extensively in talismanic operations.

Yawm يوم — Day; each day of the week is governed by a planet, affecting which operations are auspicious.

Zimām زمام — Literally "rein." In the letter-breaking method, the line of the zimām is the final line that emerges when the letters of the seeker, the one sought and the need are broken down; its letters and their sum govern the operation.

Zuḥal زحل — Saturn; the seventh classical planet, governing Saturday. Associated with subjugation, binding, severity, and operations involving constraint and domination.

al-Zuhra الزهرة — Venus; the third classical planet, governing Friday. Associated with love, beauty, harmony, attraction, and reconciliation.

The Radiant Jewels

JOHN FRIEND PUBLISHING

2026

www.ingramcontent.com/pod-product-compliance
Ingram Content Group UK Ltd.
Pitfield, Milton Keynes, MK11 3LW, UK
UKHW020720041026
15590UKWH00002B/788